Health and Medicine through History

Health and Medicine through History

From Ancient Practices to 21st-Century Innovations

VOLUME 3: Data and Documents

Ruth Clifford Engs, Editor

GREENWOOD

An Imprint of ABC-CLIO, LLC

Santa Barbara, California • Denver, Colorado

Library of Congress Cataloging-in-Publication Data

Names: Engs, Ruth Clifford, editor.
Title: Health and medicine through history : from ancient practices to 21st-century innovations / Ruth Clifford Engs, editor.
Description: Santa Barbara, CA : Greenwood, [2019] | Includes bibliographical references and index.
Identifiers: LCCN 2018055964 (print) | LCCN 2018056496 (ebook) | ISBN 9781440858925 (eBook) | ISBN 9781440858918 (set : alk. paper) | ISBN 9781440858932 (volume 1 : alk. paper) | ISBN 9781440858949 (volume 2 : alk. paper) | ISBN 9781440858956 (volume 3 : alk. paper)
Subjects: | MESH: History of Medicine
Classification: LCC R131 (ebook) | LCC R131 (print) | NLM WZ 40 | DDC 610—dc23
LC record available at https://lccn.loc.gov/2018055964

ISBN: 978-1-4408-5891-8 (set)
978-1-4408-5893-2 (vol. 1)
978-1-4408-5894-9 (vol. 2)
978-1-4408-5895-6 (vol. 3)
978-1-4408-5892-5 (ebook)

23 22 21 20 19 1 2 3 4 5

This book is also available as an eBook.

Greenwood
An Imprint of ABC-CLIO, LLC

ABC-CLIO, LLC
147 Castilian Drive
Santa Barbara, California 93117
www.abc-clio.com

This book is printed on acid-free paper ∞

Manufactured in the United States of America

For Jeff Graf and Jeff Franz

Contents

VOLUME 3 Data and Documents

Part 5 Data and Documents

Data

PART 5

Data and Documents

DATA

Population and Death Rates

1. Annual Number of Deaths by Age in London (1745–1750)

Corbyn Morris (1710–1779), a British official, collected information on the vital statistics of Great Britain, and in 1753 prepared a "bill" (registry) for the total number of births and deaths in Great Britain that had been recorded for the previous 100 years. The following table shows the number of deaths in each age group in London from 1745 to 1750. This table is important inasmuch as it is one of the first documents to report what we call today vital statistics. Although the total population is not given so as to determine percentage or rate, as can be seen from the table, infant and early childhood mortality was very high. They most likely died of diarrhea due to unhygienic conditions. The next highest groups are individuals from ages 30 to 50, which in the 21st century would be considered the "prime of life." It should also be noted that a few people lived to be 80 years and beyond.

See also: Document 21; Document 53

Source: Morris, Corbyn, William Petty, John Graunt, and Thomas Birch. *A Collection of the Yearly Bills of Mortality, from 1657 to 1758 Inclusive: Together With Several Other Bills of an Earlier Date.* London: A. Millar, 1759, 97–98.

The total extent of life, from earliest infancy to its extinction, is cut by the present bills of mortality into the following intervals, or divisions, viz.

1	Under two years old	8481
2	Between two and five	2011
3	Five and ten	851
4	Ten and twenty	762
5	Twenty and thirty	2202
6	Thirty and forty	2632
7	Forty and fifty	2771
8	Fifty and sixty	2140
9	Sixty and seventy	1673
10	Seventy and eighty	1204
11	Eighty and ninety	542
12	Ninety and hundred	72
13	A hundred and upward	8

2. Chadwick Report: Number of Deaths and Causes (1842)

This chart shows the beginning of the use of statistics in terms of percentage. Edwin Chadwick (1800–1890), the British labor and public health reformer, was the first to record death rates in the mid-19th century. He demonstrated that infectious diseases were common in Britain and often associated with home conditions. In collecting data, Chadwick visited Edinburgh, Glasgow, and other communities and inspected residences that local authorities "pointed out to be the chief seats of disease." Both external and internal conditions of their dwellings were inspected along with drainage and ventilation. As can be seen from the chart, most deaths (mortality) were caused by childhood, respiratory, or other infectious disease. Tuberculosis (consumption) rises and falls in roughly 200-year cycles, and as can be seen from the chart, it was the major cause of mortality in England at this time. Chadwick is noted for his classic public health work, The Report on the Sanitary Condition of the Labouring Population and the Means of its Improvement, London, May 1842.

Number of deaths during 1838 from death registrations and causes

Counties	Number of deaths during the year ended 31st December, 1838 from										Proportion of deaths from the preceding causes in every 1,000 of the population, 1841	Proportion of deaths from all causes of mortality in every 1,000 of the population, 1841
	1 Epidemic, endemic, and contagious diseases				2 Diseases of respiratory organs			3 Diseases of brain, nerves, and senses	4 Diseases of digestive organs	Total deaths from the four preceding classes of diseases		
	Fever: typhus, scarlatina	Smallpox	Measles	Whooping cough	Consumption	Pneumonia	All other classes					
England												
Bedford	155	75	40	66	457	97	57	304	131	1382	13	22
Berks	204	288	21	86	739	231	162	467	201	2399	15	25
Bucks	256	85	61	27	575	131	61	348	152	1696	11	19
Cambridge	231	136	57	90	686	156	70	318	189	1933	12	21
Chester	592	279	178	87	1742	366	345	1442	421	5452	14	21
Cornwall	443	135	168	491	1270	342	124	631	228	3832	11	18
Cumberland	165	188	11	83	562	75	142	278	169	1673	9	21
Derby	394	77	79	71	905	200	205	777	268	2976	11	18
Devon	615	460	287	312	1649	564	298	1237	471	5893	11	18
Dorset	137	255	80	58	571	146	106	380	159	1892	11	19
Durham	347	316	139	304	1007	362	207	1138	274	4094	13	21
Essex	417	460	83	163	1250	276	234	782	268	3933	11	19
Gloucester	352	457	440	244	1395	578	476	1142	510	5594	13	20
Hereford	84	83	17	36	333	56	57	238	62	966	8	18
Hertford	160	116	45	48	620	107	90	453	155	1794	11	20
Huntingdon	61	18	1	17	216	45	42	140	72	612	10	18
Kent	955	510	169	214	1701	564	526	1650	651	6940	13	21

(*continued*)

Number of deaths during 1838 from death registrations and causes (continued)

Counties	Number of deaths during the year ended 31st December, 1838 from: 1 Epidemic, endemic, and contagious diseases				2 Diseases of respiratory organs			3	4		Proportion of deaths from the preceding causes in every 1,000 of the population, 1841	Proportion of deaths from all causes of mortality in every 1,000 of the population, 1841
	Fever: typhus, scarlatina	Smallpox	Measles	Whooping cough	Consumption	Pneumonia	All other classes	Diseases of brain, nerves, and senses	Diseases of digestive organs	Total deaths from the four preceding classes of diseases		
Lancaster	2866	1628	898	910	8124	2660	1916	7457	3231	29690	18	25
Leicester	273	98	17	70	941	243	154	668	314	2778	13	21
Lincoln	370	138	29	88	874	248	242	1090	358	3437	9	17
Middlesex	4422	3359	487	1749	6220	3097	2334	6643	2492	30803	20	27
Monmouth	328	321	49	91	481	183	78	550	100	2181	16	24
Norfolk	515	126	63	109	1388	325	281	793	395	3995	10	19
Northampton	248	148	36	36	762	192	124	503	212	2361	12	21
Northumberland	366	149	46	113	715	287	240	709	388	3013	12	21
Nottingham	222	73	18	80	911	225	201	901	287	2918	12	20
Oxford	222	81	51	59	655	108	152	389	180	1897	12	21
Rutland	11	2	—	13	64	14	8	56	28	196	9	17
Salop	213	154	112	138	995	242	168	550	284	2856	12	21
Somerset	560	710	401	46	1446	426	373	982	473	5417	12	21
Southampton	454	164	78	148	1222	338	331	881	372	3988	17	19

Stafford	610	249	182	268	1809	539	419	1251	597	5924	12	18
Suffolk	480	325	53	158	1306	315	184	538	275	3634	12	20
Surrey	1348	814	177	565	2196	978	700	2325	763	9866	11	25
Sussex	391	80	159	88	1047	222	181	863	295	3326	11	18
Warwick	454	415	153	164	1495	678	361	978	638	5336	13	20
Westmoreland	41	40	6	41	248	33	44	154	46	653	12	21
Wilts	246	259	263	140	869	268	212	606	241	3104	12	20
Worcester	381	305	122	258	990	353	235	645	446	3735	16	29
York, E.R.	194	92	167	149	725	194	176	1009	251	2957	13	21
York, N.R.	123	28	69	114	550	102	135	553	187	1861	9	17
York, W.R.	1298	993	799	507	4253	1202	848	4374	1494	15768	14	21
Wales												
North	660	575	4	210	1227	102	223	1311	198	4510	13	18
South	1613	1004	199	398	1834	129	277	1200	380	7034	14	21
Total, 1838	24577	16268	6514	9107	59025	17999	13799	49704	19306	216299	14	22
Total, 1839	25991	9131	10937	8165	59559	18151	12855	49215	20767	214771	14	21

*The registration of the causes of death for the year 1838 is selected, as that was the year when the report was made on the sanitary condition of the laboring population in the metropolis, which has served as the foundation of the extended inquiry.

Source: Chadwick, Edwin. *Report from the Poor Law Commissioners on an Inquiry into the Sanitary Conditions of the Labouring Population of Great Britain.* London, 1842, Table, pp.1–2. http://www.deltaomega.org/documents/Chadwick Classic.pdf.

3. Population by WHO Region (1950–2100)

As can be seen in this graph using data from a 2017 report by the Department of Economic and Social Affairs of the United Nations Secretariat, global population grew from over 2 billion in 1950 to around 7.6 billion in 2018. Population is projected to increase to 8.6 billion by the mid-2030, almost 10 billion by mid-2050, and over 11 billion by 2100. This rapid population growth is a concern for the sustainability of natural resources and a public health, health care, economic, social, climate, and environmental concern. It is not known how many people the earth can successfully hold. However, with the world's population doubling from the mid-20th century to the turn of the 21st century, population pressure has already led to global water, air, and land pollution, new and reemerging diseases, food insecurity, conflicts, and a decrease in drinking water supplies. In the WHO lower-income African and Asian regions, population is projected to continue to rise. The higher-income nations in North America and Europe have almost reached a replacement level. Some reasons for the leveling off, or even decline, in these the upper-income nations include the education of women and girls, use of family planning, and desire for smaller families for a higher standard of living so as to give children greater opportunities.

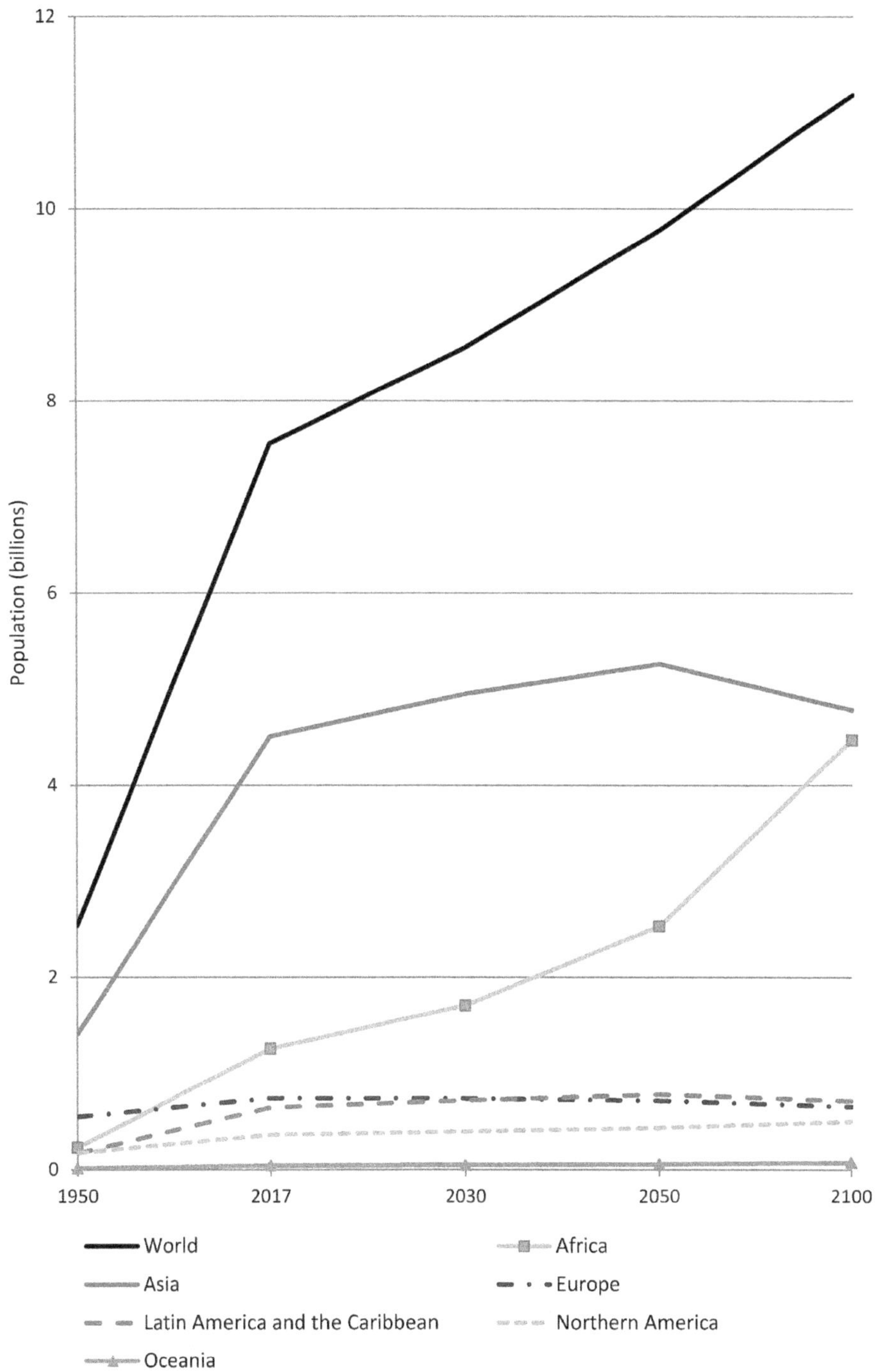

Population by WHO Region 1950–2100 (2017)

Source: Department of Economics and Social Affairs. *World Population Prospects. The 2017 Revision. Key Findings and Advance Tables* (adapted from table S.2, p. 23) https://esa.un.org/unpd/wpp/Publications/Files/WPP2017_KeyFindings.pdf

4. Hospital Admissions for All Causes during Various Wars (1991)

Infectious diseases and infections from wounds have been the major cause of morbidity and mortality in battlefield conditions since the beginning of history. During the 20th century in the wars in the Pacific and the Southeast and the Southwest Asian regions, malaria and various gastrointestinal diseases were a major cause of debility. To prevent malaria, the drug Atabrine was introduced in late 1944; penicillin had been introduced a year earlier. As can be seen in the table, a decrease in all causes for hospital admissions occurred after 1944. Disease as a percentage of all causes from 1942 through 1969 in wars in this region decreased from over 90 to less than 70 percent. Medical personnel contend this was largely due to the development of antibiotics, Atabrine to prevent malaria, immunizations, and better blood-transfusion methods. This table from the United States Army is important as it illustrates the decrease in disease as a major cause of hospitalization in these war conditions in the 20th century.

See also: Document 72; Document 73

Hospital admissions for all causes, U.S. Army, in three wars: World War II, Korea, and Vietnam, by year
[Rate expressed as number of admissions per annum per 1,000 average strength]

War	Year	All causes	Nonbattle injury	Battle injury and wounds	Disease	Disease as percentage of all causes
World War II						
China-Burma-India (CBI)	1942	1,130	81	3	1,046	92
	1943	1,081	84	6	991	92
	1944	1,191	96	18	1,077	90
	1945	745	80	4	661	90
Southwest Pacific	1942	1,035	178	25	832	80
	1943	1,229	171	12	1,046	84
	1944	1,013	139	34	840	83
	1945	990	99	48	843	85
Korea	[1]1950	1,526	242	460	824	61
	1951	897	151	170	576	64
	1952	592	102	57	433	75
Vietnam	1965	484	67	62	355	73
	1966	547	76	75	396	72
	1967	515	69	84	362	70
	1968	523	70	120	333	64
	1969	459	63	87	309	67

[1]July–December only.

Source: Neel, Spurgeon. "Health of the Command. Rates and Trends." *Vietnam Studies: Medical Support of the U.S. Army in Vietnam 1965–1970.* Washington, DC: Department of the Army, 1991, p. 33. Data from (1) World War II: Morbidity and Mortality in the United States Army, 1940–1945. Preliminary Tables Based on Periodic Summary Reports, Office of the Surgeon General, U.S. Army. (2) Korea: Korea, A Summary of Medical Experience, July 1950–December 1952. Reprinted from Health of the Army, January, February, and March 1953, Office of the Surgeon General, U.S. Army. (3) Vietnam: Health of the Army, May 1966, May 1967, May 1968, May 1969, May 1970, Office of the Surgeon General, U.S. Army.

5. How Many People Have Ever Lived? (2018)

The guestimate of how many people have every lived and world population since the beginning of humankind was compiled by demographers Carl Haub and, beginning in the mid-2010s, by Toshiko Kaneda of the Population Reference Bureau. Since the early-1930s, this nongovernmental organization has collected information and supplied statistics focused on the environment, health, and the structure of populations for academic and other research. Estimating global populations is useful for urban planning, agriculture, food resources, and medical, educational, housing, and other needs. As population increases, these resources could become inadequate, especially in developing and low-income nations. In this table, it can be seen that at the beginning of the Industrial Revolution in the mid-18th century—which began in Britain and spread around the world—the population has been steadily rising. It is estimated to rise to about 8.5 billion by 2030 and almost 10 billion by 2050. This continued increase potentially has worldwide health, economic, social, and environmental ramifications.

See also: Document 77

Estimate of how many people have ever lived on the earth

Year	Population	Births per 1,000	Births between benchmarks	Number ever born	Percentage of those ever born
8000 B.C.E.	5,000,000	80	1,137,789,769	1,137,789,769	0.4
1 C.E.	300,000,000	80	46,025,332,354	47,163,122,125	0.6
1200	450,000,000	60	26,591,343,000	73,754,465,125	0.6
1650	500,000,000	60	12,782,002,453	86,536,467,578	0.6
1750	795,000,000	50	3,171,931,513	89,708,399,091	0.9
1850	1,265,000,000	40	4,046,240,009	93,754,639,100	1.3
1900	1,656,000,000	40	2,900,237,856	96,654,876,956	1.7
1950	2,516,000,000	31–38	3,390,198,215	100,045,075,171	2.5
1995	5,760,000,000	31	5,427,305,000	105,472,380,171	5.5
2011	6,987,000,000	23	2,130,327,622	107,602,707,793	6.5

(continued)

Estimate of how many people have ever lived on the earth (continued)

Year	Population	Births per 1,000	Births between benchmarks	Number ever born	Percentage of those ever born
2017	**7,536,000,000**	**19**	**867,982,322**	**108,470,690,115**	**6.9**
2030	8,563,000,000	16	1,806,595,106	110,277,285,221	7.8
2050	9,846,000,000	15	2,833,529,982	113,110,815,203	8.7

Source: Kaneda, Toshiko, and Carl Haub. "How Many People Have Ever Lived on Earth?" (Washington, DC: Population Reference Bureau, 2018). http://www.prb.org/Publications/Articles/2002/HowManyPeopleHaveEverLivedonEarth.aspx

MATERNAL AND CHILD HEALTH

6. Comparison of Maternal Death Rates between Physicians and Midwives (1839–1846)

Hungarian/German obstetrician Ignaz Philipp Semmelweis (1818–1865) is one of the fathers of antiseptic procedures. As seen in the below table, he noticed that women in his physicians-in-training wards in a Vienna birthing hospital for poor women had more deaths from puerperal, or "childbed," fever compared to the midwives' wards. He also observed that on the days when only the physicians' wards were taking patients, "street births" were common but there were very few cases of childbed fever among these women. Since the physician wards had a reputation for many deaths, women pretended they gave birth on the way to the ward so they could still receive child benefits. Semmelweis also observed that the physicians-in-training came directly from the autopsy room to deliver babies and hypothesized that some contagion was being transferred by them to the mothers to cause illness and death. The table is important because it represents the early use of statistics that supported the hypothesis that maternity patients being attended by the medical personnel had higher death rates. Semmelweis required them to wash their hands in chlorinated lime before examining the women, and deaths in their ward declined dramatically. However, his results were not accepted by the medical establishment. It was not until Louis Pasteur (1822–1895) first identified microorganism in the 1860s that Semmelweis's work was slowly accepted along with handwashing to prevent the spread of disease.

Comparison of maternal death rates (in percent) from puerperal fever between physicians' and midwives' patients (1839–1846)

	Physicians maternity patients			Midwives maternity patients		
Year	No. births	No. maternal deaths	Death rate %	No. births	No. maternal deaths	Death rate %
1839	2781	151	5.4	2010	91	4.5
1840	2889	267	9.2	2073	55	2.6
1841	3036	237	7.7	2442	86	3.5
1842	3287	518	15.8	2659	202	7.5
1843	3060	274	8.9	2739	164	5.9
1844	3157	260	8.2	2956	68	2.3
1845	3492	241	6.8	3241	66	2.0
1846	4010	459	11.4	3754	105	2.1

Source: Adapted from Schürer von Waldheim, Fritz. *Ignaz Philipp Semmelweis, sein Leben und Wirken: Urteilder Mit-und Nachwelt.* Wien und A. Hartleben, 1905, p. 49.

7. Maternal Mortality in England (1700–1850)

This graph from a 1999 article by British obstetrician Geoffrey Chamberlain (1930–2014) examines the decline of maternal mortality in England. Causes of death among women related to pregnancy and childbirth were puerperal fever, hemorrhage, convulsions, and illegal abortion. In the 18th- to the mid-19th centuries, it was difficult to get the exact numbers of deaths. Physicians and others had to rely upon bills of mortality (list of burials usually on a weekly basis) or parish records, which were only guestimates of the number of deaths. Lack of good data, as illustrated in this graph, led to official record keeping. This occurred with the Registration of Deaths Act of 1837. At that time, maternal mortality became a measure for assessing the quality of maternity services and later the health of a nation. Around 1870, the registration of all causes of deaths was made mandatory and data concerning rates became more accurate. From the guestimate of maternal deaths, this graph appears to show that from 1700–1850 maternal deaths dropped almost in half. However, more rigorously kept data after mandatory reporting began only show a dramatic decline beginning in the late 1930s in England. This trend was also found in other developed nations due to prenatal care, antibiotics, blood-pressure control, and strict cleanliness.

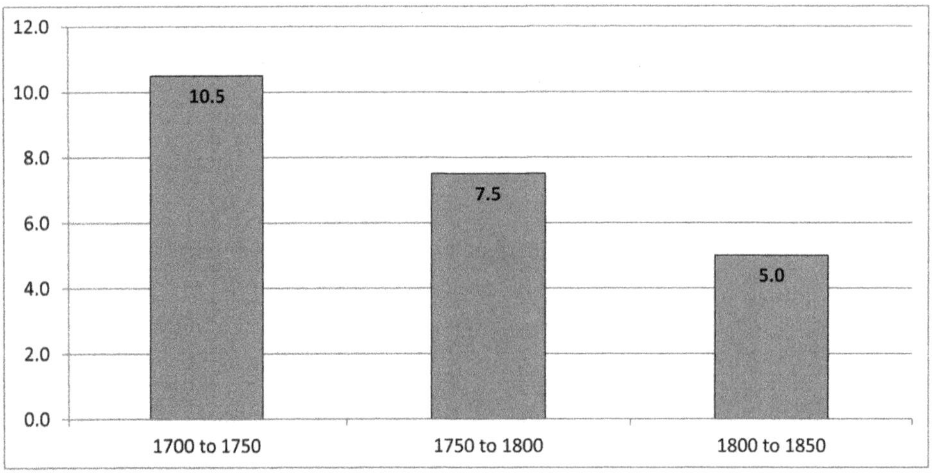

Estimates of maternal mortality rates (MMR) from records of 13 English parishes in 50-year periods
MMR per 1,000 live births

Source: Chamberlain, Geoffrey. "British maternal mortality in the 19th and early 20th centuries." *Journal of the Royal Society of Medicine* 99, no. 11 (November 1999): 559.

8. Maternal Mortality Rate in the United States (1900–1997)

The graph—developed by the American Center for Disease Control and Prevention (CDC)—shows that the maternal death rate has dramatically fallen over the 20th century. An upsurge in deaths from the late teens through the early 1930s is thought to be due to an increase in the number of women giving birth in hospital settings rather than using midwives at home. In hospitals, physicians were more likely to use surgical methods leading to fatal infection and other complications. The decrease in the 1930s was due to more aseptic hospital conditions, safer anesthesia, and the introduction of infusions of saline and other solutions and the use of the new sulfa drugs. The leading causes of maternal deaths over the 20th century were, and still are, hemorrhage, pregnancy-related hypertension and infections. These factors are the same as found in other nations, which all have had a decrease in maternal deaths. Maternal morbidity and mortality in the United States is often due to the lack of prenatal care among low-income women or because women have preexisting health conditions, which include obesity, hypertension, or diabetes. These health risks have been increasing since 1999, which have contributed to an increase in maternal deaths in the first decades of the 21st century.

See also: Data 11

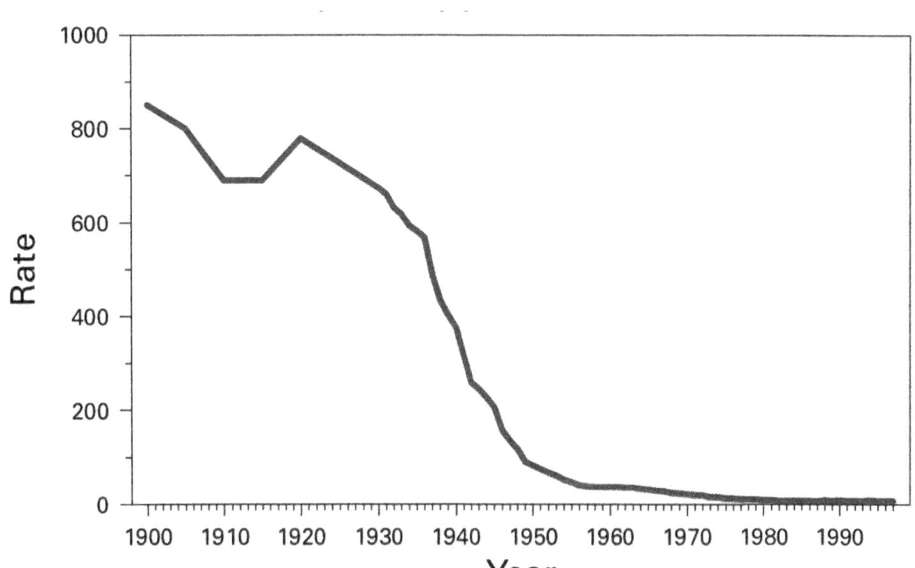

Maternal mortality rate by year, United States, 1900–1997

Source: Centers for Disease Control. "Achievements in Public Health, 1900–1997: Healthier Mothers and Babies." *MMWR Weekly* 48, no. 38 (October 01, 1999):850 https://www.cdc.gov/mmwr/preview/mmwrhtml/mm4838a2.htm.

9. Reduction in Infant Mortality (1915–1997)

This table by the CDC shows the dramatic decrease in mortality during the first year of life in the United States over the 20th century. The decline is unparalleled by other mortality reductions over this time period. This huge decrease in infant deaths was also found in other higher-income nations all of which, by 2000, had lower infant mortality rates than the United States. Congenital malformations and low birth weight accounted for a significant portion of infant mortality in the United States partially due to lack of prenatal care and poor lifestyle habits. Mortality also declined more slowly in the United States than in comparable countries between 2000 and 2014. A more gradual decline in infant mortality has been found in developing nations since the early 1900s. This table is important as it reflects the public health efforts to reduce mortality, which included improved personal hygiene and cleaner environments and living conditions in urban areas. Provisions for safe drinking water and milk along with appropriate feeding of infants were also carried out. Aseptic conditions during childbirth, prenatal care, well-baby clinics, the development of vaccines and antibiotics, and lower fertility rates and smaller families also helped with the decline of infant deaths.

See also: Document 68

Percentage reduction in infant, neonatal, and postneonatal mortality, by year—United States, 1915–1997*

	Percentage reduction in mortality		
Year	Infant (aged 0–364 days)	Neonatal (aged 0–27 days)	Postneonatal (aged 28–364 days)
1915–1919	13%	7%	19%
1920–1929	21%	11%	31%
1930–1939	26%	18%	35%
1940–1949	33%	26%	46%
1950–1959	10%	7%	15%
1960–1969	20%	17%	27%
1970–1979	35%	41%	14%
1980–1989	22%	27%	12%
1990–1997	22%	17%	29%
1915–1997	93%	89%	96%

*Percentage reduction is calculated as the reduction from the first year of the time period to the last year of the time period.

Source: Center for Disease Control. "Achievements in Public Health, 1900–1999: Healthier Mothers and Babies." *MMWR Weekly* 48, no. 38 (October 01, 1999): 849–858 https://www.cdc.gov/mmwr/preview/mmwrhtml/mm4838a2.htm.

10. United States Abortion Rate (1973–2014)

This graph from a series of academic publications based upon data collected by the Guttmacher Institute shows the abortion rates in the United States since the passage of Roe v. Wade *(1973)—the law that made pregnancy terminations legal for American women. In 2014, the lowest abortion rate of 14.6/100,000 since the passage of this law was recorded. Many factors likely contributed to the decline including education, more use of and availability of effective contraceptives, the "morning after pill" and other medications, and increased difficulty for some women to obtain pregnancy terminations due to increasingly restrictive state laws. However, the more restrictive the abortion laws, the more frequent are illegal or nonmedically supervised abortion-related illnesses and deaths. From 1990 to 2014, the maternal mortality rates (MMR) in the United States more than doubled from an estimated 12 to 28 /100,000 births—the highest of any high-income nation. Whether or not illegal, or self-induced, abortions were a factor in this increase is unclear. Of women who obtained abortions in 2014, 59 percent already had at least one birth, 75 percent were from poor or low-income backgrounds, more than half were in their twenties or older, and about 12 percent were teenagers. Medication abortions increased from 2001 to 2014 from 6 to 31 percent, respectively, although the overall abortion trend was decreasing. Trends in abortions, such as seen in this graph, can help provide material for health promotion programs to reduce the incidence of unintended pregnancy.*

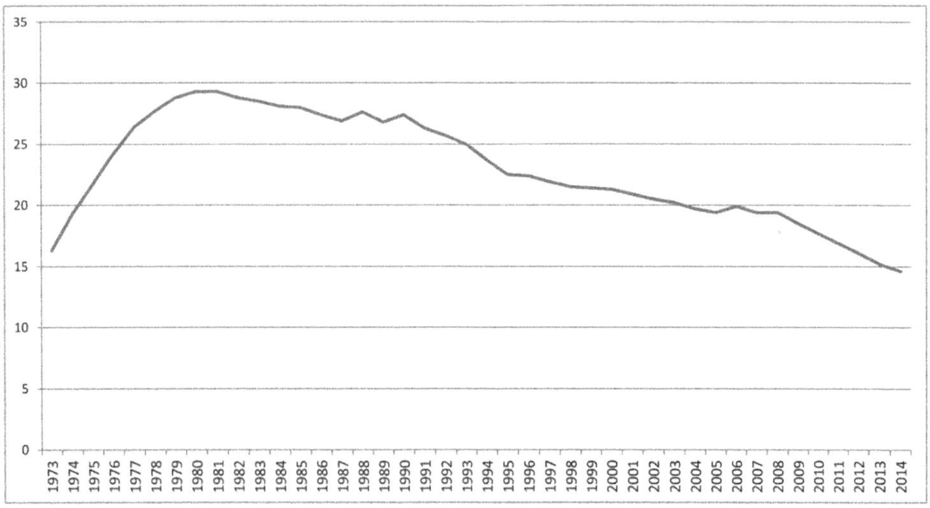

Abortions per 1,000 women aged 15–44

Sources: Jones, Rachel K. and Kathryn Kooistra. "Abortion Incidence and Access to Services in the United States, 2008." *Perspectives on Sexual and Reproductive Health* 43 no. 1 (2011): 41–50; Jones, Rachel K. and Jenna Jerman. "Abortion Incidence and Service Availability in the United States, 2011." *Perspectives on Sexual and Reproductive Health* 46 no. 1(2014): 3–14; Jones, Rachel K. and Jenna Jerman. "Abortion Incidence and Service Availability in the United States, 2014." *Perspectives on Sexual and Reproductive Health* 49 no. 1 (2017): 17–27.

11. Decrease in Maternal Mortality (1990–2015)

Based upon UNICEF data, the graph illustrates maternal mortality over a 25-year period from the late 20th century to the early 21st century. Maternal mortality refers to deaths caused by complications from pregnancy or childbirth and is an indicator of the availability and quality of health care of a nation. The graph shows that global maternal mortality decreased by almost half between 1990 and 2015. Most importantly, this decline was found in all WHO regions, although maternal deaths were still excessively high in sub-Saharan Africa. Worldwide, about 88 percent of all maternal deaths were found in sub-Saharan Africa and South Asia due to lack of health care. Most maternal deaths can be prevented, as seen by the huge differences between the higher- and lower-income regions on the graph. Adequate prenatal, childbirth, and postpartum health care can reduce deaths. The leading cause of maternal mortality is hemorrhaging. Preexisting medical conditions made worse by pregnancy, hypertensive disorders of pregnancy, infections, and complications of unsafe abortions are also major factors in maternal mortality. These causes can be reduced by prompt referral to emergency care when complications are diagnosed by skilled health care workers. Blood transfusions, antihypertensive medications, antibiotics, and surgical interventions such as caesarian C-sections can save the lives of many women.

See also: Data 8

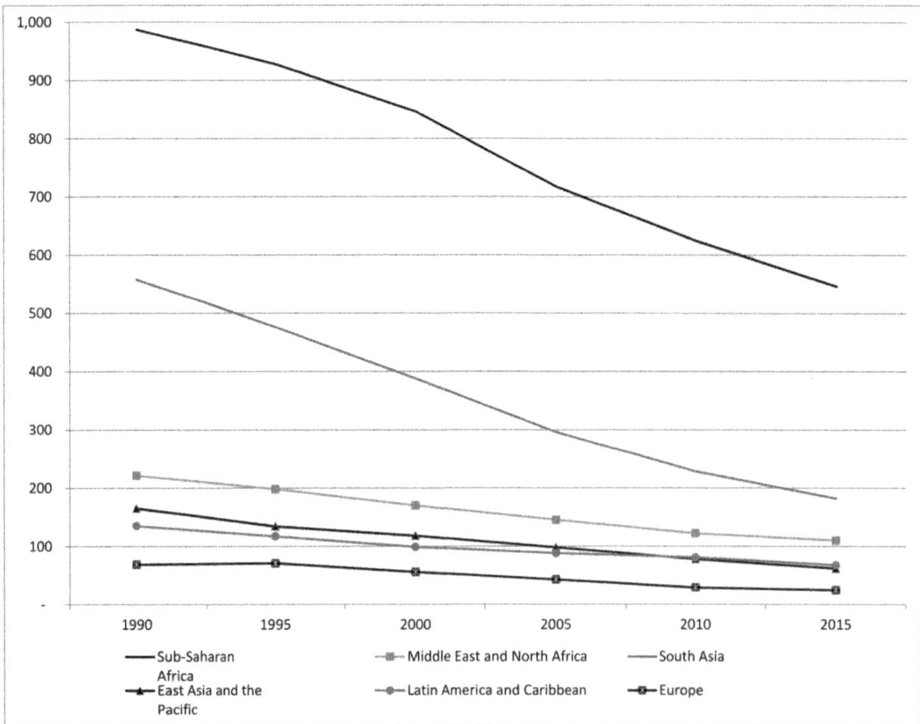

Decrease in maternal mortality in different global regions: 1990–2015

Source: "Maternal Mortality Fell by Almost Half Between 1990 and 2015." *UNICEF Data: Monitoring the Situation of Children and Women* (Updated February 2017). http://data.unicef.org/topic/maternal-health/maternal-mortality/.

12. Child Labor Around the World (2012)

In 2012, the International Labour Office in Geneva, Switzerland, published a report on child labor. A graph based upon this study shows the percentage of children who are both in the workforce and child labor situations in low- and middle-income nations. Since children were less than 1 percent of the workforce in high-income nations, they were not included in this report. A child is defined as between ages 5 and 17 years. Children in the workforce often help their families, the work can be beneficial to them as they learn skills, and they participate in normal schooling. But child labor is work that deprives children of their childhood and schooling. Of the victims of child labor, about half are employed in hazardous work that is dangerous to their health and safety, including enslavement in sweatshops, prostitution, drug trafficking, and armed conflict. This graph is important inasmuch as it points to regions of the world that need assistance in meeting the "Sustainable Development Goal 8.7" of ending all forms of child labor by 2030.

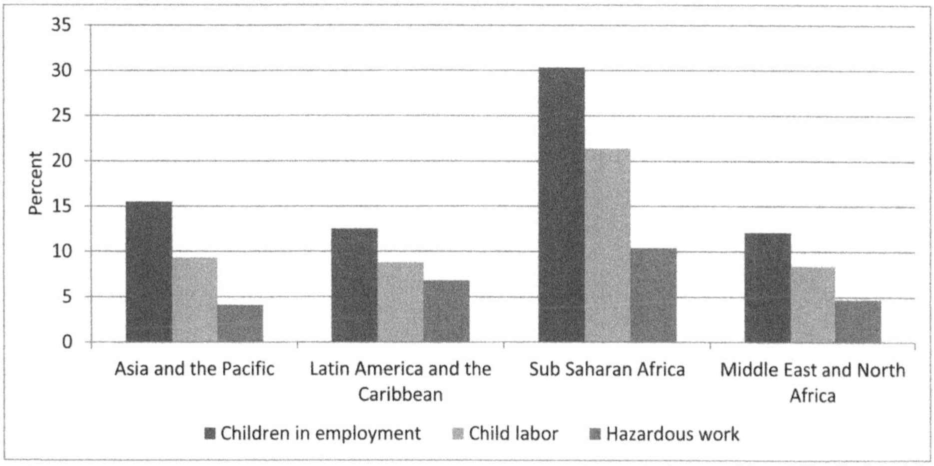

Children (ages 5–17) in employment, child labor, and hazardous work by region (2012)

Source: International Labour Office, *Marking Progress against Child Labour—Global estimates and trends 2000–2012 / International Programme on the Elimination of Child Labour (IPEC).* Geneva: ILO, 2013, 4.

13. Contraception Use and Unmet Needs Globally (2015)

This 2015 graph using data from the United Nations, based upon a global survey of 195 countries, shows that almost 75 percent of the world use contraception for family planning. On the other hand, only about 62 percent do so in the least developed nations. Around 57 percent used modern methods, and around one in ten married or "in-union women" (cohabitation or regular sexual partner) in most regions of the world had an unmet need for family planning. Easy access to family planning allows families to decide on the number of children, spaces births, and reduces maternal and infant mortality. It also allows for more schooling and higher standards of living, especially for girls and women. Determining unmet needs helps nations and global health organizations to plan for and set priorities to ensure universal access to sexual and reproductive health, family planning, and reproductive rights. Graphs such as this point out the substantial gaps in the use of contraceptive methods among couples who want to prevent pregnancy. Growth in modern contraceptive use until 2030 is expected to be found primarily in the sub-Saharan Africa and Oceania regions with the highest unmet need.

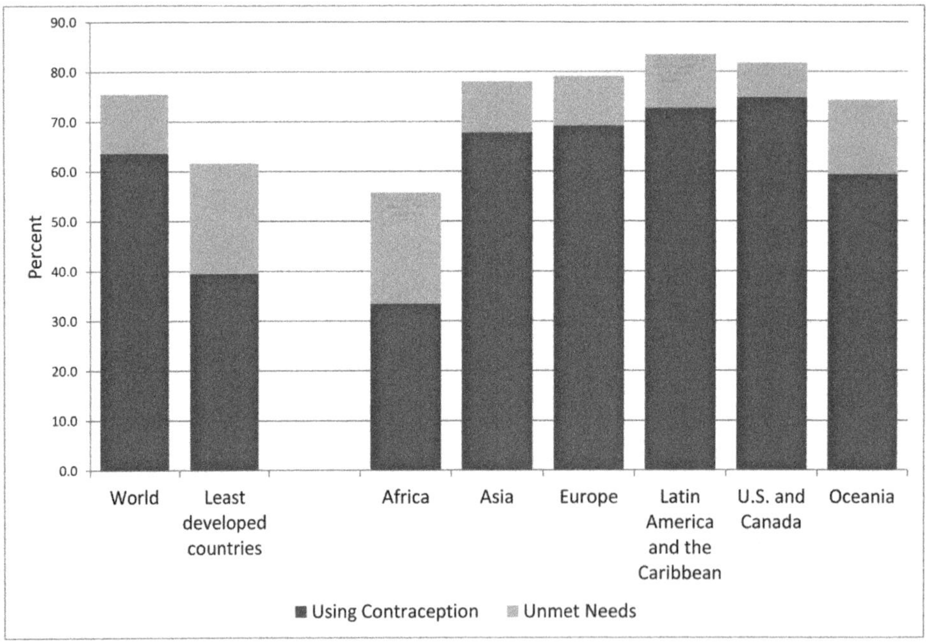

Percentage of women aged 15–49 with regular partners using contraceptions and unmet needs for family planning (2015)

Source: *Trends in Contraception use Worldwide*, 2015. New York: United Nations, 2015, 8. http://www.un.org/en/development/desa/population/publications/pdf/family/trendsContraceptiveUse2015Report.pdf.

14. Life Expectancy: Infant and Childhood Mortality Statistics (2015)

The World Health Organization, founded in 1948, has collected worldwide data on neonatal and early childhood mortality since its early years. From this information they have calculated the life expectancy at birth for individual nations and WHO regions. These data are indicators of the health of the nation and health care system. Earlier data showed that the lowest life expectancy and highest infant mortality were found in the African, Southeast Asia and Eastern Mediterranean regions. The table from data collected during 2015, for example, shows that these regions still have the lowest life expectancy and highest infant and early childhood mortality. As can be seen, these nations also have a lower percentage of births attended by skilled health care personnel. The information in the table is important as it is an indirect indication that basic health care such as sanitation and access to clean water, immunizations, and maternal/infant health care is still not widespread in these regions. The highest life expectancies and lowest maternal/child mortality are found in the region of the Americas, and the European and Western Pacific regions. Both the Americas and Western Pacific regions are a mixture of higher-income and lower-income nations.

See also: Data 11

Source: World Health Organization. "Annex B Part 1," *World Health Statistics: 2016: Monitoring Health for the SDGs*, pp. 110–111. http://www.who.int/gho/publications/world_health_statistics/2016/en/.

Infant and childhood mortality statistics and life expectancy (2015)

Member state	Total population (000s)	Life expectancy at birth (years)			Healthy life expectancy at birth (years)	Proportion of births attended by skilled health personnel (%)	Under-five mortality rate (per 1000 live births)	Neonatal mortality rate (per 1000 live births)
		Male	Female	Both sexes				
	2015	2015			2015	2006–2014	2015	2015
WHO region								
African Region	989,173	58.20	61.70	60.00	52.30	54.00	81.30	28.00
Region of the Americas	986,705	74.00	79.90	77.00	67.30	96.00	14.70	7.70
South-East Asia Region	1,928,174	67.30	70.70	68.90	60.50	59.00	42.50	24.30
European Region	910,053	73.20	80.20	76.80	68.00	99.00	11.30	6.00
Eastern Mediterranean Region	643,784	67.40	70.40	68.80	60.10	67.00	52.00	26.60
Western Pacific Region	1,855,126	74.50	78.70	76.60	68.70	95.00	13.50	6.70
Global	7,313,015	69.10	73.80	71.40	63.10	73.00	42.50	19.20

DISEASES

15. Deaths from Plague and Other Causes in London (1593)

Some of the first vital statistics were collected in London by Corbyn Morris (1710–1779), a British commissioner of customs. Two of Morris's coauthors for the Collection of Yearly Bills *had published data a century before, which were used in some of his writings. John Graunt (1620–1674) is considered one of the first statisticians and demographers and William Petty (1620–1687) may have done most of the compiling for Graunt's works. Morris, in the following table, used earlier data from the plague year of 1593 from a paper called the "The Four Great Plagues, viz. 1593, 1603, 1625, and 1636" and compared them with the weekly Bills—listing of weekly mortality—which showed the increase and decrease in plague deaths. This table is an example of one of the first epidemiological trend studies of a disease, not only from the past but also on a yearly basis. As can be seen, plague, or the Black Death (*Yersinia pestis*), was most prevalent during the warmer months with likely higher rat populations whose infected fleas then spread the disease. In the late summer and fall with the fewest deaths, a high proportion of deaths were from the plague. Although Morris did not calculate it, 45 percent of all deaths were from the plague during March through December of 1593.*

See also: Data 16; Document 21

Buried of all diseases, within London, and the liberties thereof From March to December 1593.

	Date	All diseases	Plague
March	17	230	3
	24	251	31
	31	219	29
April	7	307	27
	14	203	33
	21	290	37
	28	310	41
May	5	250	29
	12	339	38
	19	300	42
	26	450	58
June	2	410	62
	9	441	81
	16	399	99
	23	401	108
	30	850	118

(*continued*)

Buried of all diseases, within London, and the liberties thereof From March to December 1593 (continued)

	Date	All diseases	Plague
July	7	1440	927
	14	1510	893
	21	1491	258
	28	1507	852
Aug	4	1503	983
	11	1550	797
	18	1532	651
	25	1508	449
Sept	1	1490	507
	8	1210	563
	15	621	455
	22	629	349
	29	450	330
Oct	6	408	327
	13	422	323
	20	330	308
	27	320	302
Nov	3	310	301
	10	309	209
	17	301	107
	24	321	93
Dec.	1	349	94
	2	331	86
	15	329	71
	22	386	39

The total of all the burials of the time above said	25886
Whereof the plague	11503

Source: Morris, Corbyn, William Petty, John Graunt, and Thomas Birch. *A Collection of the Yearly Bills of Mortality, From 1657 to 1758 Inclusive: Together With Several Other Bills of an Earlier Date.* London: A. Millar, 1759, 1619.

16. Diseases and Casualties (1670)

The vital statistics over time including mortality from different diseases in London were compiled by British commissioner of customs, Corbyn Morris (1710–1779) and published in 1759. This work, Collection of Yearly Bills, *is based upon material published in the previous century by the coauthors John Graunt (1620–1674), who was one of the first statisticians and demographers, and William Petty (1620–1687), who may have compiled the data for most of Graunt's publications. Morris, in the following table, examines diseases and casualties (deaths) for the year 1670. As can be seen in the table, there were no deaths from plague. The leading causes of death included diarrhea, consumption (TB) and other respiratory diseases, smallpox, ague and fever (malarial type disease), and convulsions, which could be the result of high fevers. This table verifies the major causes of death as infectious diseases in this era.*

See also: Data 15; Document 21

Diseases and casualties in 1670 London

Abortive and stillborn	632	Executed	12	Overlaid	57
Aged and bedridden	923	Falling sickness	3	Palsy	22
Ague and fever	1729	Flox and small pox	1465	Pleurisy	14
Apoplexy and suddenly	76	Found dead in the streets, etc.	5	Quinsy	19
Blasted and planet	4	French pox	52	Rickets	346
Bleeding	1	Frighted	1	Rising of the lights	169
Bloody flux, scowring, and flux	142	Gout	15	Rupture	19
Burned and blown up	8	Grief	13	Scalded	5
Bursten	1	Griping in the guts	3690	Scurvy	37
Cancer, gangrene, and fistula	54	Hanged and made away themselves	13	Smothered	2
Canker and thrush	107	Jaundice	106	Sores, ulcers, broken and bruised limbs	70
Catarrh	1	Imposthume	136	Spleen	6
Childbed	288	Killed by several accidents	94	Spotted fever	121
Chrisomes and infants	746	King's evil	44	Starved	2
Cold and cough	39	Leprosy	1	Stopping of the stomach	374
Colick and wind	100	Lethargy	5	Strangury	16
Consumption and tissick	3272	Livergrown	12	Surfeit	524

(*continued*)

Diseases and casualties in 1670 London (continued)

Abortive and stillborn	632	Executed	12	Overlaid	57
Convulsion	1695	Lunatick	4	Swing pox	1
Cut of the stone and stone	42	Measles	295	Teeth and worms	1470
Dropsy and tympany	919	Megrims	5	Vomiting	76
Drowned	82	Mother	1	Wolf	1
		Murdered	11		

Christened:	Males	6278	Buried:	Males	10614	Of the plague: 0
	Females	5719		Females	9584	
	In all	11997		In all	20198	

Increased in the burials this year: 766

Decreased in the plague this year: 3

Source: Corbyn, William Petty, John Graunt, and Thomas Birch. *A Collection of the Yearly Bills of Mortality, From 1657 to 1758 Inclusive: Together With Several other Bills of an Earlier Date*. London: A. Millar, 1759, 1619.

17. Decline in Diphtheria Deaths in Chicago (1905)

B. Franklin Royer (1870–1961), an American public health physician, graphed the dramatic decline in diphtheria death rate in Chicago around 1905 before, and after, use of a diphtheria antitoxin. Diphtheria was considered a deadly childhood disease that caused a pseudo-membrane to form in the throat, preventing breathing. Royer was concerned that physicians waited too long before starting antitoxin treatment and urged early treatment with adequate doses of the antitoxin. He was one of the first physicians to advocate aggressive treatment founded upon evidence-based research. The graph clearly points out the evidence for the use of antitoxin to prevent death. A toxoid used for immunization was developed in 1921. By the 1930s, immunizations against diphtheria had reduced the use of antitoxins and prevented outbreaks of the disease particularly in developed nations. By the late 20th century, the disease had been eliminated from most higher-income nations but was still prevalent in the South Pacific, the Middle East, Eastern Europe, and sub-Saharan Africa.

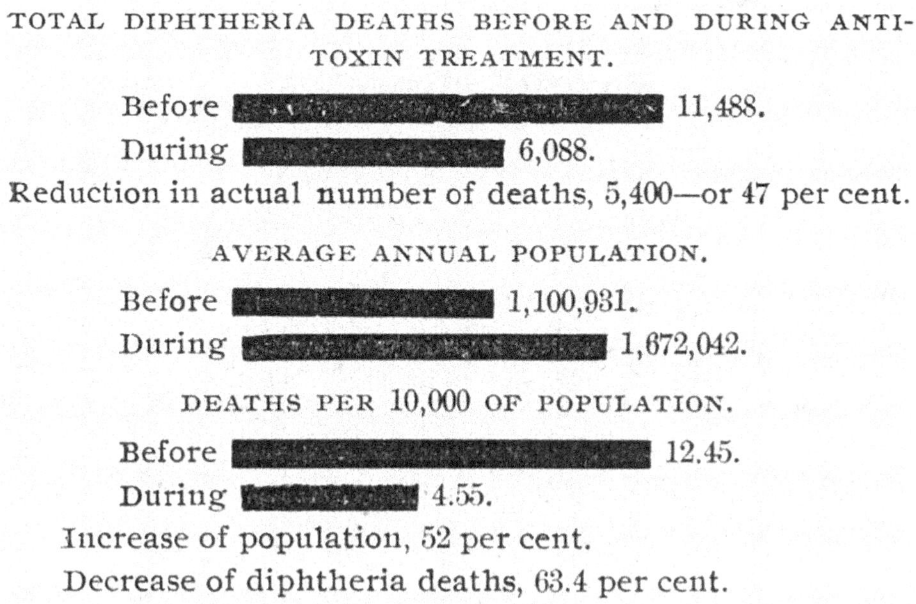

Decline in diphtheria deaths due to immunization (1905)

Source: The Historical Medical Library of the College of Physicians of Philadelphia. Royer, Franklin B. MD. *The Antitoxin Treatment of Diphtheria, With a Plea for Rational Dosage in Treatment and in Immunizing.* Detroit, Mich. E. G. Swift Publisher, 1905.

18. Global Tuberculosis Mortality Trends (1950–1970)

Up until the 1940s and 1950s, there was no cure for tuberculosis (TB) other than rest, good nutrition, and fresh air, which was only minimally successful. It was the leading cause of death at the turn of the 20th century. However, in the post-World War II (WWII) years, several drugs were developed that generally cured the disease. Rather than being a leading cause of illness and death, TB began to decline worldwide. This table by Anthony M. Lowell, of the Tuberculosis Control Division, at the Center for Disease Control in the United States, in 1976 based upon the World Health Organization's data show dramatic declines of both morbidity and mortality of TB from the beginning of antibiotic uses. The international trends of tuberculosis demonstrates the global distribution of the disease and the remarkable progress made in reducing illness and death rates The most dramatic declines were in high-income regions such as North America and Europe in addition to the eastern Mediterranean area. This dramatic decline was the result of organized modern public health prevention programs and facilities. However, these rates appeared to have plateaued in Africa due to poor public health infrastructure.

See also: Data 20

Trends, tuberculosis case rates and death rates
World regions, 1950, 1960, 1970

Region	Rate per 100,000 population			Percent change in rate	
	1950	1960	1970	1950–1960	1960–1970
Northern America	(a)				
Case rates	61.8	31.2	18.2	−49.5	−41.7
Death rates	20.6	5.9	2.6	−71.4	−55.9
Middle America	(a)				
Case rates	60.8	60.5	40.8	−0.5	−32.6
Death rates	47.9	24.6	17.0	−48.6	−30.9
South America	(a)				
Case rates	149.7	126.6	73.0	−15.4	−42.3
Death rates	73.0	41.0	20.3	−43.8	−50.5
Europe					
Case rates	204.5	114.8	63.2	−43.9	−44.9
Death rates	59.4	18.7	8.9	−68.5	−52.4
Eastern Mediterranean					
Case rates	85.7	46.4	12.2	−46.2	−73.5
Death rates	43.7	17.3	10.0	−60.4	−42.2
Africa					
Case rates	220.1	364.9	283.9	+65.8	−22.2
Death rates	119.0	33.4	18.7	−71.9	−44.0
Western Pacific					
Case rates	624.2	408.8	161.1	−34.5	−60.6
Death rates	141.5	34.5	17.4	−75.6	−49.6
Oceania					
Case rates	65.5	43.4	16.2	−33.7	−48.6
Death rates	23.2	4.8	2.0	−79.3	−58.3
All regions, total					
Case rates	202.6	135.0	69.4	−33.4	−48.6
Death rates	59.3	18.4	10.0	−69.0	−45.7

(a) Year 1951

Source: Lowell, Anthony M. *Tuberculosis in the World: Trends in Tuberculosis Incidence, Prevalence, and Mortality at the Beginning of the 3rd Decade of the Chemotherapeutic Era.* Atlanta: Public Health Service, Center for Disease Control, 1976, 18.

19. Reported Incidence of Measles in WHO Regions (1990–1995)

This graph, based upon a report from a WHO study, shows a decrease in measles from the early to mid-1990s in all regions of the world, particularly in the Americas. Plans for further decrease and complete eradication of the disease were made. The graph paints a picture of optimism and hope for the total elimination of the disease. However, this did not occur. Although measles was not wiped out as had been hoped at this meeting, between 2000 and 2016, measles vaccination resulted in an 84 percent drop in measles deaths worldwide, and in 2016 measles deaths had fallen below 100,000 per year—the first time this had occurred. The graph is important as it is a reminder that public health goals can sometimes be difficult to reach. In the 2010s, besides outbreaks in developing regions, sporadic measles outbreaks also occurred in Europe and North America due to several factors. Some developing nations feared that vaccinations were a Western plot to harm them. Refugees from these areas, or regions of conflict, who were unvaccinated, and tourists who visited or were from areas with measles, carried the disease with them. Some Europeans and North Americans frightened by bogus research that suggested autism was caused by vaccinations refused to immunize their children. These issues led to outbreaks among unvaccinated children and adults.

See also: Document 75

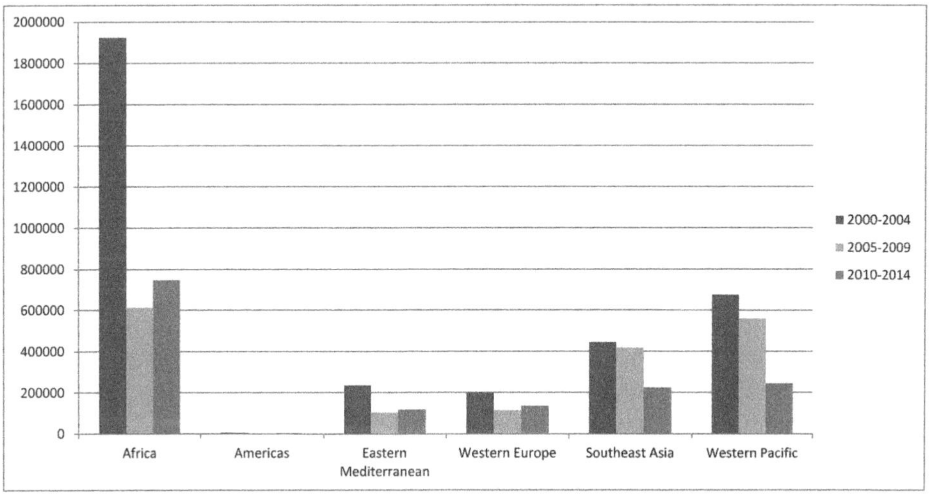

Reported incidence of measles, WHO regions, 1990–1995

Source: World Health Organization. *Measles Reported Cases*. Last update July 1, 2018. http://apps.who.int/immunization_monitoring/globalsummary/timeseries/tsincidencemeasles.html.

20. Global Burden of Disease (1990–2020)

Near the end of the 20th century, it was realized that different health conditions and diseases could have serious economic, social, and health consequences for a nation. The World Health Organization (WHO) in 1996 projected the health needs of the early 21st century based upon Global Burden of Disease (GBD) studies, which are carried out every few years. This chart illustrates the dramatic shifts that are expected. Researchers projected that in developing regions, infectious diseases and malnutrition would be replaced by depression, heart disease, and road accidents as the leading causes of disability and premature deaths. Noncommunicable diseases by 2020 were expected to account for seven out of every ten deaths in developing regions of the world. This projection was based upon the aging of the world's population, which would result in new health challenges in the third decade of the 21st century. The focus of health care would shift to older populations for the prevention of chronic conditions. The GBD studies have been instrumental in guiding global health policy development.

See also: Data 18

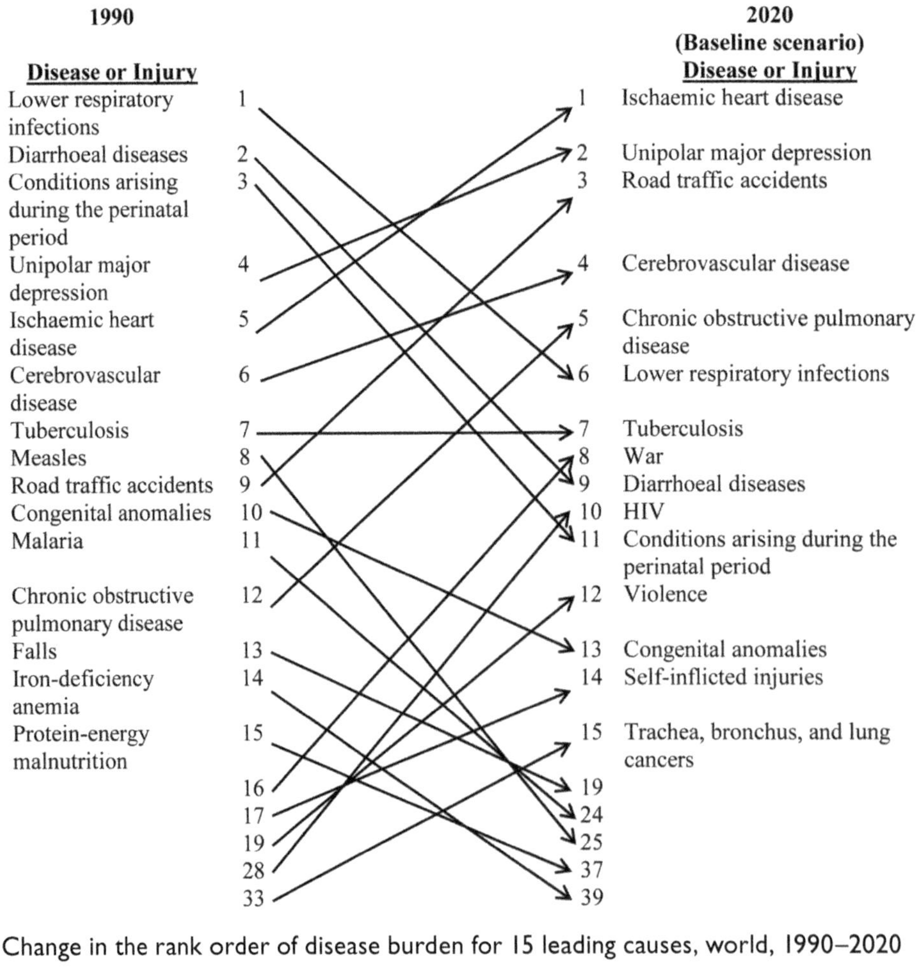

Change in the rank order of disease burden for 15 leading causes, world, 1990–2020

Source: World Health Organization, Murray, Christopher L. and Alan D. Lopez. "Disease burden measured in Disability-Adjusted Life Years (DALYs). *The Global Burden of Disease*. Geneva: World Health Organization, 1996, Figure 2, p. 5. http://www.who.int/iris/handle/10665/41864. Used with permission of the World Health Organization.

21. Impact of Increasing Average Temperature (2007)

In Climate Change 2007, *the Intergovernmental Panel on Climate Change pointed out the scientific evidence for a changing climate and its impact in different regions of the world. Although this report and the following table were published in 2007, by the late 2010s, many of these projected consequences of increased temperature were seen. These included more damaging tropical typhoons and hurricanes, increased wildfires, heat waves, massive flooding in low-lying areas, shortage of safe drinking water, and an increase in tropical diseases, such as Zika, and disease vectors such as mosquitos moving into cooler climates. This table is important as it illustrates the potential consequences likely to occur in many realms of human activities and the natural environment depending upon the degree of temperature increase. Impacts of a warmer climate will vary regionally but together were projected to cause serious problems.*

See also: Document 76

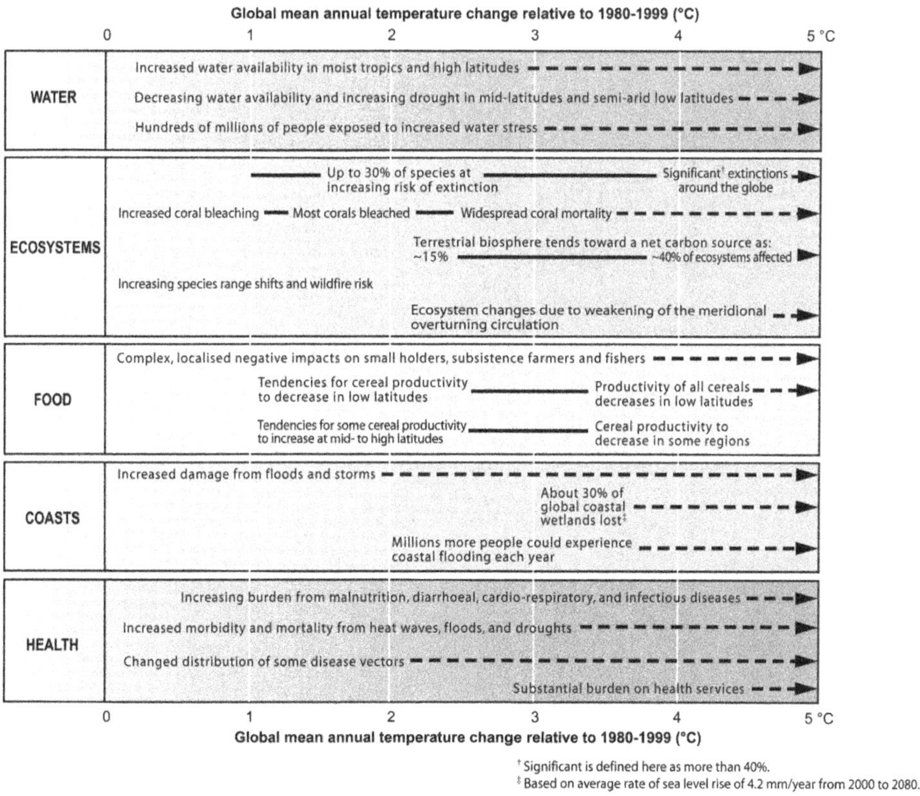

Impacts of increasing average temperature change (2007)

Source: Parry, M. L., O. F. Canziani, J. P. Palutikof, P. J. van der Linden, and C. E. Hanson, eds. "Summary for Policymakers." In *Climate Change 2007: Impacts, Adaptation and Vulnerability, Contribution of Working Group II to the Fourth Assessment Report of the Intergovernmental Panel on Climate Change*. Cambridge, United Kingdom: Cambridge University Press, 2007, 16, Figure SPM.2. Used with permission of the IPCC.

22. Death Rates from Infectious Diseases (1900–1999)

Deaths from infectious diseases in North America and higher-income nations greatly decreased over the 20th century. The graph illustrates this decline in the United States. It was developed by the Center for Disease Control and Prevention and shows what public health measures contributed to better health and longevity. The first major advancement was the creation of health departments to oversee public health on the community, state, and later national level. Sanitation and clean water supplies plus the introduction of chlorinated water contributed to a sharp drop in infant and child mortality due to death from diarrheal diseases and an increase in life expectancy. Immunizations against childhood diseases such as diphtheria and whooping cough, personal hygiene, and the elimination of garbage in the streets reduced many infectious diseases by the 1930s. The exception was a dramatic rise in deaths during 1918–1919 due to an influenza pandemic. The development of antibiotics and new immunizations against many other diseases in the post-WWII era of the 1950s and beyond led to elimination of other diseases such as smallpox and polio.

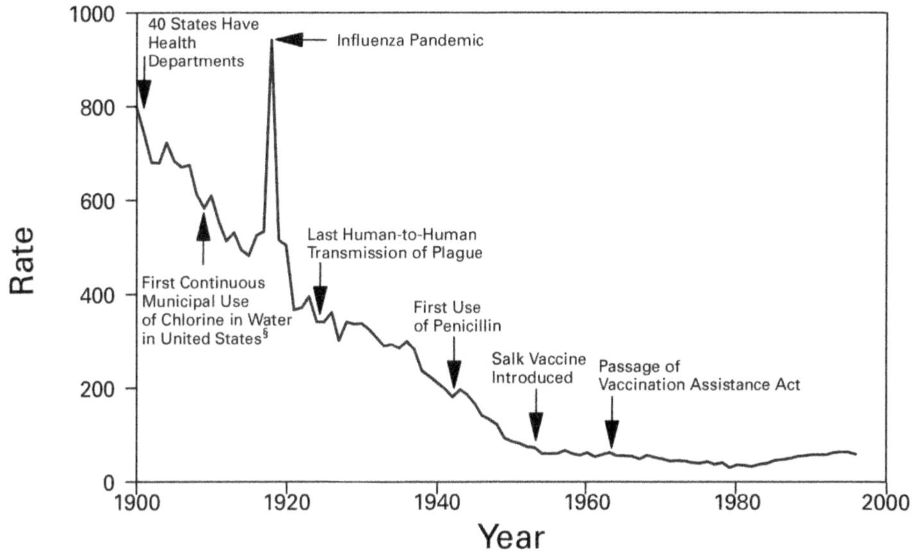

*Per 100,000 population per year.
†Adapted from Armstrong GL, Conn LA, Pinner RW. Trends in infectious disease mortality in the United States during the 20th century. JAMA 1999:281;61–6.
§American Water Works Association. Water chlorination principles and practices: AWWA manual M20. Denver, Colorado: American Water Works Association, 1973.

Crude death rate for infectious diseases—United States, 1900–1996

Source: Center for Disease Control. "Achievements in Public Health, 1900–1999: Control of Infectious Diseases. MMWR 48, no. 29 (July 30, 1999); 621–629. https://www.cdc.gov/Mmwr/preview/mmwrhtml/mm4829a1.htm

MENTAL HEALTH AND SUBSTANCE ABUSE

23. Opium Imports into China (1650–1880)

Opium was traded or smuggled into China by the British beginning in the late 17th century. Although the Chinese emperor passed many decrees and edicts against opium importation, trade and smuggling flourished in the early 1800s. The importation of inexpensive opium resulted in millions of Chinese opium addicts. However, Chinese merchants, the British, and other smugglers and traders demanded free trade with the British Empire and saw the Chinese government as blocking trade agreements. China attempted to prevent opium imports by going after the opium smugglers. This resulted in two "opium wars" in 1839–1842 and 1856–1860. However, China was defeated and forced to import opium by the British resulting in a further opium addiction. The time period between the end of the first opium war through the 1940s is called the "Century of Humiliation" by the Chinese due to intervention and colonialism by Western powers and Japan. As can be seen in the graph, a dramatic increase in opium imports into China occurred over the 19th century. Imports were not only from Britain but also from other nations, including India and Iran, and Southeast Asia.

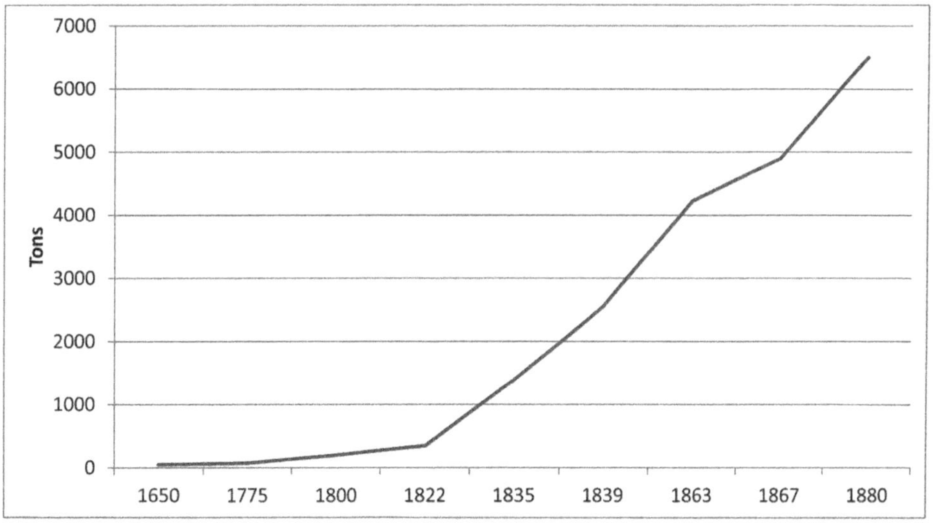

Opium Imports into China (1650–1880)*

*Original data converted into metric tons using 1 chest = 140 lbs = 63.5 kg; 1 picul = 60.453 kg. Data from: Thomas D. Reins, "The Opium Suppression Movement in China," *Modern Asian Studies* 25, no. 1 (1991); Greenberg, *British Trade and the Opening of China, 1800–1842*, UK 1979; Alfred W. McCoy, *The Politics of Heroin*, New York 1991.

Source: United Nations Office on Drugs and Crime (UNDOC) "A Century of International Drug Control." World Drug Report. Chart.: "Opium Imports into China, 1650–1880," p.23.

24. Average Number of Years Spent in Mental Institutions (1845)

British Physician and head of an "insane asylum" near York, England, John Thurman (1810–1873) published Observations and Essays on the Statistics of Insanity *in 1845 about treatment of those with mental disorders in mental hospitals. He details various conditions of the institutions he reported on, such as ventilation, lighting, grounds, and treatment including diet and exercise. Vital statistics about patients such as age, gender, social class, and so on were also collected. He felt that the new science of statistics was important to use in medicine including the field of mental illness. The purpose of this booklet was to compare the result of his mental institution to others in England through the use of statistics. This work was one of the first to use statistics in the study of mental illness in the mid-19th century. A previous tract had reported on the mortality of patients. This table from his publication, documenting the average length of time patients spent in different institutions, is important as it is one of the first studies to compare different institutions by statistical methods. He examines the average number of years a patient stays at each institution for a particular period of time.*

Showing the average duration of residence in various hospitals for the insane

Name of asylum and period	Average duration of residence in years
Cornwall, 22 years, 1820–1842	2.7
Gloucester, 9½ years, 1823–1832	1.54
Kent, 5 years, 1833–1838	1.89
Lancaster, 27 years, 1816–1843	2.23
Middlesex, 12⅓ years, 1831–1843	3.22
Nottingham, 29⅓ years, 1812–1841	1.62
Stafford, 23¼ years, 1818–1841	1.42
Suffolk, 13 years, 1818–1841	2.11
York, West Riding, 25 years, 1818–1843	2.04
Bethlem, 13 years, 1827–1839, "curable" patients	.57
St. Lukes, 83 years, 1751–1834, "curable" patients	.68
St. Lukes, 83 years, 1751–1834, "curable and incurable" patients	1.02
Asylum, York, 27⅔ years, 1814–1842	2.62
Retreat, York, 48 years, 1796–1844	4.7
Lincoln, 21⅔ years, 1820–1842	1.35
Metropolitan, licensed asylums, 6 years, 1833–1839	1.41
Metropolitan, licensed paupers, separately	1.28
Metropolitan, licensed not paupers, separately	1.56
Aberdeen, 12 years, 1830–1842	2.4
Glasgow, 28 years, 1814–1842	1.29

(*continued*)

Showing the average duration of residence in various hospitals for the insane (continued)

Name of asylum and period	Average duration of residence in years
Perth, 11 years, 1827–1838	2.56
Montrose, 16 years, 1824–1840	2.98
Dundee, 33 years, 1820–1843	2.56
Armagh, 16¾ years, 1825–1840	1.46
Ballinasloe, 8¼ years, 1833–1842	1.72
Belfast, 15 years, 1829–1844	1.78
Carlow, 10 years, 1832–1842	2.49
Clonmell, 7¼ years, 1835–1842	1.58
Cork, 9 years, 1833–1842	1.73
Limerick, 15 years, 1827–1842	2.21
Londonderry, 13 years, 1829–1842	1.8
Maryborough, 9½ years, 1832–1842	2.41
Richmond, Dublin, 11¼ years, 1830–1842	2.25
Waterford, 7 years, 1835–1842	1.9
Retreat (Friends) Dublin, 30 years, 1812–1842	4.4
New York, Bloomingdale, 20½ years, 1821–1841	.89
Frankford, U.S. 21½ years, 1817–1838	1.5
Worcester, U.S. 10 years, 1833–1843	1.13
Charenton, 8 years, 1826–1833	1.78
Schleswig, 15 years, 1820–1835	3.9
Siegburg, 15 years, 1825–1840	1.92
Milan, Senavra, 25 years, 1802–1827	1.67

Source: Thurnam, John. *Observations and Essays on the Statistics Of Insanity: Including an Inquiry Into the Causes Influencing the Results of Treatment in Establishments for the Insane: To which are Added the Statistics of the Retreat, Near York.* London: Simpkin, Marshall, & Co., 1845, 65.

25. Multilateral Agreements on Narcotics and Psychotropic Substances (1909–1988)

Over the 20th century, numerous drug trafficking treaties for international control of manufacturing and distribution of drugs took place on the global stage. The Hague Convention was the first of these treaties. Overall the treaties, as listed in the following table, based upon information by several intentional agencies, did reduce the opium problem in Asia, especially China. Various nations also passed nationwide drug laws, including the Harrison Narcotic Tax Act (1914) in the United States. By midcentury, the licit trade in narcotics had been reduced. Most importantly, 123 countries, or 95 percent of all United Nations member states, were parties to the international drug control conventions. On the other hand, illegal black markets increased and were an unintended consequence of international controls as many nations relied on opium or coca production as a major agricultural product for income and export. This continued illicit underground economy led to drug epidemics, particularly in developed nations, into the 21st century. The table points out the different treaties over the 20th century in terms of international drug control.

See also: Data 27; Document 62; Document 64

Multilateral agreements on narcotics and psychotropic substances

Date and place signed	Title of agreement	Date of entry into force
February 26, 1909 Shanghai, China	Final Resolutions of the International Opium Commission[1]	Not Applicable
January 23, 1912 The Hague, Netherlands	International Opium Convention	February 11, 1915/June 28, 1919[2]
February 11, 1925 Geneva, Switzerland	Agreement concerning the Manufacture of, Internal Trade in, and Use of Prepared Opium	July 28, 1926
February 19, 1925 Geneva, Switzerland	International Opium Convention	September 25, 1928
July 13, 1931 Geneva, Switzerland	Convention for Limiting the Manufacture and Regulating the Distribution of Narcotic Drugs[3]	July 9, 1933
November 27, 1931 Bangkok, Thailand	Agreement for the Control of Opium Smoking in the Far East	April 22, 1937
June 26, 1936 Geneva, Switzerland	Convention for the Suppression of the Illicit Traffic in Dangerous Drugs	October 26, 1939
December 11, 1946 Lake Success, New York, USA	Protocol amending the Agreements, Conventions and Protocols on Narcotic Drugs concluded at The Hague on January 23, 1912, at Geneva on February 11, 1925, and February 19, 1925, and July 13, 1931, at Bangkok on November 27, 1931, and at Geneva on June 26, 1936	December 11, 1946

(continued)

Multilateral agreements on narcotics and psychotropic substances (continued)

Date and place signed	Title of agreement	Date of entry into force
November 19, 1948 Paris, France	Protocol Bringing under International Control Drugs outside the Scope of the Convention of July 13, 1931 for Limiting the Manufacture and Regulating the Distribution of Narcotic Drugs, as amended by the Protocol signed at Lake Success, New York, on December 11, 1946	December 1, 1949
June 23, 1953 New York, USA	Protocol for Limiting and Regulating the Cultivation of the Poppy Plant, the Production of, International and Wholesale Trade in, and Use of, Opium	March 8, 1963
March 30, 1961 New York, USA	Single Convention on Narcotic Drugs, 1961	December 13, 1964
February 21, 1971 Vienna, Austria	Convention on Psychotropic Substances	August 16, 1976
March 25, 1972 Geneva, Switzerland	Protocol amending the Single Convention on Narcotic Drugs, 1961	August 8, 1975
December 20, 1988 Vienna, Austria	United Nations Convention against Illicit Traffic in Narcotic Drugs and Psychotropic Substances	November 11, 1990

1. This is the only document in the table that is not an enforceable multilateral treaty. It is included because it marks the beginning of substantial international cooperation on the control of drugs.

2. China, the Netherlands, and the United States put the Convention into force among themselves in 1915 (they were joined later that year by Honduras and Norway). Only when the Convention was made part of the Versailles Treaty in 1919 did it come into force globally.

3. As amended by the Protocol signed at Lake Success, New York, on December 11, 1946.

Source: Sinha, Jay. The History and Development of the Leading International Drug Control Conventions. The Senate Special Committee on Illegal Drugs. Library of Parliament. February 21, 2001. https://sencanada.ca/content/sen/committee/371/ille/library/history-e.htm#A.%20The%201909%20Shanghai%20Conference. Used with permission of the Senate of Canada.

26. Alcohol Consumption per WHO Region (2005)

In 2011, the World Health Organization (WHO) published the report Global Status Report on Alcohol and Health, *which examined both officially recorded alcohol consumption along with the estimate of the percentage that was unrecorded. Unrecorded consumption includes homemade and illegally produced alcohol that was not documented by official data collection and taxes. It includes smuggled alcohol, alcohol intended for industrial or medical uses, illegal distilleries, and legal homemade beverages made from fermentation of sorghum, millet, maize, rice, wheat, or fruits. As can be seen in the table, global per capita consumption of those ages 15 and older in 2005 was 6.13 liters of absolute alcohol. Almost a third of this consumption came from unrecorded sources. Unrecorded beverages, especially the distilled spirits, may contain impurities that can lead to health issues. The data in the table suggest that the highest alcohol consuming region of the world is Europe followed by the Americas. Although the eastern Mediterranean region had the lowest alcohol consumption, over 50 percent was unreported. This region has a high Muslim population where all alcoholic beverages are generally forbidden by the Qur'an—the Islamic sacred book. The table gave WHO an idea of where alcohol dependence and other issues might be prevalent.*

Total adult per capita alcohol consumption (APC), unrecorded APC, and proportion of unrecorded APC of total APC, in liters of pure alcohol, by WHO region, 2005*

WHO Region	Total APC	Unrecorded APC	Proportion of unrecorded APC of total APC (%)
Africa	6.15	1.93	31.4
Americas	8.67	2.01	23.1
Eastern Mediterranean	0.65	0.36	56.2
Europe	12.18	2.67	21.9
South-East Asia	2.20	1.52	69.0
Western Pacific	6.23	1.63	23.2
World	6.13	1.76	28.7

*Best estimates of 2005 using average recorded alcohol consumption 2003–2005 (minus tourist consumption) and unrecorded alcohol consumption 2005.

Source: World Health Organization. *Global Status Report on Alcohol and Health.* WHO, 2011, 5. Available online at http://www.who.int/substance_abuse/publications/global_alcohol_report/msbgsruprofiles.pdf Used with permission of the World Health Organization.

27. Estimated Annual Percentage of Opiate Use (1907 and 2006)

At the turn of the 20th century, the unregulated international markets and trade in highly addictive substances such as the opiates resulted in a Chinese opium epidemic. This free trade in drugs resulted in major drug dependency problems in several nations and in particular China as opium from several nations was imported into this nation. However, international pressure was brought against drug-producing nations after passage of this and other treaties. By midcentury, the illicit trade in narcotics had been reduced along with strict laws concerning use in the new People's Republic of China. This resulted in a dramatic decrease in opium use in Asia over the century that was now similar to the rest of the world as can be seen in the table below from the United Nations Office on Drugs and Crime in 2008. Adherence to international conventions was now "officially" universal although there was still a lively global illicit market for drugs.

See also: Data 25; Document 62

Estimated annual percentage of opiate use, 1907–1908 and 2006–2007

	1907–1908	2006–2007
Asia	3.3%	0.24%
World	1.5%	0.25%

Source: Data from United Nations Office on Drugs and Crime (UNDOC). A Century of International Drug Control, 2008, 90. Available online at https://www.unodc.org/documents/data-and-analysis/Studies/100_Years_of_Drug_Control.pdf.

28. Opiate Prescriptions per Year (1991–2013)

Opiate prescriptions including OxyContin and hydrocodone rapidly increased from the early 1990s in the United States as can be seen in this chart from the National Institute of Drug Abuse in 2014. The misuse of opioids including prescription pain relievers, heroin, and powerful synthetic opioids, such as fentanyl, became a serious national crisis that affected not only public health but also the social and economic welfare of the nation in the 2010s. In the late 1990s, pharmaceutical companies marketed the new opiates as nonaddictive, and health care providers began to prescribe them at greater rates. However, it was soon noticed that these drugs were highly addictive. In addition, liberal prescriptions led to widespread misuse and diversion of the drugs into a black market. By the mid-2010s, an increase in those with opiate addictive disorders and in overdose deaths was observed. Since these drugs were often injected, an increase in HIV/AIDS and hepatitis C—as needles were often shared—emerged. In 2017, the U.S. Department of Health and Human Service declared a public health emergency and announced strategies to combat the opiate crisis. This chart illustrates the decrease in prescriptions by health care professionals when dependency problems from the new opiates were discovered.

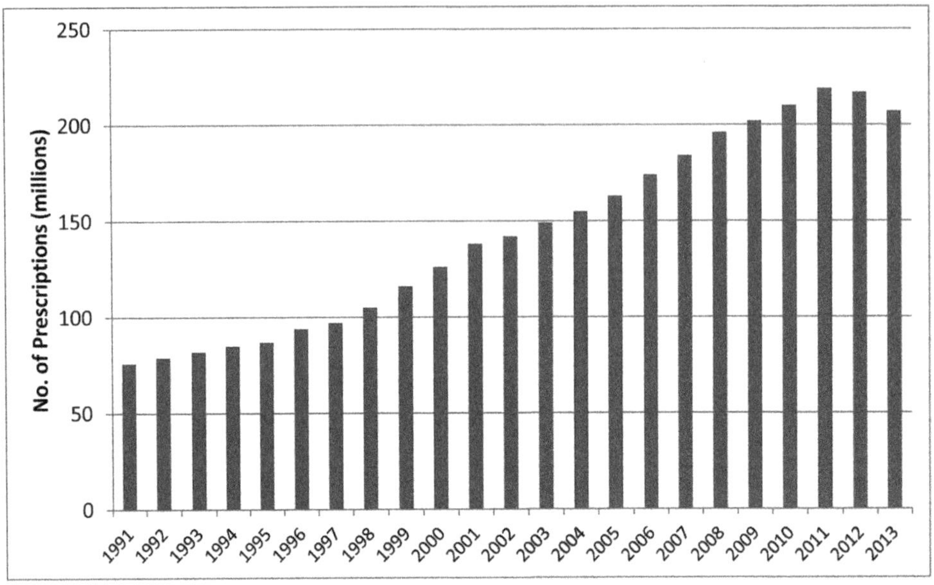

Opiate prescriptions per year (1991–2013)

Source: Adapted from Volkow, Nora D. "America's Addiction to Opioids: Heroin and Prescription Drug Abuse." Figure 1 Opioid Prescriptions Dispensed by US Retail Pharmacies. National Institute of Drug Abuse, May 14, 2014, 1. Available online at https://www.drugabuse.gov/about-nida/legislative-activities/testimony-to-congress/2014/americas-addiction-to-opioids-heroin-prescription-drug-abuse.

29. Prevalence of Tobacco Smoking (2010–2025)

The World Health Organization (WHO) published the WHO Global Report on Trends in Tobacco Smoking 2000–2025 *in 2015, which estimated the trends in tobacco use over the early 21st century. It examined several variables including tobacco use by sex and WHO global regions. The results are illustrated in the following table. The Global Report was produced under a 2013 UN mandate to address four noncommunicable diseases that are associated with tobacco use in order to reduce premature deaths, that is, deaths under 70 years of age. In 2015, smoking caused more than one in ten deaths worldwide. As can be seen in the table, smoking is projected to increase among males in the African and Southeast Asian regions but to decline in other global WHO regions. It is also projected to decline among females and in all regions by 2025. This table is useful for showing areas of the world where antismoking interventions needs to be focused.*

See also: Document 78

Prevalence of current tobacco smoking (%) by region by sex, 2010 and 2025

	2010			2025		
Region	**Male**	**Female**	**Both sexes**	**Male**	**Female**	**Both sexes**
AFRO	23.2	2.5	12.8	34.7	1.6	18.1
AMRO	24.1	14.2	19.0	16.3	8.6	12.3
EMRO	35.1	3.1	19.5	45.3	2.5	24.6
EURO	40.3	19.9	29.6	31.3	15.9	23.3
SEARO	33.1	2.9	18.2	27.5	1.2	14.5
WPRO	49.4	3.6	26.8	43.3	2.4	23.2
Global	**36.9**	**7.3**	**22.1**	**33.2**	**4.7**	**18.9**

WHO REGIONS:

AFRO: Regional Office for Africa
AMRO: Regional Office for the Americas
EMRO: Regional Office for South-East Asia
EURO: Regional Office for Europe
SEARO: Regional Office for the Eastern Mediterranean
WPRO: Regional Office for the Western Pacific

Source: World Health Organization. *WHO Global Report on Trends in Tobacco Smoking 2000–2025.* Geneva: World Health Organization, 2015, 5. Used with permission of the World Health Organization.

PRIMARY DOCUMENTS

1 Hammurabi's Laws Concerning Sickness and Medical Practice (ca. 1750 B.C.E)

The sixth Babylonian king, Hammurabi, around 1750 B.C.E. created a book of laws, or codes of behavior, that were inscribed on a stelle, a stone tablet. They were retranslated and edited by British religious scholar Chilperic Edwards in 1904. These codes were the first written documents concerning laws and legal responsibilities and included many aspects of life such as wages, contracts, inheritance, divorce, and other areas. They are the earliest known writings that describe medical conditions, expected behavior, and punishment for misbehavior; they reflect the "an eye for an eye" mentality of the era. The writings prescribed different punishments depending upon the social class of the individual and included laws regulating physicians' practices. The excerpt included here discusses laws concerning the treatment of sick women by their husbands and institutes punishments for an individual who beats a pregnant woman if the woman should miscarry or die. The excerpt also sets out payments for surgeons for different procedures on both humans and animals. Furthermore, it codifies punishments if a patient should die from treatments, again depending upon the social class of the patient.

148. If a man has married a wife, and sickness has seized her, and he has set his face to marry another; he may marry; but his wife whom the sickness has seized he shall not divorce. She shall dwell in the house he has built, and he shall support her while she lives.

149. If that woman is not content to dwell in the house of her husband, he shall return to her the dowry she brought from her father's house, and she shall go.

209. If a man strike the daughter of a free man, and causes her foetus to fall; he shall pay ten shekels of silver for her foetus.

210. If that woman die, his daughter shall be slain.

211. If he has caused the daughter of a plebeian to let her foetus fall through blows, he shall pay five shekels of silver.

212. If that woman die, he shall pay half a mina of silver.

213. If he has struck the slave of a man, and made her foetus fall; he shall pay two shekels of silver.

214. If that slave die, he shall pay a third of a mina of silver.

215. If a doctor has treated a man with a metal knife for a severe wound, and has cured the man, or has opened a man's tumour with a metal knife, and cured a man's eye; then he shall receive ten shekels of silver.

216. If the son of a plebeian, he shall receive five shekels of silver.

217. If a man's slave, the owner of the slave shall give two shekels of silver to the doctor.

218. If a doctor has treated a man with a metal knife for a severe wound, and has caused the man to die, or has opened a man's tumour with a metal knife, and destroyed the man's eye; his hands shall be cut off.

219. If a doctor has treated the slave of a plebeian with a metal knife for a severe wound, and caused him to die; he shall render slave for slave.

220. If he has opened his tumour with a metal knife, and destroyed his eye, he shall pay half his price in silver.

221. If a doctor has healed a man's broken bone or has restored diseased flesh, the patient shall give the doctor five shekels of silver.

222. If he be the son of a plebeian, he shall give three shekels of silver.

223. If a man's slave, the owner of the slave shall give two shekels of silver to the doctor.

224. If a doctor of oxen or asses has treated either ox or ass for a severe wound, and cured it, the owner of the ox or ass shall give to the doctor one-sixth of a shekel of silver for his fee.

225. If he has treated an ox or an ass for a severe wound, and caused it to die, he shall give the quarter of its price to the owner of the ox or the ass.

Source: Edwards, Chilperic, and Hammurabi. *The Hammurabi Code, and the Sinaitic Legislation: With a Complete Translation of the Great Babylonian Inscription Discovered at Susa [in English]*. London: Watts, 1904, pp. 50, 63–64.

2 Recipes to Treat Diseases of Women in Ancient Egypt (ca. 1500 B.C.E.)

The Papyrus Ebers *is considered one of the most important medical papyri of ancient Egypt and is among the oldest preserved medical documents. The* Papyrus *was supposedly found between the legs of an Egyptian mummy and was purchased in 1872 by German writer and Egyptologist Georg Ebers (1837–1898) for whom it was named. The document—written ca. 1500 B.C.E.—shows cures and incantations for many types of conditions including prevention and treatment of diseases specifically found among women. In this section, incantations and recipes of cures for diseases of women are recounted. The translator describes information about cures covered in the section. In looking at some of the formula that included manure from various creatures, it was likely that further infections occurred. Several substances mentioned in this section are unknown. However, the meanings of others are as follows to make more comprehension of this extraction from the papyrus.* Uah-*grain was likely millet or wheat;* mehit-*fish are common large fish found in the Nile;* wonderfruit *was pomegranate, which has been found to have antimicrobial properties;* hennu-*vessel was likely a boat-shaped pot; and uan-tree was likely from pine tree or similar conifer.*

CHAPTER XIV

DISEASES OF WOMEN

The women's section covers some four or five pages of the Papyrus and includes remedies for errors of menstruation and lactation, diseases of the breasts and genitalia, aids to abortion and parturition, and various valuable hints to nursing mothers. Two of these hints enable them to distinguish the quality of their milk: thus, if the milk be good, it smells like the pollen of uah-grain; if, on the other hand, the milk be bad, it smells like the entrails of the mehit-fish. Other hints enable them to prognosticate the fate of the new-born child:

PROGNOSIS FOR A CHILD ON THE DAY IT IS BORN

If it cries ni, it will live.
If it cries ba, it will die.

ANOTHER

If it lets a loud lamentation be heard, it will die.
If it looks down its face it will thereupon die.

To regulate menstruation the patient was douched with a mixture of Garlic and Wine. If this failed, a douche composed of Fennel, Wonderfruit, Honey and Sweet Beer was substituted and persisted in for four days. To protect a virgin from Leucorrheoa it was necessary to anoint her breast, body, and all the limbs with a lotion prepared by crushing the dried liver of a Swallow in Sour Milk.

To produce Milk in the breast of a woman about to suckle a child, Bones-of-the-Swordfish were warmed in Oil and her backbone smeared therewith. The same result could be brought about by mixing Fragrant Bread (which had been made from Soured Durra) with the Poppy-plant, and making her eat it while she sat cross-legged.

To bring about abortion, only one remedy is given: Dates, Onions, and the Fruit-of-the-Acanthus, were crushed in a vessel with Honey, sprinkled on a cloth, and applied to the Vulva. It ensured abortion either in the first, second or third period. To hurry on labour, however, there was no lack of remedies:

REMEDY TO CAUSE A WOMAN TO BE DELIVERED
Peppermint
Let the woman apply it to her bare posterior.

ANOTHER TO CAUSE ALL AND EVERYTHING THAT IS IN THE BODY OF A WOMAN TO FALL
Pot-of-a-new-hennu-vessel
Crush in Warm Oil and pour on her genitals.

ANOTHER TO LOOSEN A CHILD IN THE BODY OF A WOMAN
Sea-salt
Clean Grain-of-Wheat
Female Reed
Plaster the abdomen therewith.

ANOTHER
Fresh Salt
Honey
Strain and take for one day.

ANOTHER
Fennel
Incense
Garlic
sert-juice
Fresh Salt
Wasp's dung
Make into a ball and put in the Vagina. . . .

To remedy a diseased Breast one could plaster it for four days with a compound of Calamine, Cow's Brain, and Wasp's dung; or one could invoke the goddess Isis by means of a magic formula:

MAGIC FORMULA FOR THE BREAST

The Breast is the same diseased Breast of Isis who in the city of Xebt bore the gods Su and Tefnut!

She has prepared for it this Magic Formula to be said over aat-plant, Health-corn, over the Fruitful-Part-of-Reeds, over the Hair-of-the-abt-plant, which we bring here to drive out all kinds of Deadly Diseases, as many as there are, cleansing by a discharge in the Left Side.

Prepare it against all kinds of Deadly Diseases. Neither express, nor rub, nor bleed. Prevent the dryness of the Eyes which ensues.

SPEAK OVER AAT-PLANT, OVER HEALTH-GRAINS, OVER THE-FRUITFUL-PART-OF-REEDS, OVER HAIR-OF-THE-HEAD-OF-THE-ABT-PLANT.

LET IT POUR OUT ON THE LEFT SIDE.

MAKE SEVEN PORTIONS AND GIVE THEM.

The Vulva could be protected against the entry of disease by injecting a douche in which Garlic and Horn-of-a-Cow figure as ingredients. Should this prophylactic fail and inflammation ensue, the douche was changed to one of Bile-of-the-Cow, Cassia, and Oil. If the disease progressed and corrosion occurred, the Cow was discarded for the Hog, and a douche of Fresh Dates and Hog's Bile administered.

To correct the displaced uterus, the remedies recommended were almost as ingenious as they were useless:

REMEDY TO ALLOW THE WOMB OF A WOMAN TO SLIP INTO ITS PLACE

The-Film-of-Dampness-which-is-found-on-the-Wood-of-Ships (mould)

Rub in Yeast-of-Fermented-Beer and let her drink it.

ANOTHER

Put an Ibis-of-Wax on the coals and allow the fumes thereof to penetrate into her sex-organs.

ANOTHER

Dried Human excrement

Put in Incense; the woman bends herself over the same and lets the fumes thereof penetrate into her sex-organs.

ANOTHER

Oil-of-the-Earth (? Petroleum) with peddu (manure)

Keep in Honey and rub the body of a woman therewith.

ANOTHER

Dried Excrement

Froth-of-Beer

Rub the finger of the woman therewith and put it to all her limbs against her sufferings. (Joachim suggests that she was to smear the prolapsed uterus.)

With one more extract from the women's section we may pass on:

WHEN THOU EXAMINEST A WOMAN WHO HAS LIVED many years without her Menstruation having appeared; she vomits something like foam and her body is as though a fire were under it, but she recovers after the vomiting; then say thou to her: This is a rising of Blood to the Womb. So soon as she has spoken the Magic Formula, and has had coitus, make thou for her:

Berry-of-the-uan-tree	1/32
Caraway	1/64
Incense	1/64
uah-grain	1/16

Put Cow's Milk to the Fire with Thigh-tallow. Add Milk thereto and let her take for four days.

Source: Bryan, Cyril P. Translator. *Ancient Egyptian Medicine: The Papyrus Ebers.* Translated from the German. [S.l.: s.n., 1930?], pp.82–87.

3 Circulation of the Blood As Seen by Ancient Egyptians (ca. 1500 B.C.E.)

The Papyrus Ebers *is one of the first written medical documents that discusses treatment of many diseases. It contains 110 pages on anatomy and physiology, herbal and other remedies, toxicology, spells, and treatment and was written around 1500 B.C.E. This papyrus is considered one of the most important medical works from ancient Egypt and was written in priestly Hieratic Egyptian cursive writing. It contains the largest compilation of ancient Egyptian medical knowledge compared to other writings. Some information from Egyptian antiquity, such as the information in this document, found its way into ancient Greek medical thought which influenced medical thinking of western medicine. The papyrus was found by German Egyptologist and author Georg Ebers (1837–1898) in Luxor in 1893–1894. It includes such topics as herbal, organic and mineral recipes and cures, the importance of the gods, cures for the alimentary, urinary and circulatory systems, mental illness, diseases of women and diseases of ears, skin, and eyes. Although they knew the heart contained a number of vessels going out to various parts of the body to carry blood, other fluids such as blood, tears, urine and semen, were also thought to be carried by the blood. The following section is on the circulation system and should be compared to the writings of other physicians over the centuries as advancement in medical knowledge emerged.*

See also: Document 2

CHAPTER XX

THE HEART AND CIRCULATORY SYSTEM

To the student the most interesting section of the Papyrus is undoubtedly the chapter dealing with the Heart, or rather with the vascular system. At first sight one is in danger of assuming that the knowledge of the Heart and of its action enjoyed by these Ancients was much greater than it was in reality. But as one reads on it is clearly established that they made the fatal mistake of regarding the Heart not as a pump but as a mere well. Perhaps had they made a closer examination of the Heart itself they would have discovered the existence of the all-important valves, when (it is not too much to believe) they would in a flash have grasped the real function of the organ.

THE BEGINNING OF THE SECRET BOOK OF THE PHYSICIAN

THE SCIENCE OR THE ACTION OF THE HEART AND OF THE HEART ITSELF

In the Heart are the vessels to the whole of the body. As to these every physician, every sexet-priest, every magician, will feel them when he lays his finger on the head, on the back of the head, on the hands, on the Stomach (? heart) region, on the arms, on the legs. Everywhere he feels his Heart because its vessels run to all his limbs. Therefore it is called the centre of the vessels to all the limbs.

There are four vessels to the Nostrils, two of which convey mucus and two blood.

There are four vessels in the inside of either Temple. After they have given blood to the Eyes all kinds of diseases of the Eyes arise through them because they are open to the Eyes. When water comes out of them it is the Pupils of the Eyes that give it. Or according to another authority sleep in the Eyes brings it forth.

There are four vessels which divide in the Head and spread out in the back thereof. These afterwards bring forth a great mass of hair. (Uncertain.)

When the breath goes into the Nose it makes its way to the Heart and Intestines, and the last-named vessels give to the body richly thereof. If one hears something below it is caused by the two vessels that go to the Collar-bone; or if one hears them thereunder, behold it is those that are in the upper Cheek-bones of a person in that it is the rough wind that cuts into him when he draws his breath therefrom. Or when the Heart absorbs Water his limbs fade away completely. When the Heart is struck it is that vessel whose name is 'Fasser' that does it; it gives water towards the Heart or towards the Eye when it is stopped up. When he hears through the opening of his mouth all his limbs show themselves benumbed after a mist has gripped his Heart. When anger arises in his Heart, behold it is a seething-up of the parts of the Intestine and the Liver. His Ear is on the alert, his vessels fall after their rising heat has dissolved everything.

There are four vessels to his Ears, two to the Right side and two to the Left. Breath-of-Life goes in the Right Ear and Breath-of-Death into the Left. Or in other words Breath-of-Life goes to the Right side and Breath-of-Death to the Left.

There are six vessels that run to the Arms, three to the Right and three to the Left, and they lead right down to the Fingers.

There are six vessels that lead to the Feet, three to the Right and three to the Left. They reach down to the Soles of the Feet.

There are two vessels to his Testicles which convey the Semen. There are two vessels to the Kidneys, one to one Kidney, the other to the second Kidney.

There are four vessels to the Liver which convey to it Moisture and Air. Afterwards they cause all sorts of disease to arise therein being mixed with Blood.

There are four vessels to the Intestines and to the Spleen which likewise convey Moisture and Air. There are two vessels to the Bladder which convey the Urine.

There are four vessels which end in the Rectum. They give and bring forth in it Moisture and Air. Afterwards they turn towards the Rectum, each vessel to the Right and Left side right down to the Feet, mixing itself with the excrement.

When the Heart is sad, behold it is the moroseness of the Heart, or the vessels of the Heart are closed up in so far as they are not recognizable under thy hand. They grow full of Air and Water.

When the Heart feels an aversion, behold it is the Bitterness of the Heart because of Inflammation in the Anus. Thou findest it big and something forms itself in his Abdomen as in his Eye.

When his Heart spreads out, behold the vessels of the Heart are with excrement.

When any kind of dehert-disease enters the Left Eye and comes forth from the Navel, behold it is the Breath from the hollowed hand of the Priest that is allowed by the Heart to enter his vessels. Fire of every kind is locked up in his Flesh. His Heart is sick thereof because the Fire comes forth and the vessels of his Heart absolutely deny him their service.

Source: Bryan, Cyril P., translator. *Ancient Egyptian Medicine: The Papyrus Ebers.* Translated from the German. London, 1930, pp. 124–127.

4 Duties of a Physician in Ancient Ayurvedic Medicine (ca. 1500–400 B.C.E.)

This late 19th-century excerpt is from a translation of the ancient practice of Ayurvedic medicine originally written from around 1500 to 400 B.C.E. It was translated from ancient Sanskrit into English by renowned Indian scholar and translator, Manmatha Nath Dutt (1855–1912). The work, and this excerpt, is important because the translation describes the qualities and duties expected of a physician in antiquity. As can be seen, most of the qualities and duties of a physician are similar to what would also be expected today of a physician or healer. Ayurvedic medicine was, and still is, practiced in India and other nations where immigrants from South-Asian nations have migrated. The system is grounded on text-based classical knowledge, literature and apprenticeships. Students learn this material under a master or teacher often in a school and the training is usually considered an academic discipline within the culture. It is one of the major world's medical traditions. However, unlike modern Western medicine, it is generally not based upon scientific studies but years of tradition. A major concept is that diseases results when the body's physical, mental, spiritual, and social systems are out of balance.

See also: Document 5

The ancient medical works of the Hindus also give a very beautiful account of how the physicians should behave themselves towards their patients. The Rishis gave a particular stress upon four circumstances relating to the cure of a disease—namely the acquirements of the physician, the proper diagnosis of the disease, proper medicines and good nurses and a reasonable patient. These four circumstances are essentially necessary for the cure of a malady.

First of all a qualified physician is required. The Hindu never placed any confidence in a quack; learning in a physician was greatly admired. Sushruta thus describes the requirements of a medical practitioner. "He should be of a good family, of healthy body, handsome, pure, vigorous, modest, discrete, patient and intelligent. He should keep his nails and beard short, his body pure and his clothes clean."

It was essentially [necessary] for a medical man to know well both the theory and practice of his Science. A student knowing the Shastras i.e. theoretical portion and not the practical part of the profession is described as " . . . carrying a heavy load of fragrant wood, without discovering and enjoying the fragrance of his burden." If the practitioner does not know his duty well the cure of the disease will be greatly retarded and imperfect.

The nature and temperament of the physician is thus described:—"The physician should always be dignified in his deportment, correct in his manners and habits, gentle and kind, amiable, cheerful and collected. His language should be mild, candid and encouraging, rather like that of a friend than an acquaintance and he should always be ready to assist the sick. His heart should be pure and charitable and he should carefully follow the instructions of his Guru and his predecessors. Such a physician should possess a character for strict veracity, be of calm temper and of the greatest sobriety and chastity. He should be a man of sense and benevolence and his constant thought should he how he is to do good. A person may be afraid of his father and mother, friends and master but not of his physician; so the physician should be more kind and considerate to the sick than a father, a mother, a friend or a master. To these qualities should be added that of affection for learned friends and the constant habit of visiting the sick and seeing them treated by experienced persons."

These are the qualities which a physician should possess for becoming a successful practitioner. As a professional man he should be acquainted with the causes and varieties of disease and the means of preventing and curing them. A good physician is described as one perfectly acquainted with his own profession. To perform his daily duty he must have a knowledge of (i) Sutrasthdna or the relation of customs and habits; (2) Sari'sastk ana—physiology and anatomy; (3) Chikitsasthana and Upasaya or a knowledge of regimen and medicines which cure disease; (4) Nidanasthana—invasion and symptoms of disease; (5) Upadrava or unusual symptoms such as delirium, thirst etc.; (6) Kalpasthana or use of poisons.

This list, we dare say, gives an exhaustive account of the amount of theoretical knowledge which a medical practitioner should possess is not only the theoretical knowledge, to which the Rishis paid every attention, practical knowledge was equally necessary for a medical man. A real and good physician must have in him a combination of theoretical and practical knowledge. Without a knowledge of books a medical man is like a soldier afraid in the time of battle. Such a man, the Sliastras enjoin, is a great sinner and should be capitally punished by the Rajah. On the other hand without a practical knowledge a physician's senses will be bewildered when called on to treat acute diseases. Such a person is considered as a murderer—and the medicine, prescribed by him, is like a poison. That a real physician should combine in him both theoretical and practical knowledge. . . .

Source: Dutt, Manmatha Nath. *Ayurveda: or the Hindu System of Medical Science.* Calcutta: Society for the Resuscitation of Indian Literature, 1899, pp. 44–48.

5 Impregnation and Pregnancy in Ancient Ayurvedic Medicine (ca. 1500–400 B.C.E.)

This colorful description of when a women is fertile, how fertilization takes place, and signs of pregnancy are from a translation into English of an ancient Sanskrit document written around 1500 to 400 B.C.E. The late-19th-century and early 20th-century Indian scholar and translator, Manmatha Nath Dutt (1855–1912), was renowned for translating many ancient Sanskrit documents into English including medical texts. Although the excerpt depicts various suppositions about menstruation, pregnancy, and fertility, some which are not accurate by modern standards, the description gives early insight into the process of fertilization and pregnancy. One error is that the best time to get pregnant is during menstruation. Various suggestions are given for health care during menses and pregnancy. This suggests the basic process of reproduction was known to the ancient Indians and the concepts were important for Ayurvedic medical practitioners.

See also: Document 4

The human body is the object upon which the Science of Medicine is founded and therefore the Hindu sages paid great attention to its growth. It is thus described by a great oriental scholar:—

As the mould receives the seed which is to form the future plant, so the menses of the female receive the semen of the male and germination takes place therein. The menses are stated to be of a red colour like the blood of a hare; and they should neither stain cloth when they fall upon it nor have any smell. They are derived from the two vessels of the uterus which discharge their contents, under the influence of the vital air into the uterus and vagina. The menses make their appearance generally about the twelfth year and remain till the fiftieth. At the monthly period the female is moist, plump and happy with her hairs flying about, her eyes languishing, her sides, eyes, arms, breasts, thighs, and navel are in a state of excitement; this period continues for sixteen days when the female may be impregnated. During this time the mouth of the uterus, like the mouth of the ruefish, is open as the flower of the water-lily when exposed to the sun; as the rays of the light concentrated by a lens produce fire so is generation produced. After this period the mouth of the uterus closes like the petals of the lily when the benign of influence of the sun is absent.

During the period of menses much attention is required regarding the conduct of the woman. During the first three days the woman should remain pure, sit and sleep in purified situation, avoid cold and fatigue and eat temperately. Both parents should be young and healthy. The semen conveyed through the eurethera of the male passes into the vagina, is received into the menses, as a seed, is dropped into a good soil and like it germinates, thus constituting conception. When the mixture has taken place and the resulting body has become solid by the respective qualities of cold and heat the soul is added. When the germ has more the qualities of the semen a male child is formed and when of the menses a female child is the result.

Should conception take place on the first or second day of the menses the child, becomes weak and dies soon after birth. If it takes place on the third the child is weak and deformed and dies at an early age. And if it is on the fourth, sixth, eighth or tenth day the child becomes strong and healthy.

The signs of conception described by the Hindu sages are interestingly accurate. During pregnancy the skin round the nipples becomes dark and the hair upon the body becomes more distinct and prominent. The person feels weak, the eyelids are heavy and closed. Much saliva proceeds from the mouth and nose and the woman has no appetite, feels sick and vomits. In this condition a woman must avoid approaching her husband, fasting, vomiting, strong purgatives, grief and fear, scratching and severe coughing, dragging heavy weights, riding on horse back, sleeping during the day and sitting up at night. During pregnancy the woman should be given everything she wants and be kept gratified.

Source: Dutt, Manmatha Nath. *Ayurveda: or the Hindu System of Medical Science.* Calcutta: Society for the Resuscitation of Indian Literature, 1899, pp. 53–56.

6 Empedocles: Poem on Elements, Creation, and Conception (Fifth Century B.C.E.)

The theory of disease, health, and medical treatment from antiquity into the mid-19th century were based upon the four elements: earth, air, fire, and water, along with ether, or spirit, that is sometimes considered air. Based upon Egyptian beliefs, this excerpt by philosopher and physician Empedocles (490–430 B.C.E) is one of the first writings that puts forth the theory that the four elements were present in different amounts in all matter including solids, liquids, gases, and living material. This theory suggested that personality temperaments and humors (blood, yellow bile, black bile, and phlegm) needed to be in balance with each other in order for a person to be well both mentally and physically. Ancient Asian medicine also had as a similar philosophy in terms of elements and humors. In Empedocles' excerpt, he discusses the origin of the universe, a creation story, and also conception, pregnancy, and birth of different creators including humans. The sex of a child, for instance, was thought to be due to sperm meeting a cold or hot womb thus producing a girl or boy respectively. In terms of treatment originating from this system, hot, cold, moist, and dry were also used in different combinations depending upon the patient's temperament and affliction.

The World as it now is

38. Come! I will name the like-primeval Four,
Whence rose to sight all things we now behold—
Earth, many-billowed Sea, and the moist Air,
And Aether, the Titan, who binds the globe about.

Earth and Air Not Illimitable

39. If Earth's black deeps were endless, and o'er-full
Were the white Ether, as forsooth some tongues
Have idly prated in the babbling mouths
Of those who little of the All have seen . . .

Sun and Moon.

40. Keen-darting Helios and Selene mild.

41. But the sun's fires, together gathered, move
Attendant round the mighty space of heaven,
And the sun's beams
The moon, in passing under, covers o'er,
And darkens a bleak tract of earth as large
As is the breadth of her, the silver-eyed.

43. As sunbeam striking on the moon's broad disk.

44. Toward Olympus back he darts his beams.
With fearless face.

45. Round earth revolves a disk of alien light.

46. Even as revolves a chariot's nave, which round
The outmost . . .

47. For toward the sacred circle of her lord
She gazes face to face.

48. But earth makes night for beams of sinking sun.

The Darkling Night.

49. Of night, the lonely, with her sightless eyes.

Wind and Rain.

50. Iris from sea brings wind or mighty rain.

Fire.

51. And fire sprang upward with a rending speed.

The Volcano.

52. And many a fire there burns beneath the ground.

Air.

53. For sometimes so upon its course it met,
And ofttimes otherwise.

Things Passing Strange.

54. In Earth sank Ether with deep-stretching roots.

55. Earth's sweat, the sea.

56. The salt grew solid, smit by beams of sun.

Strange Creatures of Olden Times.

57. There budded many a head without a neck,
And arms were roaming, shoulderless and bare,
And eyes that wanted foreheads drifted by.

58. In isolation wandered, every limb,
Hither and thither seeing union meet.

59. But now as God with God was mingled more,
These members fell together where they met,
And many a birth besides was then begot
In a long line of ever varied life.

60. Creatures of countless hands and trailing feet.

61. Many were born with twofold brow and breast,
Some with the face of man on bovine stock,

Some with man's form beneath a bovine head,
Mixed shapes of being with shadowed secret parts,
Sometimes like men, and sometimes woman-growths.

62. But come! now hear how 'twas the sundered Fire
Led into life the germs, erst whelmed in night,
Of men and women, the pitied and bewailed;
For 'tis a tale that sees and knows its mark.
First rose mere lumps of earth with rude impress,
That had their shares of Water and of Warm.
These then by Fire (in upward zeal to reach
Its kindred Fire in heaven) were shot aloft,
Albeit not yet had they revealed a form
Of lovely limbs, nor yet a human cry.
Nor secret member, common to the male.

The Process of Human Generation To-day.

63. But separate is the birth of human limbs;
For 'tis in part in man's . . ,

64. Love-longing comes, reminding him who sees.

65. Into clean wombs the seeds are poured, and when
Therein they meet with Cold, the birth is girls;
and boys, when contrariwise the meet with Warm

66. Into the cloven meads of Aphrodite.

69. For bellies with the warmer wombs become
Mothers of boys, and therefore men are dark,
More stalwart and more shaggy.

68. On the tenth day, in month the eighth, the blood becomes white [milk]
[. . .]

71. And if belief lack pith, and thou still doubt
How from the mingling with the elements,
The Earth and Water, the Ether, and the Sun,
So many forms and hues of mortal things
Could thus have being, as have come to be.
Each framed and knit by Aphrodite's power.

Source: Empedocles. Translated by William Ellery Leonard. *The Fragments of Empedocles*. Chicago: Open Court, 1908, pp. 33–39.

7 Celsus: Fevers and Cures from Roman Antiquity (10 C.E.)

Scottish physician James Greive (1753–1805) in 1756 translated a medical work written by Roman physician Aulus Cornelius Celsus (25 B.C.E.–50 C.E.) around 10 C.E. Greive felt that ancient observation might be useful in treatment. It was reprinted in 1814. In one section, Celsus describes different types of fevers. In the following excerpt, the malaria cycles that generally begins with feeling cold, shivering, and a high fever, followed by sweating as the fever declines, is explained. In the excerpt, quartan and tertian describe the four- and three-day cycles of malarial fever, respectively. Quotidian fever usually occurs once a day at the same time. These terms are still used today, which is an example of medical terminology from antiquity being carried into modern times. We now know that different plasmodia, or malaria parasites, tend to cause different fever cycles. The fever is related to the time new broods of parasites are released from the red blood cells. In regions of the world with stable endemic malaria, older children and adults may not have fever despite having the parasite. Cures discussed in this excerpt were not likely very effective. Today drugs are used to both prevent and cure the disease; however, malaria is still a problem in Africa, Southeast and South Asia.

See also: Document 8

CHAP. III.

OF THE SEVERAL KINDS OF FEVERS.

We next proceed to the cure of fevers, which is a kind of disease, that affects the whole body, and is the most common of all. Of these one is a quotidian, another a tertian, and a third a quartan. Sometimes some fevers also return after a longer period, but that seldom occurs. With regard to the former, they are both diseases in *themselves*, and a cure *for others.*

But quartan fevers are more simple. They begin commonly with a shuddering; then a heat breaks out; after the paroxysm is over, the patient is well for two days. So that it returns upon the fourth day.

Of tertians again there are two kinds. One of them both beginning and ending like the quartan; with this difference only, that there is one day's intermission, and it returns upon the third. The other kind is much more fatal, which indeed returns upon the third day, but of forty-eight hours, thirty-six are occupied by the fit (and sometimes either less or more,) nor does it entirely cease in the remission; but is only mitigated. This kind most physicians call semitertian [intermittent fever].

But quotidians are various, and different in their appearances. For some of them begin with a heat, others with a coldness, others with a shuddering. I call that a coldness, when the extremities of the limbs are chilled; a shuddering, when the whole body trembles. Again, some end, so as to be followed by an interval quite free from indisposition; others so, as that though the fever somewhat abates [. . .] Some again are attended with a very vehement heat, others more tolerable; some are equal every day, others unequal, and alternately milder one day and more severe another: some return at the same time the following day, others either later or sooner: some by the fit and the intermission take up a day and a night, some less, others more: some, when they go off, cause a sweat, others do not; and in some a sweat leaves the patient well, in others it only renders the body weaker . . . Sometimes too the fits are so irregular, that neither their durations nor intermissions can be observed . . .

CHAP. IV.

OF THE DIFFERENT METHODS OF CURE.

This then is the general nature of fevers. But the methods of cure differ, according to their different authors. Asclepiades says, that it is the duty of a physician to effect the cure safely, speedily, and with ease *to the patient.* This is to be desired: but generally too great haste and too great indulgence both prove dangerous. What moderation must be used in order to obtain all these ends as far as possible, the principal regard being always had to the safety *of the patient*. . . when we treat of the particulars of the cure.

And the first inquiry is, how the patient is to be treated in the beginning of the distemper. [. . .] Asclepiades laying aside the use of medicines, ordered clysters [enemas] . . . in almost every distemper. And he professed his principal cure for a fever was the disease itself [. . .].

Now I grant that medicinal potions and clysters, ought to be used but sparingly. And yet I do not think these are to be administered with a view to destroy the patient's strength: because the greatest danger arises from weakness. Wherefore it is proper only to diminish the redundant matter; which is naturally dissipated, when there is no new accession to it. For this reason the patient must abstain from food in the beginning, and in the day-time be kept in the light, unless he be weak, because even that contributes to the discharge. And he ought to lye in a very large room.

As to thirst and sleep, the best mean is, that he be awake in the day-time, and rest in the night, if possible; and neither drink plentifully, nor be too much tormented with thirst. His mouth also may be washed, when it is both dry, and has a fetid taste; although such time is not seasonable for drinking. And Erasistratus very justly observed, that often the mouth and fauces require moisture, when there is no want of it in the internal parts; and that it is of no consequence, that the patient is uneasy. Such then ought to be the treatment at first.

Now the best medicine is food seasonably administered: when that must be given first, is a question. Most of the ancients were slow in giving it; often on the fifth or sixth day: and that perhaps the nature of the climate in Asia or in Egypt admits of. Asclepiades, after he had for three days fatigued the patient in every way, appointed the fourth for food. But Themison of late considered, not when the fever had begun, but when it had gone off, or at least was abated; and waiting for the third day from that time, if the fever had not returned, he gave food immediately;

if it did come on, when it had ceased; or if it continued constantly, when at least it was mitigated.

Now none of these rules is always to be followed. For it may be proper to give food on the first day, it may on the second, it may on the third, it may not before the fourth or fifth; it may after one fit, it may after two, it may after several. For the qualities of the distemper, constitution, air, age, and season of the year make some difference. And no time can be universally fixed in things so widely different from each other.

Source: Celsus, Aulus Cornelius. *Of Medicine: In Eight Books*. Translated by James Greive. Edinburgh: Printed at the University Press for Dickinson and Company, 1814, pp. 89–92.

8 Celsus: Treating Fractures in Roman Antiquity (10 C.E.)

Scottish physician James Greive (1753–1805) in 1756 translated a medical work written by Roman physician Aulus Cornelius Celsus (25 B.C.E.–50 C.E.) around 10 C.E. It was reprinted in 1814. In one section, Celsus describes the treatment of fractures. Different types of fractures are depicted along with their treatment. For compound fractures, a wine and oil-soaked cloth is placed over the fracture. Hot water was also put on the wound. Wine and hot water, acting as an antiseptic, likely prevented some severe infections and the onset of gangrene. The Romans were aware that in displaced fractures, tendons and muscles would often contract and further separate the two bones if they were not straightened with traction. If a leg or arm was not put into traction, Celsus observes it could be crooked when healed. This excerpt is an example of successful treatment that was not necessarily carried out continuously from the Roman era over the centuries in Western cultures. Use of hot water was again suggested in 1896. If the procedure had been adopted after the translation of Celsus, many limbs might have been saved during the wars of the early and mid-19th century.

See also: Document 7; Document 36; Document 50; Document 69

CHAP. X.

OF FRACTURES OF THE HUMERUS, FORE-ARM, THIGH, LEG, FINGERS, AND TOES.

THE cases which occur in the arms and thighs, and their methods of cure, are in a great measure similar. There are also some general things that belong equally to the arms, fore-arms, thighs, legs, fingers, and toes; for a fracture in the middle of these is least dangerous; but the nearer the fracture is, either to the superior or inferior head, so much the worse: for it both creates greater pain, and is more difficult to cure. Of fractures, the most innocent is a simple transverse one; worse, where it is oblique, and where there are fragments; worst of all, when these are sharp. Sometimes the bones in these parts being fractured, continue in their places: but they much more frequently give way, and one part lies over the other. This circumstance ought to be first of all considered; and there are certain marks for knowing it. If they are displaced, they are bent, and cause the sensation of pricking, and are unequal to the touch. But if they meet one another, not directly, but obliquely (which happens, when they are not in their place) that limb is shorter than the other, and the muscles of it swell.

Therefore, if this is found to be the case, it is proper to extend the limb immediately: for the tendons and muscles being in *a natural state kept* stretched by the bones, are *in this case* contracted; neither do they return to their place, unless they be extended by force. Again, if that is neglected for some days at first, an inflammation comes on during which, it is both difficult and dangerous to use violence to the tendons; for there follows a convulsion or gangrene; or at least, which is the mildest of the bad consequences, a suppuration; therefore, if the bones have not been replaced before *the inflammation*, they must not be reduced till after it is gone. Now one person alone may extend a finger, also any other member, if it be of a child by taking hold of one part with his right hand, and the other with his left. A stronger limb requires two to pull different ways. If the tendons are very firm, as is the case in robust men, and chiefly in their thighs and legs, the ends of the joint, on both sides must be tied with straps or linen rollers, and pulled contrary ways by several persons; and when this force has stretched the limb a little beyond its natural length, then the bones must be pressed by the hands into their place; and the sign of a bone's being reduced, is the removal of the pain. The limb being made equal with the other, must be wrapped up in cloths two or three times doubled, dipped in wine and oil; for which purpose linen is best.

Six bandages are generally required. The first to be applied, the shortest; which should be rolled about the fracture, and ascend spirally like a screw; and it is sufficient for it to go round in this manner thrice. The second is one half longer than this; which, if the bone project any part, must begin there; if it be every where equal, it may begin any where upon the fracture, and go in an opposite direction to the former, tending downwards and returning again to the fracture, end in the upper part beyond the former bandage. Over these must be laid cerate, upon a broad piece of linen, to keep them on. And if the bone is prominent in any part, a cloth, three times doubled moistened in the wine and oil before mentioned must be laid upon it. These are to be secured by a third and a fourth bandage, in such a manner, that the following move always in a contrary direction to the former the third alone must end in the lower part, and the other three in the superior; because it is better to make several convolutions, than to bind it tight; for a strict bandage disorders a part, and makes it liable to a gangrene. We ought to bind an articulation as little as possible; but if the fracture of the bone is near the joint, there is a necessity for it.

When the limb is bound up, it must be kept so to the third day, and the bandage should be such, as on the first day not to hurt *by its stricture*, and yet not to seem lax; on the second it should be a little laxer; the third almost loosened. Therefore, the limb must then be bound up again, and a fifth roller must be added to the former; after which it must be again opened on the fifth day, and then secured by six rollers, in such a manner, that the third and fifth may end below, and the rest above. As often as the limb is opened, it must be fomented with hot water. But if the fracture be near a joint, wine, with the addition of a small proportion of oil, must be dropped upon it for a long time, and all the other directions observed, till the inflammation leave it, or the limb become smaller than ordinary: which, if it does not happen on the seventh day, will certainly be effected by the ninth. Then the bones are handled with great ease.

Therefore, if they are not well joined to each other, they must be set again [. . .].

Source: Celsus, Aulus Cornelius. *Of Medicine: In Eight Books.* Translated by James Greive. Edinburgh: Printed at the University Press for Dickinson and Company, 1814, pp. 406–408.

9 Galen Debates Other Physicians and Philosophers (180 C.E.)

British physician Arthur John Brock (1878–1947) in the early 20th century translated Greek physician and surgeon Galen of Pergaman's (130–ca. 200 C.E.) debate with other physicians from Latin into English. Galen, based upon Hippocrates as discussed in the excerpt, "Aphorisms of Hippocrates for Medical Students (Fifth Century B.C.E, 1817)" expanded Hippocrates's beliefs that disease was caused by natural processes and not evil spirits. Different theories of disease have existed from antiquity, and Galen in the following excerpt does not agree with the theory of the Erasistratus (304–250 B.C.E.), who had founded an anatomy school in the past. Galen observed that disease is due to predisposing, exciting, and environmental factors. However, Galen, who treated Roman gladiators and was familiar with anatomy, still theorized that disease was based upon the four humors or temperament. Galen and other Greek physicians believed that the human body had the powers to restore humeral equilibrium, and it was the physician's primary role to assist in this healing process. These theories were not discredited until the mid- to late 19th century when the germ theory of disease was accepted.

See also: Document 6

IX

For this reason the things that we have said are not to be looked upon as proofs but rather as indications of the dullness of those who think differently, and who do not even recognize what is agreed on by everyone and is a matter of daily observation. As for the scientific proofs of all this, they are to be drawn from these principles of which I have already spoken—namely, that bodies act upon and are acted upon by each other in virtue of the Warm, Cold, Moist and Dry. And if one is speaking of any activity, whether it be exercised by vein, liver, arteries, heart, alimentary canal, or any part, one will be inevitably compelled to acknowledge that this activity depends upon the way in which the four qualities are blended. Thus I should like to ask the Erasistrateans why it is that the stomach contracts upon the food, and why the veins generate blood. There is no use in recognizing the mere fact of contraction, without also knowing the cause; if we know this, we shall also be able to rectify the failures of function. "This is no concern of ours," they say; "we do not occupy ourselves with such causes as these; they are outside the sphere of the practitioner, and belong to that of the scientific investigator." Are you, then, going to oppose those who maintain that the cause of the function of every organ is a natural eucrasia [normal], that the dyscrasia [abnormal]is itself known as a disease, and that it is certainly by this that the activity becomes impaired? Or, on the other hand, will you be convinced by the proofs which the ancient writers furnished? Or will you take a midway course between these two, neither perforce accepting these arguments as true nor contradicting them as false, but suddenly becoming sceptics—Pyrrhonists, in fact? But if you do this you will have to shelter yourselves behind the Empiricist teaching. For how are you going to be successful in treatment, if you do not understand the real essence of each disease? Why, then, did you not call yourselves Empiricists from the beginning?

Why do you confuse us by announcing that you are investigating natural activities with a view to treatment? If the stomach is, in a particular case, unable to exercise its peristaltic and grinding functions, how are we going to bring it back to the normal if we do not know the cause of its disability? What I say is that we must cool the over-heated stomach and warm the chilled one; so also we must moisten the one which has become dried up, and conversely; so, too, in combinations of these conditions; if the stomach becomes at the same time warmer and drier than normally, the first principle of treatment is at once to chill and moisten it; and if it become colder and moister, it must be warmed and dried; so also in other cases. But how on earth are the followers of Erasistratus going to act, confessing as they do that they make no sort of investigation into the cause of disease? For the fruit of the enquiry into activities is that by knowing the causes of the dyscrasiae one may bring them back to the normal, since it is of no use for the purposes of treatment merely to know what the activity of each organ is.

Now, it seems to me that Erasistratus is unaware of this fact also, that the actual disease is that condition of the body which, not accidentally, but primarily and of itself, impairs the normal function. How, then, is he going to diagnose or cure diseases if he is entirely ignorant of what they are, and of what kind and number?

Source: Galen. Translated by Arthur John Brock. *On the Natural Faculties, with an English Translation by Arthur John Brock.* Cambridge, MA: Harvard University Press, 1916, pp. 195–199.

10 Chinese Medicine from the Yellow Emperor (ca. 200 C.E.)

German-American medical historian Ilza Veith (1915–2013) translated into English the Inner Canon of the Yellow Emperor. *This medical text is the basic source for traditional Chinese medicine. The text was written in approximately 200 C.E., although the original theories are thought to be over 2,000 years old. Much of the work is in the format of questions and answers between the mythical Yellow Emperor and his six legendary physicians. This book is divided into two parts. The first one is known as the "Basic Questions." It covers the theoretical foundation of Chinese medicine. It describes various diagnostic and treatment methods and includes the concept of balance and yang and yin. It also describes the theory of earth, fire, water, wood, and metal, which is associated with different organs of the body. The second text presents acupuncture theory. Acupuncture was one of the treatment methods to cure illnesses. This extract discussed wine making and brewing for making liquid medications based upon the balance of life forces as believed by Chinese medical practitioners. It also mentions surgery for some conditions.*

See also: Document 19

Treatise on the Treatment with Hot Water, Liquid Medicines, the Lees of Wine, and Sweet Wine

The Yellow Emperor asked: "How can one prepare soups and clear liquids and even lees of wine and sweet wine from the five kinds of grain?" [The five grains are glutinous millet, wheat, millet, rice, and beans].

Ch'i Po replied: "One must use paddy rice and steam it. The stalks of the paddy rice serve as firewood. When the steaming of the rice is completed, the rice (extract) is strong."

The Emperor inquired: "How is this possible?"

Ch'i Po answered: "The effect is obtained by mixing the products of Heaven and Earth, the exalted and the base substances, in proper proportion. Hence if this can be done and the plants be cut at the proper season, the potion will be strong."

The Emperor said: "In ancient times, although the sages prescribed soups and hot water, the lees of wine and sweet wine as medicines, they did not know how to use them. Is this the case?"

Ch'i Po answered: "From olden times the sages prescribed soups, liquids, the lees of wine and sweet wine and medicines, but their special emphasis was on the preparation. Thus from olden times these soups and liquid medicines were prepared but not swallowed as medicines.

"In medieval times, when morality deteriorated, these medicines were first taken at the time when evil influences appeared and they worked very effectively."

The Emperor said: "The present generation should not be like the medieval world."

Ch'i Po said: "The present generation must respect (Chinese character) the poisonous medicines, which assault the diseases within their bodies, and they should hold in awe acupuncture and treatment with moxa, which cure the diseases of the external body."

The Emperor asked: "When the body is worn out and the blood is exhausted, is it still possible to achieve good results?"

Ch'i Po replied: "No, because there is no more energy left."

The Emperor inquired: "What does it mean, there is no more energy left?"

Ch'i Po answered: "This is the way of acupuncture: if man's vitality and energy do not propel his own will his disease cannot be cured.

"Nowadays vitality and energy are considered the foundation of life; in order to keep them flourishing they must be protected and the life-giving force must rule. When this force does not support life, its foundation will dissolve, and how can a disease be cured when there is no spiritual energy within the body?"

The Emperor said: "Thus life itself is really the beginning of illness! Minute particles first enter the body through the skin, and all physicians of skillful workmanship, those who are renowned, call this group 'stubborn diseases.' If they cannot be cured by means of acupuncture, not even good medicine can bring a cure. Nowadays the good physicians all have developed a definite method: they guard the fate of the parents, of kin, of brother, of strangers and of close friends. They perceive the sounds and noises of the day with their ears and they observe the colors of the day with their eyes; and how could they relax before the illness has improved?"

Ch'i Po replied: "Illness is comparable to the root; good medical work is comparable to the topmost branch or a beacon. If this root is not reached, the evil influences cannot be subjugated. This is what I want to say."

The Emperor said: "Those who are not obedient to the smallest fraction can yet live; but Yang, the principle of life within their five viscera, is exhausted. Saliva and liquid secretions act as rim for their animal (or inferior) soul, which dwells in isolation. The spirit is confined to the interior of the body, while wasteful and destructive airs attack from the outside. The body can no longer wear clothes and protect its four extremities. Thus distress can move into the lungs (center), and the entry of life-giving force is impeded from within while the body is neglected at the outside. How can a cure be effected under these conditions?"

Ch'i Po answered: "The fairest treatment is to weigh and to consider carefully removal, as well as cutting and scooping out exposed and spoiled particles. Even if they are ulcerated one should move the four extremities slowly and clothe them warmly. One should criticize and correct the faults in the patients' mode of life; one should restore their bodies and open the anus so that the bowels can be cleansed, and so that the secretions come at the proper time and serve the five viscera which belong to Yang, the principle of life.

"One should put in order the five viscera which were remiss and cleanse and purify them. Then the secretions are certain to produce life, and the body contains flourishing bones and flesh without further help; they all help and protect each other, and thus the life-giving force becomes strong and peaceful."

The Emperor said: "Wonderful indeed!"

Source: Veith, Ilza and Linda L. Barnes. *The Yellow Emperor's Classic of Internal Medicine.* University of California Press, 2015, pp. 151–153, excerpted from chapter 7. Used with permission of the University of California Press.

11 Aphorisms of Hippocrates for Medical Students (ca. Fifth Century C.E.)

The ancient Greek physician Hippocrates (370–460)—often called the father of clinical medical observations including diagnosis and treatment—wrote the aphorisms as a reference book for medical student. American physician Elias Marks (1790–1886) translated it from the Latin translation of Lucas Verhoofd, an earlier Greek translator. In Marks's work, Latin was on one side of the book, and on the other side was a literal translation with explanatory notes. The aphorisms were used into the mid-19th century for medical training in Western cultures and are sayings that contain observations and advice that were considered based upon fact. Hippocrates believed that disease was caused by natural processes and not spirits or punishments from gods for sinful ways and that human emotions and behaviors were caused by an excess or lack of fluids, or humors, in the body, which included blood, yellow bile, black bile, and phlegm. Different personality temperaments of hot, cold, dry, and moist mentioned by him were still accepted by mid-19th century physicians. Through his teachings, he taught young physicians to focus on clinical observations that are found in his writings. In this excerpt, attention to nutrition for the type of illness, different stages of an illness, physical shape of and the age of an individual, and the season of the year are explained to the medical students.

1. Life is short, art long, occasion brief, experience fallacious, judgment difficult. It is requisite that the Physician exhibit what is essential, and that the patient, attendants and all which surrounds him, concur therein.

2. In diarrhoea and spontaneous vomiting, if the matter voided be of a nature that ought to be expelled, let the patient be purged, for in this case, the evacuations are beneficial and are easily supported; but if the effect be otherwise, the contrary is indicated. The same rule obtains in vascular depletion; when it is judiciously had recourse to, it is beneficial and is easily supported: but if it be otherwise, the contrary is indicated. We ought, therefore, to bear in mind the climate, the season, the age and the disease and thence infer whether these things be beneficial or otherwise.

3. In those having an excess of health, violent exercise is dangerous; for in such constitutions an equilibrium of health cannot be maintained. And as their temperament of health is neither stationary nor progressive, it must, of necessity, have a retrograde tendency. For these reasons, therefore, we should speedily set about reducing this extreme of health, in order that the body may take upon itself a new principle of nutrition. Neither should this reduction be carried too far, for we should be guided by the strength and constitution of the patient. Thus the extremes of repletion and depletion are equally to be avoided as both are attended with danger.

5. The sick frequently err in the adoption of a spare diet. They are therein the more injured. In the choice of regimen, more evil results from abstraction than from a small excess.

6. The greater the evil—the more vigorous the remedy.

7. In acute diseases the most violent symptoms supervene: the severest regimen is, therefore, to be observed. But if these symptoms be wanting, a more generous diet is to be permitted.

8. When the disease attains most vigour—then it is, that the severest regimen is required.

9. In the prescribing of regimen, we are to consider, whether it be sufficient to support the patient until the disease attain its height; whether before this period, the patient may sink from an inability to support the regimen; or, whether the malady will, thereby be previously broken and overcome.

10. In those diseases which quickly arrive at their climax, a thin regimen should immediately be adopted. In those which attain it at a somewhat later period, we should at, or before that period, subtract from their diet: but until then, sufficient nourishment should be allowed, that the strength of the patient may be supported.

11. During the exacerbations, food is to be suspended: to administer it at that time would be injurious. When the returns are periodical, the diet is to be withdrawn on the coming on of the paroxysms.

12. The nature of diseases, with their paroxysms, are ascertained by regarding the time of the year—the comparative succession of periods;—observing also, whether the exacerbations occur each day, or on alternate days, or at greater intervals. The same result is obtained by attending to present symptoms; as in pleurisy, if the flow of saliva take place at the commencement, the duration of the disease will be short; if at a later period—it will be more extended [. . .].

13. Old men bear abstinence best; next, those who have attained their climacteric adolescence, less; and infancy, least;—but of all these, the vivacious support it most easily.

14. The growing body has most of innate heat, and, therefore, requires moist aliment; otherwise the constitution suffers. Old men have less heat, and, therefore, needless food. An over quantity would injure them. It, therefore, follows that fevers have not that acute tendency with the aged which they have with the youthful; with the former the body is cold.

15. In winter and in spring the stomach is necessarily warmer, and the sleep more extended. In those seasons, therefore, a more generous diet is to be permitted; for the augmentation of innate heat demands a more plentiful aliment. This is observable in youth, and in the habits of the Athlete.

16. A moist aliment accords well with febrile constitutions—remarkably well with children—and with all those to whom use has made it essential.

17. Note well the constitution, wherein food is daily required either once, or twice—in greater or less quantities, or by a graduated allowance. But we are to take into consideration habit, season, country, and age.

18. In summer and autumn, digestion is difficult; in winter, vigorous; in spring, indifferent.

19. In those diseases wherein the exacerbations are periodical, neither give nor force anything, but let the food be withdrawn before the coming on of the paroxysm.

20. When the paroxysm is well ascertained, do not disturb it either by medicines or any new irritation: leave it to itself.

21. That which is excrementitious, should be drawn off at the point to which it most tends, by the most convenient outlets.

22. Purgatives should be administered after the food on the stomach is concocted, not while it is yet crude; neither should they be given at the commencement of disease, lest turgescence [swelling] ensue; though the latter rarely occurs.

24. In acute affections, and especially at their commencement, purgatives ought rarely to be used, and when permitted, are to be administered with care.

25. If the matter voided be of a nature that ought to be expelled, let the patient be purged, for then, the evacuations are beneficial, and are easily supported; but if the effect be otherwise, the contrary is indicated.

Source: Hippocrates. Translated by Elias Marks. *The Aphorisms of Hippocrates, from the Latin version of Verhoofd, with a literal translation on the opposite page, and explanatory notes. The work is intended as a book of reference to the medical student.* New York, Collins & co., 1817, pp. 30–37.

12 Three Kinds of Hindu Indian Treatments (ca. Sixth Century C.E.)

The Indian Ayurvedic medical tradition is based upon myths and customs passed down through centuries. The system was still used by Hindus into the 21st century often combined with Western medicine. The tradition describes three doshas—life forces or energies—that govern the mind, body, and spirit. They in turn are influenced by the five elements (air, space fire, water, earth). When the three energies are in balance, the person is healthy, but when they are out of balance, the person becomes mentally, physically, or spiritually sick. This excerpt discusses treatment practices to keep the energies in balance or to cure sickness. One depends upon prayers, offerings, and various rituals to a deity or several deities. The second includes foods and herbs while the third is calming of the mind through meditation. When the body is out of balance, three types of treatment are used that touch the body. The first is external and includes massage or substances rubbed or placed on the skin. The second is internal. It involves ingesting medicines, herbs, or certain foods. Surgery is the last treatment if other methods fail. The excerpt also advises that the wise will seek treatment when they first become sick and not wait until they are near death.

See also: Document 47

Medicines are of three kinds; those that depend for their action upon the deities and invisible influences; those that depend for their application and action upon knowledge and reason; and those that appertain to the subjugation of the mind.

Among these, *mantras*, herbs and plants of invisible virtue (if kept in contact with the body), gems, auspicious rites, offerings in sacrifices, offers of articles to the deities in course of worship or religious rites, libations of meat and ghee on the sacred fire, practice of vows, expiatory ceremonies and rites, fasts, propitiatory rites, bows to the deities, and pilgrimage to sacred waters and shrines, constitute medicines of the first kind.

Diet and articles of medicinal virtue that are applied with the aid of knowledge and reason are medicines of the second kind. The subjugation of the mind by withdrawing it from every kind of injurious or harmful acts and objects of the senses, constitutes medicine of the third kind.

When the sources of the faults of the body (*viz*., wind, bile, and phlegm) become disordered, it is very generally seen that three kinds of medicines, all of which must be brought in contact with the body, become necessary. These three kinds are (1) those for internal application, (2) those for external application, and (3) the application of surgery.

Those medicines which are taken internally and which, entering the body, destroy the disorders thereof, are said to be medicines for internal application.

Those medicines which are applied to the skin and which destroy disease by means of being rubbed gently, or by producing perspiration, or by being used as plaster, or by fomentation, or by being rubbed with force, are said to belong to the second class of medicines, *viz*, those for external application.

Application of surgery includes lopping, breaking, piercing, cutting, tearing extracting, puncturing, sewing, exploring (by needles and catheters and tubes), burning by salts, and applying leeches.

Here occur some verses.

It is said that—When disease manifests itself, the man of wisdom, dispelling it, attains to health by external or internal application of medicines or by help of surgical operation.

A person destitute of intelligence, without doubt, fails, through stupefaction or error of judgement, to notice a disease as soon as it arises, even as a fool fails to detect a foe (before the latter ruins him outright).

Appearing at first in a very subtile [*sic*] form, disease afterwards increases, till, driving its roots deeply, it destroys the strength and cuts short the period of life of the man of little intelligence.

The man of little intelligence does not awake to a consciousness of his situation till he is sorely afflicted by disease. When he becomes sorely afilicted [*sic*], it is then only that he sets his mind upon the cure of his ailment. It is then that summoning his sons and spouses and kinsmen he says unto them,—Let some physician be brought even if I have to give away the whole of my property!"—But what physician is there that is able to rescue such a person who, afflicted with disease, has been reduced in strength, who has become emaciated, whose senses have been weakened in respect of their functions, who has become exceedingly cheerless, and who is on the point of death ?" Such a man of foolish understanding, from want of a rescuer, has to give up his life, even as a reptile of the iguana species gives up its life when dragged by the tale by a strong foe.

Hence, before an ailment is contracted, or while it is new, it should be counteracted with the aid of medicines by one who wishes for one's own happiness.

Source: Caraka. *Charaka-samhita: Translated into English. Published by Avinash Chandra Kaviratna.* Calcutta: Printed by G. C. Chakravarti [etc.], 1896, pp. 130–132.

13 Amputation in Antiquity (ca. Seventh Century C.E.)

The Seven Books of Paulus Ægineta *was written by seventh century Greek physician Paulus Aegineta (625–690), who is considered the father of early medical textbooks written in Greek. He was greatly admired by Arab physicians, who translated his works into Arabic and kept some of the ancient practices alive. This work was translated from the Greek into English by Scottish physician Francis Adams (1796–1861) between 1844 and 1847 and was one of the first translations into English from ancient medical manuscripts. The excerpt concerns the procedure for amputating limbs with massive fractures or those that had developed gangrene. Adams comments on techniques from an early 19th century perspective of other physicians of antiquity. This was before the acceptance of the germ theory of disease and the use of antiseptics and an aseptic environment were recognized as being important to prevent infections. He describes cauterization of bone and arteries, which may have prevented some infection.*

See also: Document 8

SECT. LXXXIV. ON AMPUTATION OF THE EXTREMITIES.

Sometimes the extremities, such as a hand or a foot, having mortified, so that the bones themselves are corrupted, either from having been fractured by some external means, or from having become putrid owing to some internal cause, it is necessary to saw them off; before doing which the parts surrounding the bones must be divided. But since, when this is done first, as a considerable time is required for the sawing, there is danger of a hemorrhage taking place, Leonides properly directs us not to divide all the parts at once unless they are completely mortified, but first to cut the part where not many nor very large veins or arteries are known to be situated, down to the bone quickly; then to saw the bone as expeditiously as possible, applying a linen rag to the parts which have been cut lest they be torn by the sawing and occasion pain, and then having cut through what remains, to apply red-hot irons to the vessels and stop the hemorrhage thereby with compresses of lint, and to apply proper bandages with the dressings suitable to suppurations.

Commentary. Hippocrates and Galen recommend amputation to be performed in general at a joint. Hippocrates says complete excision may be performed at the joints of the hand and foot, and at those of the wrist and ankle, and generally with safety, unless the patient be cut off by fainting, or continual fever supervene on the fourth day. When gangrene attacks a fractured limb, his rule of practice is to let the parts drop off, and he remarks, many persons thus recover, even when the fracture is seated in the femur. When gangrene comes on without being preceded by fracture, he directs the soft parts, as soon as they have lost all sensibility, to be removed at the nearest joint below, and the surgeon is to wait until the bone also separates. He says he had seen the bone of the thigh thus separate on the eightieth day; in that case the limb below had been removed at the knee on the twentieth day. In a similar case of gangrene of the leg, the bones separated on the sixtieth day. He pronounces gangrene of the extremities to be more formidable in appearance than in reality. He recommends a mild and anti-inflammatory treatment, and that the limb should be laid in an elevated position as long as there is any fear of hemorrhage [. . .]

It would appear from Thucydides and Lucretius that it was not uncommon to amputate in cases of gangrene in the days of Hippocrates . . . In cases of gangrene Celsus directs us to make an incision of the flesh, between the sound and corrupted part, down to the bone, which is to be sawed across, and after the asperities have been removed from the end of the bone, the skin is to be brought over the stump . . . He gives us no particular description, however, of amputation of the extremities. [. . .]

Archigenes begins by stating the circumstances which require recourse to be had to amputation. They are, the presence of some intractable disease, such as gangrene, necrosis, putrefaction, cancer, certain callous tumours, and sometimes wounds inflicted by weapons, and the like. Before attempting the operation he recommends us to consider well if the patient's strength will enable him to endure it. The operator must then tie or sew the vessels which pass to the parts; in certain cases a ligature is to be applied round the whole limb, cold water is to be poured upon it, and some are to be bled. Amputation near the joints is not to be attempted. In such as are of a full habit of body, a circular band is to be put round the limb, to draw up the skin with, and to direct the incision. After cutting down to the bone, the tendons are to be retracted, and the bone scraped and sawn. When much blood is discharged, red-hot irons are to be applied, and a double compress laid on the part from which the blood proceeds. Having loosened the band, a cataplasm of leeks, bread, and salt is to be applied to the stump; and the parts about the jawbone are to be anointed with cerate [wax mixture] of iris and old oil, doubtless in order to obviate the danger from tetanus.

Heliodorus states that a limb may require to be amputated owing to gangrene or any other cause that occasions the death of it. In the extremities, then, he remarks, amputation may be performed with less danger; but above the knee or elbow the danger of hemorrhage from the great vessels being wounded is very considerable. Some, he says, from too great anxiety for despatch, cut through all the bodies (the soft parts?) at one incision, and then saw the bones. But this method of removing the limb is not unattended with danger, as many vessels pour forth blood at the same time. "Wherefore," he adds, "it appears to me better first to divide those parts of the limb where there is least flesh, as on the anterior part of the leg, and then to saw the bone; and I myself am in the practice of first applying a ligature above the part of the limb which is to be sawn across, and then of operating in the manner described. In sawing the bone the plate of the saw ought to be applied even, in order that the sawing of the bones may be even. When the bones are sawed the other parts which remain undivided are straightway to be cut through with a scalpel, and large pledgets applied along with suitable compresses. External to these, sponges with suitable bandages are to be put on. After the third or fourth day, when all fear of hemorrhage is over, suppuration is to be promoted by suitable dressings."

Source: Aegineta, Paulus. Translated by Francis Adams. *The Seven Books of Paulus Ægineta. Translated from the Greek. With a commentary embracing a complete view of the knowledge possessed by the Greeks, Romans, and Arabians on all subjects connected with medicine and surgery, Vol. II.* London, Printed for the Sydenham Society, 1844–47, pp. 409–411.

14 Treatment for Respiratory Illnesses and Tuberculosis (1412)

British surgeon John de Arderne (1307–1392) is considered one of the fathers of surgery [Cirurgia] in 14th-century England. His parchment manuscripts written in Latin included elaborate drawings on various diseases and their cures and were assembled into a book in 1412. In 1922, it was translated by British surgeon and medical historian D'Arcy Power (1855–1941) based upon a transcript made by Eric Millar from a replica in the Stockholm Wellcome Historical Medical Museum. Arderne was also an expert in the pharmacology of the day and recommended different mixtures for different diseases. His surgical techniques and recipes for cures were often accompanied with illustrations. In this excerpt, he describes various concoctions for colds, coughs, TB, and other ills using a blend of various medicinal plants and herbs. Some of them are still used today such as opiates, but others are considered highly poisonous, such as ground ivy sometimes called Creeping Charlie. This excerpt gives an example of the complexity of mixing various medications many of which may not have been very effective in the 14th century. (Note: ʒ equals one dram and āā means "of each").

Of hoarseness from shouting, watching and fatigue. Give a bath and poached eggs and conserve of apples and orach and lovage and a confection of linseed and bean flour . . .

Observe that phlebotomy should not be done for hoarseness unless it is of hot and moist cause.

For severe hoarseness pills of asafoetida and fenugrec and orobus and make an electuary for this is of much service in hoarseness from a cold cause . . .

If the materies morbi is of a moist cause dried figs and decoctions of calamint with tragacanth and gum arabick are helpful. Dried figs are serviceable in all causes.

For roughness of the voice. Make a poultice of sieved bran with milk of almonds, sugar candy and the whites of eggs.

Against a cough whether cold or hot. . . Dried figs, raisins āā. . . . broth a third part. Digest them with liquorice and honey and make a decoction with maidenhair, origanum and hyssop āā. Let the patient avoid acid and salt things and let him live with moderation.

A cure for a cough from cold and moist cause. Let the breath be held because it warms the lung and the whole chest.

Likewise pills of myrrh and storax with honey held under the tongue.

Likewise sulphur rubbed up with poached eggs.

Likewise rubbing with warm oils as oil of lilies with red wax and costus and spikenard and cummin.

Let a dried fig be given.

Against Cold Rheum[discharge from nose]. . .

Absinthe and white horehound a handful of each; ground ivy a third part.

Let them be digested in white wine or in water and let the patient be made drowsy by the steam (inhaled) through his mouth and nostrils with the head covered.

But note that chewing three grains of white incense daily is useful against all rheums from a cold cause and . . . Liquorice juice ʒxii; of the seeds of citron melons ʒv ;

tragacanth and gum acacia āā. ʒi.

Make it into lozenges and let one be kept under the tongue until it is dissolved and let the liquorice juice be swallowed.

It is useful in every rheum.

In hot and cold cases Rx. Liquorice juice ʒ10: melon and quince
seeds ʒv : gums tragacanth and arabic āā. ʒij; make lozenges
and let one be held under tongue until it is dissolved and let
the liquorice juice be swallowed. This is useful in every fever.

Against a cold cough.

A water of sieved bran wonderfully cleanses the lung and chest if horehound, calamint, hyssop, figs and liquorice be digested with it.

Against dryness of the Chest.

Rx. Violets ʒ1/2 ; figs ʒi; horehound and poppies of each ʒi.
Make a decoction with sugar.
Also let an electuary be used of iris, mint and horehound.

If anyone is full of phlegm.

Rx. Hyssop; mint; maiden hair āā. a handful; horehound half a handful; agrimony a quarter of a handful; cinnamon ʒ1/2 orrice ʒii; gum arabic and tragacanth aä. ʒ1/2 liquorice ʒiv. Make a syrup with a tisane of barley and beans and add to it one pound of sugar and an equal quantity of honey.

Against phthisis [*TB*] ***with fever***.

Rx. Endive; maidenhair; scolopendra; enula campestris; shepherd's purse; horsehoof; duckweed āā. ʒi; barley sugar ʒii, etc.; gum arabic and liquorice āā. ʒii; four seeds of the cleansing cold seeds ʒi; of quince seeds and of cotton seeds āā, ʒii; and of all the saunders āā. ʒ1/2; of water-lily flowers ʒii; sugar q.s.

Without fever.

Rx. Calamint; hyssop; maidenhair; scolopendrium, a handful; agrimony half a handful; lily root; smallage seeds; pine cones; mallows ʒ1/2; figs and juice of liquorice āā, one quarter.

Make a syrup. To be given in a tisane made of barley and beans with honey 1 1/2.

Against Vomiting of Blood by the Mouth.

Rx. Hypoquistidist ; acacia; balaustines: ; psyllium; white coral and red coral powdered; hematite; plantain seeds; quince seeds; bole armoric; terra sigillata; dragon's blood; juice of green mint; juice of roses and of sumach āā ʒxv.

Make a syrup with three pounds of sugar and make the syrup with rain water or with rosewater.

It is excellent in bleeding from the mouth and for dysentery.

A Syrup for the Consumptive for the hectic, the wasted, the phthisical, for those who cough, and for the Asthmatic, since it cleanses and purifies, soothes and feeds and is useful in healing and for driving out discharges as well as for its strengthening virtues. . .

Rx. Root of iris and hyssop āā ʒi; maidenhair three handfuls; four seeds of the greater and lesser celandine; coriander seed; mallow seed; seed of the white poppy; cotton; fenugrek; bitter vetch; marmalade of liquorice; marmalade of raisins; marmalade of pines and of almonds; marmalade of husked barley āā ʒi.

Cook them over a slow fire with dry sticks in sweet well water without sediment and add half a pound of bread and two pounds of sugar. Make a syrup.

Source: Arderne, John. Translated by D'Arcy Power. *De Arte Phisicali et de Cirurgia of Master John Arderne*, Surgeon of Newark, Dated 1412. New York: W. Wood, 1922, pp. 11–14.

15 Paracelsus: Theses on Medicine (1500s)

American-born British poet, astrologer, and mystic A. E. Waite (1857–1942) wrote numerous occult texts and translated The Hermetic and Alchemical Writings of Aureolus Philippus. . . *by Paracelsus into English from the Latin. Paracelsus was a Swiss physician and alchemist born Theophrastus von Hohenheim (1493–1541) but generally was known as Paracelsus in his writings. This excerpt discusses medical knowledge that he strongly believed needed to be kept secret and known only to physicians. He felt that the mixing of medicines—which we would now call pharmacology—must be prepared with the guidance of the stars or astrology. Paracelsus believed that salt, sulphur, and mercury were the three basic elements of all substances and denounced the antiquated systems of Galen and other earlier physicians. The following excerpt is important because Paracelsus was the first to use zinc and other metallic and mineral substances in the treatment of diseases. It also demonstrates that astrology and alchemy were often part of medical practice during 16th-century Europe.*

See also: Document 9

We have drawn our medicine by experiment, wherein it is made clear to the eye that things are so. Then, coming to its practice, we divide this our book of Archidoxies [ancient doctrine or practice] into ten, as a sort of aid to the memory, so that we may not forget these matters, and at the same time may speak of them so far openly that we may be understood by our disciples, but not by the common people, for whom we do not wish these matters to be made too clear. We do not care to open our mind and thoughts and heart to those deaf ears, just as we do not wish to disclose them to impious men; but we shall endeavour to shut off our secrets from them by a strong wall and a key. And if by chance this our labour shall not be I sufficiently safeguarded from those idiots who are enemies of all true arts, we shall forbear writing the tenth book, concerning the uses of those which precede it, so that we may not give the children's meat to the dogs. Nevertheless, the other nine will be sufficiently understood by our own disciples.

And, to speak more plainly of these matters, it must be known that in this treatise on the microcosm are proved and demonstrated all those points which it contains, which also embrace medicine, as well as those matters which are interconnected therewith. The subject of the microcosm is bound up with medicine and ruled by it, following it none otherwise than a bridled horse follows him who leads it, or a mad dog bound with chains. In this way I understand that medicine attracts Nature and everything that has life. Herein three things meet us, which shew by what forces they are filled and produced. Firstly, in what way the five senses are assisted by the mysteries of Nature, though those senses do not proceed from Nature, nor spring naturally as a herb from its seed, since there is no material which produces them. Secondly, the mobility of the body is to be considered: whence it proceeds, by what power it is moved and exercised, and in what manner it is ministered to. Thirdly, there must be a knowledge of all the forces in the body, and what forces apply to each member, and are transmuted according to the same nature as the particular limb, when originally they are identical in Nature. [. . .]

Medicine is most rude and unpolished. How can man be more rude than when he eats raw flesh, clothes himself in undressed hides, and has his dwelling in the nearest rocks, or is exposed to the rains? In the same way, how can a physician be more dense, for the preparation of **medicine** than what ointment-sellers use for decocting substances? Nothing can be more objectionable than this method for pounding, subduing, and mixing medicines, or for polluting them in any other different way. As its own special art dresses the hide, so does its own special art prepare the medicament. And since, in this place, the true basis of preparing remedies, in which lies the whole essence of **medicine**, is laid down and established, be well assured of this, that such a foundation must be extracted from the most secret recesses of Nature, and not from the imaginative brain, as a cook dresses a mess of pottage, according to his own judgment. For in this preparation the extreme and ultimate condition of things is posited. Thus, if philosophy and astrology—that is, the nature of diseases and their remedies, with all their combinations and conjunctions—be understood, it follows next in order, and is chiefly necessary, that you should decide how you will use and avail yourself of your knowledge. Nature, indeed, of herself teaches you on these subjects, and you should give her your chief attention in order that you may reduce your medical science down to practice.

As summer puts forth the pears and the grapes, so should you do with your **medicine**. If you act thus you will assuredly compass the results you covet. And if it so be that as summer puts forth its fruits, so you do with your **medicine**, be certain that summer does this by means of the stars, and in no case without their aid. Now, if the stars accomplish this, take care so to regulate your preparation in this case also that it shall be duly directed by the stars. These it is which complete and perfect the work of the physician. Now, if the stars have this effect, it is right that **medicine** should be understood, and naturalized in all respects, with reference to them. Let it not be said; This is cold, this warm, this moist, this dry; but rather let it be said: This is Saturn, this Mars, this Venus, this the Pole-star. In such a way the physician proceeds by a straight road, especially if, beyond this, he also knows how to subject, conjoin, and harmonize the astral Mars with that which is produced from it. For here is situated the covering or nucleus which none of the physicians from first to last before me has ever arrived at. This must be understood, that **medicine** should be prepared with reference to the stars, so that they exert their astral influences. The higher stars weaken and cause death, but they also heal.

If any of these effects is to be produced, it cannot be done without the stars. But if this is to be done by the help of the stars, it will be done after such a manner, and in such a way, that the preparation will be reduced to practice, so that **medicine** will be compounded and prepared by means of heaven.

Source: Paracelsus. Edited and translated by Arthur Edward Waite. *The Hermetic and Alchemical Writings of Aureolus Philippus Theophrastus Bombast, of Hohenheim, Called Paracelsus the Great: Now for the First Time Faithfully Translated into English*; Edited, With a Biographical Preface, Elucidatory Notes, a Copious Hermetic Vocabulary, and Index. London: James Elliott and Co., 1894, 5–6, 148–149.

16 Aztec Smallpox Victims (ca. 1520)

Berdardino de Sahagún (1499–1590), a Franciscan missionary priest went to Mexico in 1529. Over his many years there, he compiled an oral history of Aztec history and customs from Aztec elders and is considered one of the first anthropologists. His General History of the Things of New Spain, *also known as the* Florentine Codex *has a description of the spread of the smallpox epidemic that lasted from 1517–1521. Smallpox arrived in the fall of 1520 to the capital city, Tenochtitlán (now Mexico City), even before the battle, siege, and fall of the city. It was likely transmitted by a sailor on of the Spanish ships to soldiers and then on to native peoples. A smallpox victim was covered with pustules and had high fever. If the pustules were few and far apart on the skin, the patient generally lived. However, if there were many, the patient usually did not survive. This pen-and-ink from the* Codex *shows smallpox patients. As described by the Aztec elders, victims had no energy, laid in bed, could not move, and many died of starvation as there was no one to feed them. From about a third to a half died from the disease, and some went blind. The epidemic in the city lasted for about sixty days.*

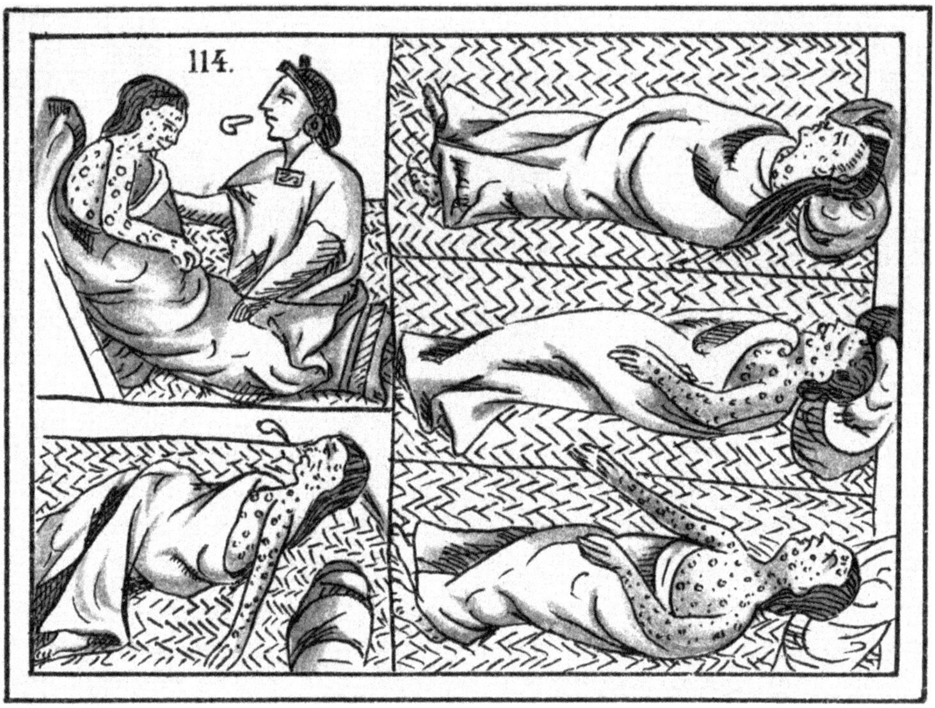

Aztec smallpox victims

Source: Courtesy of the Peabody Museum of Archaeology and Ethnology, Harvard University, PM# 2004.24.29636

17 Girolamo Fracastoro: Description of Syphilis (1530)

Italian Physician and poet Girolamo, or Hieronymus, Fracastoro (1478–1553) described in a poem the sexually transmitted disease (STD) syphilis in 1530. American physician Solomon Claiborne Martin (1871–?) translated it into English in 1911. The outbreak of syphilis in Europe first occurred in 1494/1495 in Naples, Italy, during a French invasion. The Italians considered it the French disease while France and other areas of the continent considered it the Italian disease or blamed their enemy nation for causing the disease. Fracastoro thought it might be of astrological origins. On the other hand, he proposed the germ theory of diseases with particles spreading through clothing, contact, or through the air. This was more than 300 years before the theory was tested by Louis Pasteur and Robert Koch in the 19th century. Fracastoro also suggested using mercury to treat it. The disease was named after a shepherd in his poem who has been given the disease as punishment from the gods. The following excerpt is important as it pinpoints the first detailed description of the disease soon after the return of the explorers from the new world. However, there is still some debate as to whether or not it was brought to the old world by Columbus's men or if it had already existed but had become more virulent (deadly).

See also: Document 54

The introduction to the work by the publisher suggests:

> "To the author is due the credit of having given this name which, not only supplanted the many others which had been given to it, but which has persisted to the present day and is in universal use. Whilst this poem is filled with mythological allusions it affords a good clinical description of the symptoms of the disease."

This disease does not affect the dumb inhabitants of the wave, nor the wild beasts of the forests, nor the birds of the sky, nor horses nor cattle. It only has to do with man; man alone is its prey. In the human body, it is the blood that it attacks at first, and, feeding on naught but fat and viscid humors, it is on the fat and corrupted parts of this fluid that it preferably attaches itself.[. . .]

One of the most surprising of facts is that, after having contracted the germ of the contagion, the victim attacked by the scourge does not often present any lesion that is well marked before the moon has four times accomplished its travels. The disease, in fact, does not show itself at once by accusing symptoms directly that it has penetrated the organism. For a certain time it broods in silence, as if it were gathering its forces for a more terrible explosion. During this period, at all events, a strange languor seizes the patient and depresses his whole being; his mind seems heavy, his limbs are soft, and weakening, fail for work; the eye loses its flash and the face is depressed in its expression and has become pale.

It is on the organs of generation that the virus first is transported, to irradiate from there to the neighboring parts and on the regions of the groin.

Soon after, more well defined symptoms show themselves. When the light of day disappears to give place to the shades of night, at the time when the inner heat of living bodies leaves the peripheral parts to concentrate upon the viscera, atrocious pains suddenly burst forth in the limbs charged with vitiated humors and torture the articulations, the arms, the shoulders, the calves. It is because at that moment, vigilant Nature, an enemy of all impurity, is at work to react against the putrid ferments which the disease has introduced into the veins and with which it has penetrated all the humors, all the nourishing juices of the organisms. She strains to drive them away; she energetically fights against them. But they resist; thick, viscid, not displacing themselves except slowly, they fix themselves on the muscles, they attach themselves to the exsanguined framework of the tissues, and give rise to horrible sufferings wherever they adhere.

The most subtle of these morbid humors, those which are the most easily evacuated, take refuge either in the skin or in the extremities of the limbs. They then produce hideous eruptions on those points and these exanthems soon spread over the whole body and cover the face with a repulsive mask.

Unknown up to our days, these eruptions consist of pustules and conical pimples, which, gorged with corrupted liquids, are not slow in opening to allow the escape of a mucous and virulent sanious liquid. Even, sometimes, the pimples that are similar develop in the depths of organs and noiselessly corrode the tissues. It is thus that horrible ulcers are seen covering the limbs, denuding the bones, eating the lips and penetrating the throat, from which there only issues a weak and plaintive voice.

At other times, again, there exhales from the skin thick humors which dry into fearsome crusts on the surface of the integument. Like these are seen the viscid juices which come from the cherry tree or the almond tree condensing in a gummy callus on the bark of these trees.

Ah! how many patients, sorrowful victims of this plague have contemplated with horror their faces and their bodies covered with the hideous taints, deploring their youth destroyed in its bloom, and have cursed the gods and threatened the sky! Unfortunates! Night which pours sweet repose upon all nature, has no more charms for them, in the same manner, aurora comes without attractions, for them, for sleep has fled from their eyes. Day like night recalls their pains.

Source: Fracastoro, Girolamo. Translated by Solomon Claiborne Martin. *Hieronymus Fracastor's Syphilis, From the Original Latin; A Translation in Prose of Fracastor's Immortal Poem.* St. Louis, Mo., The Philmar Company, 1911, 20–23.

18 Vesalius: Anatomy of Bones and Cartilages of the Head (1543)

Andreas Vesalius (1514–1564) a 16th-century Flemish (Dutch) anatomist and physician who worked as court physician in Spain published one of the most influential book on human anatomy. He is often considered the father of modern human anatomy. His major work, De Humani Corporis Fabrica *(*Fabric of the Human Body*), was published in 1543. The* Epitome *was a brief descriptive anatomical work condensed from his larger volume for use by students. He was noted for correcting many anatomical inaccuracies of Galen, the early Greek anatomist and physician. However, like Galileo and Copernicus and other scholars and scientists of his day, he was subject to questions from the Inquisition for his autopsies. He was accused of doing a dissection on a person whose heart was still beating. The* Epitome *was first translated into English in 1949 from the Latin original. The entry here was one of the first to give a fairly accurate description of various boney parts of the head.*

CONCERNING THE BONES AND CARTILAGES,

OR THOSE PARTS WHICH SUPPORT THE BODY

CHAPTER I

ALL of the parts of the human body are either similar, or simple to the senses, such as the bones, cartilages, ligaments, fibers, membranes, flesh, and fat, or dissimilar, instrumental agencies, such as the veins, arteries, nerves, muscles, individual fingers, and the remaining organs of the entire body. These latter parts are made all the more instrumental to the degree that they (e.g., the hand and head) are composed of many similar parts and also of many functional mechanisms.

The bones are the hardest and driest parts of the entire body. The cartilages are softer than the bones, but of the parts of the body they are next in hardness to the bones. The whole body is supported by bones and cartilages in combination, and all its parts are attached to, and stabilised by, them. The skull, which contains the brain and the sense organs, is composed of several bones; one bone frequently makes up the forehead, especially in women; in the occiput of the head there is likewise one; two bones are at the vertex, and one at each ear or temple, in which a cavity is formed suitable for the reception of the organ of hearing. This cavity encloses two small bones, one of which resembles an anvil or molar tooth, while the other is like a small hammer The bone of the temple has connected to it the cartilage supporting the structure of the ear. In addition it has three processes: first, it bears the mastoid process posteriorly; second, the styloid process, like a bodkin or cock's spur; third, a process which turns anteriorly, is closely joined in the external structure of the orbit to the bone of the upper jaw, and at the level of this junction constitutes the part of the skull which we call the os jugale. Inferiorly the temporal bone joins the base of the occipital bone to form that region of the skull which we may compare to a broken rock, not only from the standpoint of hardness but also in appearance. In the base of the skull is a noteworthy bone which professors of dissection compare to a wedge; it is polymorphous and gives forth projections very much like the wings of a bat. Near it, above the nose, there is another bone which is pervious in form like a sieve or more like a sponge; it forms the septum of the nose, and in company with the seven bones previously listed it makes up the cavity which contains the brain.

In the upper jaw we count twelve bones in addition to the teeth: one on the lateral and two on the medial aspect of each eye socket, and one pair in the inferior part of the orbits; these last bones are regarded as by far the largest of the group and contain small cavities for the reception of the upper teeth. A pair of bones is found at that end of the palate at which the apertures of the nasal cavities become continuous with the pharynx. Finally, the prominent part of the nose is composed of two bones which connect with the cartilages of the nose by which the wings of the nostrils are supported; like the other bones of the upper jaw, they have no special name.

Thus far most of the bones mentioned are held in place by sutures, of which the one passing transversely in the sinciput is called the coronal; the one creeping transversely in the occiput receives its name from its resemblance to the Greek letter Λ; and the one passing along the length of the skull from the top of the occiput to the middle of the coronal suture is called the sagittal. Those bony junctions which are equidistant from the sagittal suture and which pass superior to the ears do not look like sutures but are more like two overlapping scales, from which appearance they are called squamous conglutinations. The remaining connections between the bones of the skull do not show the appearance of a suture as well as do the three which have been named; in fact, in some places they appear more like a simple line and should receive the name of "harmony" rather than that of "suture".

The lower jaw consists of a single bone, with the exception of very young children, in whom it forms from two bones fusing at the point of the chin; indeed, most of the bones of children are composed of several bones which later unite into single bones in those who have reached their full growth. The lower jaw articulates on either side with a bone located near the ear, and in addition with its special cartilage intervening here, where the heads of these bones and their corresponding sinuses fit together, the articular surface is covered in the manner of a rind and a joint is thereby provided that turns readily, rendering it free from the injuries of continuous friction of the bones against each other. There are at most sixteen teeth in each jaw: four incisors, two canines, and ten molars; not only do they differ in appearance when examined in place in the mouth, but they are also fixed in their sockets with differing numbers of roots.

In the pharynx, the bone at the root of the tongue has more the shape of the Greek letter v than of Λ; it is bound together with many small bones. The lower of these are joined at their extremities to the rough artery of the head (which we call the larynx rather than the gullet or throat) and, more specifically, to a cartilage which resembles a shield.

Source: Vesalius, Andreas. *The Epitome of Andreas Vesalius.* Translated by Levi Robert Lind. New York: Macmillan, 1949, pp. 1–3.

19 Chinese Vaccination Procedure (ca. 1549)

Smallpox has been documented for centuries and was a major killer until the late 19th century. Some evidence exists that the Chinese variolated (vaccinated) or inoculated against smallpox as early as 1000 C.E. Chinese physicians found that when someone had become sick with smallpox and survived, they did not get it again. They also discovered that when healthy people, in particular children, were exposed to material from the smallpox scabs or pustules, they acquired a milder case of the disease and generally did not get it again. The Chinese used several methods to inoculate. As illustrated in the picture, ca. 1549, a common method of inoculation was to crush smallpox scabs into powder and store them in a container for several weeks. Then the powder was placed into the nose or the person breathed the powder through the nose from a bag. Another method was to put a sample of the matter from a pustule on a piece of cloth and insert it into the nose. Still another method was to make a scratch on the arm and rub some of the powdered smallpox scab or matter into the wound. In most cases, the person developed a mild case of the disease.

See also: Document 10; Document 25

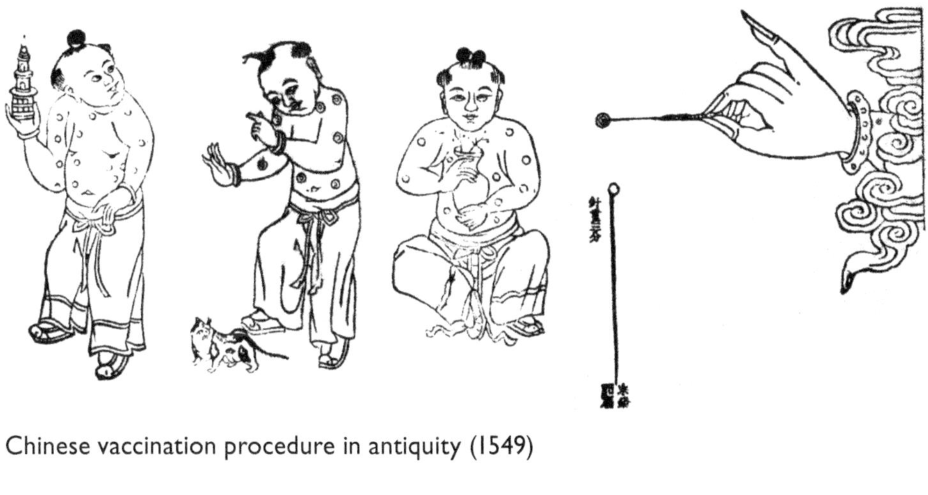

Chinese vaccination procedure in antiquity (1549)

Source: Burroughs Wellcome and Company. *The History of Inoculation and Vaccination for the Prevention and Treatment of Disease: Lecture Memoranda.* American Medical Association, Minneapolis, 1913, p. 20.

20 William Harvey: Circulation of the Blood (1628)

English physician William Harvey (1578–1657) wrote De Motu Cordis *in 1628 on the circulation of the blood. Scottish physician and medical historian Robert Willis (1799–1878) translated it from Latin as* An Anatomical Disquisition on the Motion of the Heart & Blood in Animals. *It was published in 1847 by the Sydenham Society, a publisher of medical and historical works. The translation was reprinted in 1906. Although others had mentioned valves in the veins, Harvey was the first to demonstrate valves in veins of human and other mammals. Most importantly, he demonstrated the circulation of blood. He showed that oxygenated blood flows from the left ventricle of the heart out to the extremities by arteries and back again to the heart through two large veins that flow into the right atrium and into the ventricle. The veins had valves to help prevent the blood from flowing backward. From the left ventricle, the blood is sent to the lungs for oxygen and then back into the heart to be circulated again. This excerpt is the classic Harvey report on circulation.*

CHAPTER XIII

THE THIRD POSITION IS CONFIRMED: AND THE CIRCULATION OF THE BLOOD IS DEMONSTRATED FROM IT

Thus far have we spoken of the quantity of blood passing through the heart and the lungs in the centre of the body, and in like manner from the arteries into the veins in the peripheral parts and the body at large. We have yet to explain, however, in what manner the blood finds its way back to the heart from the extremities by the veins, and how and in what way these are the only vessels that convey the blood from the external to the central parts; which done, I conceive that the three fundamental propositions laid down for the circulation of the blood will be so plain, so well established, so obviously true, that they may claim general credence. Now the remaining position will be made sufficiently clear from the valves which are found in the cavities of the veins themselves, from the uses of these, and from experiments cognizable by the senses.

The celebrated Hieronymus Fabricius of Aquapendente, a most skilful anatomist, and venerable old man, or, as the learned Riolan will have it, Jacobus Silvius, first gave representations of the valves in the veins, which consist of raised or loose portions of the inner membranes of these vessels, of extreme delicacy, and a sigmoid or semilunar shape. They are situated at different distances from one another, and diversely in different individuals; they are connate at the sides of the veins; they are directed upwards or towards the trunks of the veins; the two—for there are for the most part two together—regard each other, mutually touch, and are so ready to come into contact by their edges, that if anything attempt to pass from the trunks into the branches of the veins, or from the greater vessels into the less, they completely prevent it; they are farther so arranged, that the horns of those that succeed are opposite the middle of the convexity of those that precede, and so on alternately.

The discoverer of these valves did not rightly under their use, nor have succeeding anatomists added anything to our knowledge: for their office is by no means explained when we are told that it is to hinder the blood, by its weight, from all flowing into inferior parts; for the edges of the valves in the jugular veins hang downwards, and are so contrived that they prevent the blood from rising upwards; the valves, in a word, do not invariably look upwards, but always towards the trunks of the veins, invariably towards the seat of the heart. I, and indeed others, have sometimes found valves in the emulgent veins, and in those of the mesentery, the edges of which were directed towards the vena cava and vena portae. Let it be added that there are no valves in the arteries [save at their roots], and that dogs, oxen, &c, have invariably valves at the divisions of their crural veins, in the veins that meet towards the top of the os sacrum, and in those branches which come from the haunches, in which no such effect of gravity from the erect position was to be apprehended. Neither are there valves in the jugular veins for the purpose of guarding against apoplexy, as some have said; because in sleep the head is more apt to be influenced by the contents of the carotid arteries. Neither are the valves present, in order that the blood may be retained in the divarications or smaller trunks and minuter branches, and not be suffered to flow entirely into the more open and capacious channels. [. . .]

CHAPTER XIV: CONCLUSION OF THE DEMONSTRATION OF THE CIRCULATION

And now I may be allowed to give in brief my view of the circulation of the blood, and to propose it for general adoption. Since all things, both argument and ocular demonstration, show that the blood passes through the lungs, and heart by the force of the ventricles, and is sent for distribution to all parts of the body, where it makes its way into the veins and porosities of the flesh, and then flows by the veins from the circumference on every side to the centre, from the lesser to the greater veins, and is by them finally discharged into the vena cava and right auricle of the heart, and this in such a quantity or in such a flux and reflux thither by the arteries, hither by the veins, as cannot possibly be supplied by the ingesta, and is much greater than can be required for mere purposes of nutrition; it is absolutely necessary to conclude that the blood in the animal body is impelled in a circle, and is in a state of ceaseless motion; that this is the act or function which the heart performs by means of its pulse; and that it is the sole and only end of the motion and contraction of the heart.

Source: Harvey, William. *An Anatomical Disquisition on the Motion of the Heart & Blood in Animals.* Translated from the Latin by Robert Willis. London: Dent, 1628, 1906.

21 John Graunt: Mortality Rates in Britain in the 17th Century (1662)

John Graunt (1620–1674) is considered one of the first statistician and demographers. He kept statistics on the number of deaths and illnesses from various diseases in a bill, or mortality or morbidity records entitled Natural and Political Observations Made upon the Bills of Mortality *(1662). Various honors were bestowed on him by the leading scientists of the day. However, later some suggested that a coauthor of another book, William Petty (1620–1687) may have done most of the compiling. In his book, Graunt alludes to syphilis as the French pox and describes its characteristics, which should be compared to descriptions from the 16th and late 19th centuries. He also discusses rickets, now known to be caused by a lack of vitamin D, scurvy from lack of vitamin C, gout, and the malaria-type illness, the Ague. Data for these statistics were gathered by pensioned elderly women called "seachers," whose job was to examine corpses and report their findings to the parish clerk who then entered the cause of death into the bill. Graunt also comments on new diseases by comparing their symptoms. He does not make a table but explains his statistics in writing. The spellings of the 17th century and numbering of the paragraphs have been kept as is in the document.*

See also: Data 15; Data 16

15. We finde one *Casualty* in our Bills, of which though there be daily talk, . . . this *Casualty* is the *French-Pox*, gotten, for the most part, not so much by the intemperate use of *Venery* (which rather causeth the *Gowt*) as of many common Women.

16. I say, the Bills of *Mortality* would take off these Bars, which keep some men within bounds, as to these extravagancies: for in the afore-mentioned 229250 we finde not above 392 to haved died of the Pox. Now, forasmuch as it is not good to let the World be lulled into a security, and belief of Impunity by our Bills, which we intend shall not be onely as *Death's-heads* to put men in minde of their *Mortality,* but also as *Mercurial Statues* to point out the most dangerous ways, that lead us into it, and misery . . .

17. Forasmuch as by the ordinary discourse of the world it seems a great part of men have, at one time, or other, had some *species* of this disease, I wondering why so few died of it, especially because I could not take that to be so harmless, whereof so many complained very fiercely; upon inquiry I found that those who died of it out of the Hospitals (especially that of *King's-Land*, and the *Lock in Southwark)* were returned of *Ulcers*, and *Sores*. And in brief I found, that all mentioned to die of the *French-Pox* were retured by the *Clerks* of Saint *Giles's*, and Saint *Martin's in the Fields* onely; in which place I understood that most of the vilest, and most miserable houses of uncleanness were: from whence I concluded, that onely *hated* persons, and such, whose very *Noses* were eaten of, were reported by the Searchers to have died of this too frequent *Maladie*[. . .]

19. My next Observation is, that of the *Rickets* we finde no mention among the *Casualties;* until the . . year 1634, and then but of 14 for that whole year.

20. Now the Question is, whether that Disease did first appear about that time; or whether a Disease, which had been long before, did then first receive its Name?

21. To clear this Difficulty out of the Bills (for I dare venture on no deeper Arguments:) I enquired what other Casualties before the year 1634, named in the Bills, was most like the *Rickets;* and found, not onely by Pretenders to know it, but also from other Bills, that *Liver-grown* [enlarged liver] was the nearest. For in some years I finde *Liver-grown, Spleen*, and Rickets, put all together, by reason (as I conceive) of their likeness to each other. Hereupon I added the Liver-growns of the year 1634, *viz*. 77, to the Rickets of the same year, viz. 14. making in all 91. which Total, as also the Number 77. it self, I compared with the Liver-grown of the precedent year, 1633, *viz*. 82. All which shewed me, that the *Rickets* was a new Disease over and above.

22. Now, this being but a faint Argument, I looked both forwards and backwards, and found, that in the year 1629, when no *Rickets* appeared, there was but 94 *Liver-growns;* and in the year 1636. there was 99 Liver-grown, although there were also 50 of the *Rickets:* onely this is not to be denyed, that when the *Rickets* grew very numerous (as in the year 1660, viz. to be 521.) then there appeared not above 15 of Liver-grown.

23. In the year 1659 were 441 *Rickets*, and 8 *Liver-grown*. In the year 1658, were 476 Rickets, and 51 Liver-grown. Now, though it be granted that . . . these Diseases were confounded in the judgment of the *Nurses*, yet it is most certain, that the Liver-grown did never but once, viz. Anno 1630, exceed 100. whereas *Anno* 1660, *Liver-grown*, and *Rickets* were 536.

24. It is also to be observed, That the Rickets were never more numerous then now, and that they are still increasing; for Anno 1649, there was but 190, next year 260, next after that 329. and so forwards, with some little starting back-wards in some years, untill the year 1660, which produced the greatest of all.[. . .]

33. The *Stone* seemed to decrease: for in 1632, 33, 34, 35, and 36. there died of the *Stone*, and *Strangury,* 254. And in the Years 1655, 56, 57, 58, 59, and 1660, but 250, which numbers although . . indeed they be almost equal, yet considering the Burials of the first named five Years were but half those of the latter, it seems to be decreased by about one half.

34. Now the [kidney] *Stone*, and *Strangury* [frequent urination generally caused by enlarged prostate] , are diseases, which most men know, that feel them, unless it be in some few cases, where (as I have heard Physicians say) a Stone is held up by the *Filmes* of the *Bladder*, and so kept from grating, or offending it.

35. The *Gowt* [gout] stands much at a stay, that is, it answers the general proportion of Burials; there dies not above one of 1000 of the *Gowt,* although I believe that more die *Gowty.* The reason is, because those that have the Gowt, are said to be Long-livers, and therefore, when such die, they are returned as *Aged.*

36. The *Scurvy* hath likewise increased, and that gradually from 12. Anno 1629. to 95. Anno 1660 [. . .]

38. *Agues* and *Fevers* are entred promiscuously, yet in the few Bills, wherein they have been distinguished, it appears, that not above one in 40, of the whole are *Agues*.

Source: Graunt, John. Edited by Willcox, Walter Francis. *Natural and Political Observations Made upon the Bills of Mortality*. Baltimore: The Johns Hopkins Press [1662], 1939, 13–16.

22 Symptoms of Depression and Other Mental Conditions (1686)

German physician Johann Dolaeus (1651–1707) wrote Systema Medicinale, *and it was translated from Latin by English physician William Salmon (1644–1713). Dolaeus divided the book into diseases and conditions found in different parts of the body such as head, chest, belly, heart, etc. He discusses sexually transmitted diseases such as the French Pox (syphilis) and gives theories of its origins, including suggesting it was Columbus's men who brought it back to the old world. The book describes signs, symptoms, and causes of various conditions and diseases. He also includes herbal recipes for treatment. In this excerpt, he describes depression and suggests there are two kinds. One arises in the brain and one in the body. He also gives symptoms such as delusions, paranoia, hallucinations, and fear that suggest psychotic and mood disorders. The excerpt is important as it suggests that mental disorders were not classified into separate illnesses. Depression was lumped together with other disorders and psychotic behaviors, which were all thought to be different aspects of melancholia or depression. It was not until the turn of the 20th century when mental illnesses began to be classified into separate entities.*

Chap. III.

Of Melancholy.

In the preceding Chapter we treated of the Animal spirits, when tumultuary and ungovernable, here we find them, on the other Hand, so much dejected and declined from their Natural Briskness, that they are scarce able to perform any Function aright.

1. Definition

This distemper is commonly defin'd by others, A certain sort of Delirium or Dotage, without a Fever and Rage, proceeding from a melancholy Humor; which in our Opinion is well enough, but for Perspicuities sake we give this Definition, A Delirium without a Fever and Rage, arising from the Dulness and Unactiveness of the Animal Spirits.

The Essential Cause of this Distempter (if it be not clearly explain'd already) is, the Imagination's being so disturb'd as to fancy strange and monstrous Things, but yet with Fear and Sadness; whereby it comes to pass that the Animal Spirits, forgetful, as it were, of their Duties, flow less plentifully into the several Organs to perform their Offices, so that the Viscera being defrauded of their Spirits, have not their due Fermentation, without which they cannot perform their proper Actions, whence the Body becomes fill'd with acid, viscous and tenacious Flegm; and then those few Spirits being entangled, and as it were agglutinated in the tough Matter, are insensibly wafted every Day more and more, upon the loss of which the disease Person lives very miserably. But to come nearer the Business, and to give the Genus of our Definition. In this Disease are found various Deliriums, and (as Willis says) fabulous Antiquity has scarce invented any Metamorphosis of Man, which some or other have not fancied in themselves.

2. Division
We divide this disease into Melancholy Cephalic, and Hypchondriac. A Cephalic is when the Disorder is in the Brain, and the Hypochondria are not in fault. The Hypchondriac is when the Disease has its Seat about the lower Part of the Abdomen.

3. Part affected
Now we come to the Part affected, which according to the Opinion of the Ancients is the Brain itself, and they say it is hurt as it is a peculiar Part; for they derive all the chief Faculties of the Soul from thence, and will have in this Case the principal Faculty thereof, that is, the Imagination, not the Cogitation or Memory, to be hurt. The excellent Hippocrates asserts . . . that the Soul in this Distemper, is distinctly affected, and, as it were, without the Body and Brain. The Brain, say others, is hurt essentially, and that then there are no Signs of the Pracordia, Hypochondria, or of any other Part being affected, and that in that Case the Symptoms are more favourable, and that a Lividness appears in the Face: If the Brain be hurt by Communication or Consent; as by the Spleen, Hypchondria, or by the Womb, when a melancholy Humor is generated there, that then the Symptoms commonly ascribed to the Womb do appear in those Parts affected. For they tell us that in Childbearing Women, whose Lochia are stopt, or in Maids when their Terms do not flow, the Blood is spoil'd, and becomes more fixt, and is turn'd into a melancholy Dyscrsy, and that by this Means this Distemper arises. For which Reason the Ancients blame the Spleen; but Our Opinion is, that rather the morbid Product than the Disease itself, lies there. The famous Willis thinks that both the Heart and Brain in this Case are affected. Some take the Corporeal Soul to be the Subject of it. Helmont thinks that it lies out of the Brain in the Pracordia, and about the Mouth of the Stomach. Our own Opinion, in short, is, That it has its Residence in the globous Frame of the Brain, which being the principal Part, and the Fountain from whence the Animal Spirits issue out into every Corner of the Body, if they be dull, languid and unactive, the Hypochondria, Spleen, Liver, Pancreas, Mesentery, Womb, etc. being thereby deprived of their Fermentations, must needs suffer in the common Calamity, and be the Receptacles of latent Evils.

4. Signs
The two principal Signs of this Disease are Fear and Sadness; all melancholy People are extraordinary fearful and sad; which the famous Willis (as we have heard above) ascribes to the Passion of the Heart; for it must needs be a Fellow-Sufferer, when the Animal Spirits are so dull and sleepy that they cannot irradiate and puff it up. For whereas naturally and in a sound state they ought to be brisk, lively, clear, fine and lucid, now they are sad, dark, and as if they were dead, and as terrible as the dismal blackness of Night, which may make the boldest Courage shake. A joyful Spirit, on the contrary . . . *makes the days of a Man's Life pleasant and flourishing; whereas a sad Spirit causes the Bones to dry, and brings a speedy Death.* Those that are affected with this Disease are weary of their Lives, infected

with frightful and very intent Thoughts, have strange Convulsions of their Limbs, and are Epileptical through the whole Body. They begin to talk idly, and without any Order. They also often fall a weeping, and take Pleasure in being alone, and anon dislike what they so lately delighted in. They are so jealous that they think every body cheats and lays Snares for them, and are even afraid of Poison in their Bread. They sleep so little that the Nightingale is not more vigilant; and this short Repose is attended with strange frightful Dreams, which many Physicians erroneously ascribe to Vapors arising from the Spleen, which We (with those of better Judgment) impute rather to Spirits got out of their proper Sphere.

These were the General Signs, now we come to the Special. Some Melancholy People have always a foolish silly Laughter like Democritus; others again never cease Weeping, as if by a Pythagorean Metempsychosis, the Soul of Heraclitus had transmigrated into them. Many imagine themselves Prophets and prophesy of things to come. Some do vainly fancy that they are great Kings or Princes, and that the Staff they carry in their Hands in a Scepter. Others believe that they are transform'd into a new Species, whence it is that they imitate the Sounds and Gestures of Cuckows, Cocks, Wolves, Dogs, and other Creatures. Many think themselves earthen Pots, and therefore are afraid of meeting any Body left they should be broken. Others that they are made of Glass, and are much concern'd left by being too hard grasp'd they should be crusht to Pieces. Some that they are dead, and are very importunate to be carried to their Graves. Many think they see an evil Spirit in this or the other Pot or Chest, and for that Reason they are thought by the Vulgar to be possess'd by the Devil. Others, though they fear Death, yet some wish for it. And sometimes do lay violent Hands upon themselves; three Examples of which, I myself have known. Some think they want their Heads. Some all their Members, as Arms, Feet, etc., and fancy to themselves such a mangled Body as Aeneas in Virgil saw Deiphobus have. . .

Some supposing themselves to be dead, refuse to eat. Many think that Soldiers and Officers are ready to seize them and carry them to Prison. . . Many are afraid that the Earth will open and swallow them up. Some are intent upon Battles, Contentions, Quarrels, Studies, Prayers, or such other Employment and Course of Life as they have been conversant in . . . and some that are awake, are not unlike to others in a Dream.

Source: Doläus, Johann, 1651–1707. *Systema Medicinale, a Compleat System of Physick, Theorical and Practical: In Six Books.* London: Printed for T. Passinger, T. Sawbridge, and T. Flesher, 1686, 35–37.

23 James Lind: Experiments on Scurvy (1753)

Scottish physician James Lind (1716–1794) is often considered the father of naval medicine. In 1739, he entered the navy as a surgeon's mate and served in the Mediterranean and in the West Indies. Scurvy, which often occurred on long voyages, killed more people than naval battles. The condition is caused by a lack of vitamin C, which was not known until the early 20th century. In order to cure it, Lind conducted one of the first clinical trials to determine the best cure for the disease. Others had noted that citrus fruit appeared to prevent scurvy as did eating the ships' rats. All animals except primates (humans, monkeys, apes, etc.) make vitamin C. In 1747, he divided sailors into several groups. Each group received a different substance that was thought to cure the disease. These included oranges, cider, vinegar, sea water, a garlic mustard paste, and diluted sulfuric acid. At the end of a week, those who ate the citrus fruits were well enough to take care of the others. However, it took several decades for the British navy to accept these findings and supply citrus fruit to sailors on long voyages. This extract from his work, A Treatise on the Scurvy *(1753), describes the experiment.*

The following are the experiments.

On the 20th May 1747, I selected twelve patients in the scurvy, on board the *Salisbury* at sea. Their cases were as similar as I could have them. They all in general had putrid gums, the spots and lassitude, with weakness of their knees. They lay together in one place, being a proper apartment for the sick in the fore-hold; and had one diet in common to all, viz., water gruel sweetened with sugar in the morning; fresh mutton broth often times for dinner; at other times light puddings, boiled biscuit with sugar etc.; and for supper barley and raisins, rice and currants, sago and wine, or the like. Two of these were ordered each a quart of cyder a day. Two others took twenty five drops of elixir vitriol [diluted sulfuric acid] three times a day upon an empty stomach, using a gargle of it for their mouths. Two others took two spoonfuls of vinegar three times a day upon an empty stomach, having their gruels and their other food sharpened with vinegar, as also the gargle for their mouth. Two of the worst patients, with the tendons in the ham quite rigid (a symptom none of the rest had) were put under a course of sea water. Of this they drank half a pint every day and sometimes more or less, as it operated, by way of gentle physic. Two others had each two oranges and one lemon given them every day. These they eat with greediness, at different times, upon an empty stomach. They continued but six days under this course, having consumed the quantity that could be spared. The two remaining patients took the bigness of a nutmeg three times a day of an electuary [medicated paste with honey] recommended by an hospital surgeon made of garlic, mustard seed, horseradish, balsam of Peru and gum myrrh, using for common drink, barley water boiled with tamarinds, by which, with the addition of cream of tartar, they were gently purged three or four times during the course.

The consequence was, that the most sudden and visible good effects were perceived from the use of oranges and lemons; one of those who had taken them being at the end of six days fit for duty. The spots were not indeed at that time quite off his body, nor his gums sound; but without any other medicine than a gargle for his mouth, he became quite healthy before we came into Plymouth, which was on the 16th of June. The other was the best recovered of any in his condition, and being now deemed pretty well, was appointed to attend the rest of the sick.

Next to the oranges, I thought the cyder had the best effects. It was indeed not very sound. However, those who had taken it, were in a fairer way of recovery than the others at the end of the fortnight, which was the length of time all these different courses were continued, except the oranges. The putrefaction of their gums, but especially their lassitude and weakness, were somewhat abated, and their appetite increased by it.

As to the elixir of vitriol, I observed that the mouths of those who had used it by way of gargle, were in a much cleaner and better condition than many of the rest, especially those who used the vinegar; but perceived otherwise no good effects from its internal use upon the other symptoms. I indeed never had a great opinion of the efficacy of this medicine in the scurvy, since our longest cruise in the *Salisbury*, from the 10th of August to the 28th of October 1746; when we had but one patient in the scurvy, a marine, who, after recovering from a quotidian ague in the latter end of September, had taken the elixir vitriol by way of restorative for three weeks; and yet at length contracted the disease, while under a course of a medicine recommended for its prevention.

There was no remarkable alteration upon those who took the electuary and tamarind decoction, the sea-water, or vinegar, upon comparing their condition, at the end of the fortnight, with others who had taken nothing but a little lenitive electuary and cream of tartar occasionally, in order to keep their body lax, or some gentle remedies in the evening, for relief of the breast.

Source: Lind, James. *A Treatise on the Scurvy, Third Edition.* London: Printed for S. Crowder, 1772, pp. 149–152.

24 Matthew Carey: Scourge of Yellow Fever (1794)

Irish-American journalist and publisher Matthew Carey (1760–1839) wrote about the yellow fever epidemic that ravaged Philadelphia in the fall of 1793. He gives a detailed description of the symptoms of the disease from its onslaught to recovery or death. He also discusses various treatments for a disease that was unknown among physicians of the time. The noted physician Benjamin Rush (1745–1813) tried purging with salt water but all patients died. He next tried a West Indies bark, wine, laudanum (opium derivative), and the cold bath, but this was not successful. Other treatments were tried, such as bleeding and calomel—a purgative that contained mercury. Some physicians concluded that strong purges with the use of calomel and jalap [purgative root] and bleeding were the best treatments. Carey also mentions that normal civility of social life was broken down during the epidemic. This excerpt shows that in the face of an unknown epidemic, various cures were undertaken using the trial and error method. However, there is no cure for this disease.

See also: Document 57

THE symptoms which characterized the first stage of the fever, were, in the greatest number of cases, after a chilly fit of some duration, a quick, tense pulse–hot skin–pain in the head, back and limbs–flushed countenance–inflamed eye–moist tongue–oppression and sense of soreness at the stomach, especially upon pressure–frequent sick qualms, and retchings to vomit, without discharging anything, except the contents last taken into the stomach–costiveness, etc. And when stools were procured, the first generally showed a defect of bile, or an obstruction to its entrance into the intestines. But brisk purges generally altered this appearance.

These symptoms generally continued with more or less violence from one to three, four, or even five days; and then gradually abating, left the patient free from every complaint, except general debility. On the febrile symptoms suddenly subsiding, they were immediately succeeded by a yellow tinge in the opaque cornea, or whites of the eyes—and increased oppression at the præcordia—a constant puking of everything taken into the stomach, with much straining, accompanied with a hoarse, hollow noise.

If these symptoms were not soon relieved, a vomiting of matter, resembling coffee grounds in color and consistence, commonly called the black vomit, sometimes accompanied with, or succeeded by haemorrhages from the nose, sauces, gums, and other parts of the body—a yellowish purple colour, and putrescent appearance of the whole body, hiccup, agitations, deep and distressed sighing, comatose delirium, and finally, death. When the disease proved fatal, it was generally between the sixth and eighth days. This was the most usual progress of this formidable disease, through its several stages. There were, however, very considerable variations in the symptoms, as well as in the duration of its different stages, according to the constitution and temperament of the patient, the state of the weather, the manner of treatment, etc.

In some cases, signs of putriscency [rotten smell] appeared at the beginning, or before the end of the third day. In these, the black vomiting, which was generally a mortal symptom, and universal yellowness, appeared early. In these cases, also, a low delirium, and great prostration of strength, was constant symptoms, and coma came on very speedily.

In some, the symptoms inclined more to the nervous than the inflammatory type. In these, the jaundice colour of the eye and skin, and the black vomiting, were more rare. But in the majority of cases, particularly after the nights became sensibly cooler, all the symptoms indicated violent irritation and inflammatory diathesis. In these cases, the skin was always dry, and the remissions very obscure.

The febrile symptoms, however, as has been already observed, either gave way on the third, fourth, or sixth day, and then the patient recovered; or they were soon after succeeded by a different, but much more dangerous train of symptoms, by debility, low pulse, cold skin, (which assumed a tawny colour, mixed with purple) black vomiting, haemorrhages, hiccup, anxiety, restlessness, coma, etc. Many, who survived the eighth day, though apparently out of danger, died suddenly in consequence of an haemorrhage.

This disorder having been new to nearly all our physicians, it is not surprising, although it has been exceedingly fatal, that there arose such a discordance of sentiment on the proper mode of treatment, and even with respect to its name. Dr. Rush has acknowledged, with a candour that does him honour, that in the commencement, he so far mistook the nature of the disorder, that in his early essays, having depended on gentle purges of salts to purify the bowels of his patients, they all died. He then tried the mode of treatment adopted in the West Indies, viz. bark, wine, laudanum, and the cold bath, and failed in three cases out of four. After wards he had recourse to strong purges of calomel and jalap, and to bleeding, which he found attended with singular success.

The honour of the first essay of mercury in this disorder, is by many ascribed to Dr. Hodge and Dr. Carson, who are said to have employed it a week before Dr. Rush. On this point, I cannot pretend to decide. But whoever was the first to introduce it, one thing is certain, that its efficacy was great, and rescued many from death. I have known, however, some persons, who, I have every reason to believe, fell sacrifices to the great reputation this medicine acquired; for in several cases it was administered to persons of a previous lax habit, and brought on a speedy dissolution.

I am credibly informed that the demand for purges of calomel and jalap, was so great, that some of the apothecaries could not mix up every dose in detail; but mixed a large quantity of each, in the ordered proportions; and afterwards divided it into doses; by which means, it often happened that one patient had a much larger portion of calomel, and another of jalap [dried tuberous root of a Mexican plant], than was intended by the doctors. The fatal consequences of this may be easily conceived.

Source: Carey, Matthew. *A Short Account of the Malignant Fever Lately Present in Philadelphia Lately Prevalent in Philadelphia: with a statement of the Proceedings that took place on the subject, in different parts of the United States—to which are added, Accounts of the Plague in London and Marseilles; and a List of the Dead, From August 1, to the middle of December 1793, Fourth Edition, Improved.* Philadelphia: Printed by the author. January 15, 1794, pp. 13–16.

25 Edward Jenner: An Inquiry into Cowpox (1798)

British physician Edward Jenner (1749–1823) was the first to vaccinate against smallpox using the matter from a cowpox pustule. Insertion of matter from a smallpox pustule, a procedure called "variolation," prevented smallpox. It had been noted since antiquity that once a person had survived the disease, he or she did not get it again. In the early 1700s, African slaves used variolation and rarely contracted or died from smallpox. In 1718, British wife of the ambassador to Turkey, Lady Mary Montague (1689–1762), had her son variolated with smallpox matter based upon the Turkish practice that prevented the disease. Since it was successful, she spread the idea as a method of preventing the disease in England. However, about 2 percent of individuals inoculated died from the procedure. Jenner had heard stories that dairymaids were protected from smallpox after having suffered from cowpox. He hypothesized that cowpox protected against smallpox and the disease could be transmitted from one person to another. In this excerpt, Jenner in 1796 vaccinates a young boy with cowpox matter and then exposes him to smallpox, which he did not get. The procedure was found to be safer than live smallpox vaccination. His work represented the first scientific attempt to control an infectious disease by the deliberate use of vaccination.

See also: Document 19

CASE XVI.—Sarah Nelmes, a dairymaid at a farmer's near this place, was infected with the cow-pox from her master's cows in May, 1796. She received the infection on a part of her hand which had been previously in a slight degree injured by a scratch from a thorn. A large pustulous sore and the usual symptoms accompanying the disease were produced in consequence. The pustule was so expressive of the true character of the cow-pox, as it commonly appears upon the hand, that I have given a representation of it in the annexed plate. [In original.] The two small pustules on the wrists arose also from the application of the virus to some minute abrasions of the cuticle, but the livid tint, if they ever had any, was not conspicuous at the time I saw the patient. The pustule on the forefinger shews the disease in an earlier stage. It did not actually appear on the hand of this young woman, but was taken from that of another, and is annexed for the purpose of representing the malady after it has newly appeared.

CASE XVII.—The more accurately to observe the progress of the infection I selected a healthy boy, about eight years old, for the purpose of inoculation for the cow-pox. The matter was taken from a sore on the hand of a dairymaid, who was infected by her master's cows, and it was inserted, on the 14th of May, 1796, into the arm of the boy by means of two superficial incisions, barely penetrating the cutis, each about half an inch long.

On the seventh day he complained of uneasiness in the axilla, and on the ninth he became a little chilly, lost his appetite, and had a slight headache. During the whole of this day he was perceptibly indisposed, and spent the night with some degree of restlessness, but on the day following he was perfectly well.

The appearance of the incisions in their progress to a state of maturation were much the same as when produced in a similar manner by variolous matter. The only difference which I perceived was in the state of the limpid fluid arising from the action of the virus, which assumed rather a darker hue, and in that of the efflorescence spreading round the incisions, which had more of an erysipelatous look than we commonly perceive when variolous matter has been made use of in the same manner; but the whole died away (leaving on the inoculated parts scabs and subsequent eschars) without giving me or my patient the least trouble.

In order to ascertain whether the boy, after feeling so slight an affection of the system from the cow-pox virus, was secure from the contagion of the smallpox, he was inoculated the 1st of July following with variolous matter, immediately taken from a pustule. Several slight punctures and incisions were made on both his arms, and the matter was carefully inserted, but no disease followed. The same appearances were observable on the arms as we commonly see when a patient has had variolous matter applied, after having either the cow-pox or smallpox. Several months afterwards he was again inoculated with variolous matter, but no sensible effect was produced on the constitution.

Here my researches were interrupted till the spring of the year 1798, when, from the wetness of the early part of the season, many of the farmers' horses in this neighbourhood were affected with sore heels, in consequence of which the cow-pox broke out among several of our dairies, which afforded me an opportunity of making further observations upon this curious disease.

Source: Jenner, Edward. *The Three Original Publications on Vaccination Against Smallpox* Vol. XXXVIII, Part 4. *The Harvard Classics*. New York: P.F. Collier & Son, 1909–1914.

26 Fluid Movement into Organs Causes Complex Changes (1809)

Jean-Baptiste Lamarck (1744–1829), a French botanist, originated the theory of inheritance of acquired characteristics. His theory underpinned the hereditarian concerns (diseases passed from one generation to the next) of the mid-19th century and the initial surge of the early-20th-century eugenics movement to improve the health of the human race. Lamarck crafted a theory of inheritance and evolution based upon environmental influences, and he was the first scientist to acknowledge the adaptability of organisms. Lamarck first mentioned his theory around 1800, detailing it in Philosophie Zoologique *(1809). In this work, he explains how complex life forms evolved from simpler ones. Lamarck formulated four laws, and in his last and most famous law, he argued that all characteristics acquired by an organism from its environment could be transmitted to offspring. This theory of inheritance was accepted until the 1910s when it was disproved by the new field of genetics based upon the work of Gregor Mendel (1822–1884). In this excerpt from his* Philosophie, *Lamarck explains the development of new organs based upon his theory of acquired characteristics.*

If we admit on the one hand that every living body whatever is a mass of cellular tissue, in which are embedded various organs of a number proportionate to the complexity of organisation; and if on the other hand we also admit that all bodies contain within them fluids that move faster or slower according as the state of organization allows of a more or less active or energetic life, we are forced to the conclusion that it is to the movement of fluids in the cellular tissue that we have primarily to attribute the formation of every kind of organ in the midst of this tissue, and hence that each organ must be invested by it both in its gross outlines and in its most minute parts, as indeed we actually find.

With regard to animals, I have no need to show that in various of their internal parts the cellular tissue is squeezed aside by the moving fluids, which open a passage through it; and that in these regions it has been forced back upon itself; it has then been compressed and transformed into investing membranes round about these running streams of fluid; while on the outside these living bodies are incessantly compressed by the environing fluids (either water or atmospheric fluids) and modified by external impressions and by deposits upon them. Their cellular tissue has thus come to form that universal investment of every living body, that is called skin in animals and bark in plants.

I was then fully justified when I said " that the function of the movement of fluids in the supple parts of living bodies, and especially in the cellular tissue of the simplest among them, is to carve out routes, places of deposit and exits, to create canals and thereafter diverse organs, to vary these canals and organs in accordance with the diversity of the movements or character of the fluids causing them, finally to enlarge, elongate, divide, and gradually solidify these canals and organs. This is effected by the substances which are incessantly being formed in the fluids, and are then separated from them, and in part assimilated and united to the organs, while the remainder is rejected."

I was equally justified when I said "that the state of organization in every living body has been gradually acquired by the increasing influence of the movement of fluids (firstly in the cellular tissue and afterwards in the organs formed in it), and by the constant changes in the character and state of these fluids owing to the continual wastage and renewals proceeding within them."

Lastly, I was authorised by these principles in saying " that every organisation and every new shape, acquired by this agency and contributing circumstances, were preserved and transmitted by reproduction, until yet further modifications had been acquired by the same method and in new circumstances." It follows from the above that the function of the movement of fluids in living bodies, and consequently of organic movement, is not merely the development of organisation, for this development continues so long as the movement is not weakened, through the hardness which overtakes the organs during life; but that this movement of fluids has in addition the faculty of gradually increasing the complexity of organisation and of multiplying the organs and their functions according as new modes of life or new habits acquired by individuals stimulate it in various ways, create a necessity for new functions, and consequently for new organs.

Source: Lamarck, Jean Baptiste. Translated by Hugh Elliot. *Zoological Philosophy: An Exposition With Regard to the Natural History of Animals.* London: Macmillan, 1914, pp. 232–233.

27 Sylvester Graham: Intemperance, the Cause of Cholera (1832)

American diet and anti-alcohol reformer, Sylvester Graham (1794–1851), presented a lecture in New York in 1832 where he denounced drinking any form of alcohol as he thought it would weaken the constitution and predispose a person to cholera. During the 1830s when cholera was originally transmitted to Europe and the United States, it was first thought to be a disease associated by immorality, drunkenness, poverty, and filth. Graham noted that Paris had a higher rate of cholera compared to London. Campaigns in London advised people not to drink as a method of preventing the disease. Graham supposes that the heavy meat-eating and wine-and-brandy-drinking French contracted the disease because of their lifestyle. On the other hand, in London where the cholera rate was lower, he thought that drinking tea, rather than alcohol, saved them from the disease. Drinking hot tea would have killed the cholera bacterium, which likely reduced the disease in the country. This excerpt from his lecture is important as it shows that boiling water for tea would have reduced waterborne diseases, but its significance at the time went unnoticed.

See also: Document 30

Writers in Paris inform us, that almost everybody in that city, has more or less of the premonitory symptoms of cholera, and therefore it is inferred that the epidemic cause is atmospheric: but it ought to be known that such a state of things may be produced by panic alone, without the action of any other cause; and therefore, men ought not rashly to increase the horrors of this disease, by throwing the awfulness of mystery over the public mind [. . .].

It has been a favorite doctrine with some of our wine-loving countrymen, and one which they have zealously endeavored to promulgate that in wine countries there is little, or no intemperance, in the use of intoxicating liquors. But this is altogether erroneous. The excesses in Paris according to the number of the population, are at least equal, and probably much greater, than in London. An American gentleman in Paris writing to this country on the subject of the cholera, says, "Narrow damp streets, houses that are dripping half the time in wet weather, cold floor, excessive dirt, and drunkenness, of which you have no conception in America, are the causes why the disease has been so bad here. There are perhaps one hundred thousand souls in Pans that are intoxicated more or less, once or twice a week, and in this class the mortality has been fearful." For excessive lewdness, which is another most powerful, predisposing cause of cholera, Paris has long been exceedingly notorious ; and we learn that it is among the unfortunate citizens of that character, that the disease has committed its most terrible ravages. [. . .]

But there are other facts of equal, if not more importance in their bearing on this subject. For a considerable time before the cholera appeared in London, great, and somewhat extensive efforts had been made, in (the Temperance cause, against the use of all intoxicating liquors: and when the terrible disease was believed to be approaching that city, every laudable measure was taken, to spread over the whole population, a solemn impression that every drinker of strong drink, and every one given to excess, must expect to fall a sure victim of the cholera. Handbills advertising this, were posted up in every part of the city, and newspapers reiterated the warning in every quarter : and no medical gentleman came out with his professional advice, against the warning ; no physician renowned for his experience and knowledge of the disease, publicly recommended the use of "generous wine, and brandy, and gin." [. . .]

[On the other hand], in Paris a "generous diet of flesh, and wine, and brandy," became the popular doctrine of conservation, and for awhile, was believed to constitute an insuperable barrier, over which the "vulgar disease," could not lift its destroying energies; and behind which, he that was able to erect it, might stand in safety, and laugh at the storm that was raging below him ; or, for his amusement, ludicrously masquerade the dismay, and agonies, and convulsive sufferings of the "vulgar herd."

But the respectable citizens of Paris, little thought that their "generous diet," which they deemed their bulwark of security, would prove the very means by which the "ignoble disease" would be enabled to elevate his enginery of death to a level with their own breasts! Nevertheless, the consequences were inevitable! Excesses in eating and drinking, were as universal in Paris, as the means of indulgence ; and thus, the higher classes of society brought themselves, in liability to the disease, on to the level with "the herd," whose sufferings they had treated with sneering commiseration, and compassionate ridicule. And the gay and reckless Parisians were the first to learn, and to demonstrate to the terrified world, that the cholera was not confined, in its work of death, to the destitute, the miserable, and the abandoned: but it had the audacity to fold, in its unclean embrace, even persons of titled rank and distinction, and to breathe its pestilential breath into the very atmosphere that surrounded the throne! [. . .]

They are asked why the cholera prevails so much more extensively and fatally in Paris than in London. They gravely set themselves about the solution of the question, and finally come to the sapient conclusion, that *"the general and constant use of tea, by the English, saved them from the severity with which the disease attacked the French; and therefore they recommend the use of tea as a specific against the violence of the cholera."* [emphasis mine]. . .To suppose that this is absolutely, in any degree a specific against the violence of the cholera, is an absurdity which would be disreputable to the empirics of the nursery.

It is very certain that the sour wines which are so habitually so universally, and so abundantly used in Paris as a common beverage, predispose the body to the cholera far more than the weak tea generally used in England. But pure water, in reasonable quantities, is an infinitely better substitute for such wines than tea, or any other alcoholic or narcotic drink.

Source: Graham, Sylvester. A lecture on epidemic diseases generally: and particularly the spasmodic cholera: delivered in the city of New York, March 1832. New York: Mahlon Day, 1833, pp. 42–58.

28 Digitalis: An Advance in Drug Treatment from the Beginning of Modern Therapeutics (1847)

British botanist and professor of materia medica *(now called pharmacology), John Forbes Royle (1798–1858), was on the medical staff of Kings College, London. He spent several years in India as part of the Bengal army and as superintendent of the botanical garden at Saharanpur. One of his major interests was traditional botanical remedies used by Hindu native healers. Royle wrote a classic* materia medica *in 1847. This pharmacology text covered the identification of plants, how to make drug preparations, what the substance was prescribed for, side effects, and possible antidotes in case of poisoning. He also gives the history of various medicinal plants. The following excerpt on digitalis is taken from this major work and is important as it demonstrates that digitalis, from the foxglove (*Digitalis purpurea*) leaves, was the most important drug used for heart disease at least since the 17th century in Europe. This antiarrhythmic drug at the beginning of modern pharmacology was a forerunner of cardiac drugs developed in the later 20th and 21st centuries.*

See also: Document 53

Digitalis Folia, L. D. (Digitalis, U. S.) Leaves, E. and Digitalis Semina, L. Seeds of Digitalis Purpurea, *Linn*. Foxglove.

Foxglove does not appear to have been known to the ancients. Fuchsius was the first to describe it, and to name it Digitalis, from the resemblance of its flowers to the finger of a glove. It was admitted into the L. P. of 1668 and 1721, rejected in that of 1745. Withering brought it into permanent notice in 1775.

Biennial. Root fibrous. In the first year a tuft of radical leaves is thrown up, from the midst of which rises, in the second year, a stem 1–5 feet high, which is erect, wandlike, and leafy, slightly angled and downy, in some varieties with a purple tinge, as well as on the lower surface of the leaves. Leaves alternate, ovate-lanceolate, or oblong, crenate, and rugose, downy, especially on the under surface, tapering at the base into winged footstalks. Racemes terminal, long, and lax, on which the pendulous flowers appear on one side in slow succession. Flowers crimson, purple, marked with eye-like spots, and hairy within, sometimes white. . . . Seeds very small, of a pale brownish colour, and pitted.—Indigenous and also common chiefly in the western parts of the Continent: found on pastures and exposed hill-sides, as also in plantations: begins to flower in June and July, and ripens its seed in August and September

Both the leaves and seeds are officinal, but the latter are seldom employed. The roots, collected in the autumn or winter of their first year, are possessed of active properties. The leaves of this plant, like the leaves of all biennial plants, Dr. Houlton says, should be gathered in the second year of their duration, and as soon as possible after the first flowers have expanded: he also prefers those of the plants having a purplish stem. Dr. Christison, however, thinks this is a needless—it is at least a safe—restriction. He has observed that their bitterness, which probably measures their activity, is very intense both in February and September, and that their extract is highly energetic as a poison in the middle of April, before any appearance of the flowering stem. Full-grown and perfect leaves should be chosen, especially of such plants as grow spontaneously in open situations. They should be carefully dried in a dark airy room, and the midrib separated, and kept so that the light be excluded. They should be renewed annually, have a dull, but when powdered, a fine green colour, a slight odour, with the strong bitterness of the recent plant. The juice of the fresh plant may be expressed and evaporated to the consistence of an extract, or its active properties imparted to water or Spirit. The leaves of Digitalis have been found to contain traces of Volatile Oil, Fixed Fatty matter, a red extractiform Colouring matter, Chlorophylle, Albumen, Starch, Sugar, Gum, salts of Potash, of Lime, and of Magnesia, but also an acid, partly free and partly combined, probably with a Bitter principle (*Digitaline*), on which the activity of the plant seems to depend. (*Homolle.*) This Bitter matter is soluble in Alcohol, a little so in Ether, and dissolves in water with the aid of the substances with which it is combined and mixed. . . . It is easily reduced to a yellowish-white powder, which must be kept from air and light. From its solution in Spirit it may be separated in beautiful white scales. Dr. Morries Sterling, by the destructive distillation of the dried leaves, obtained an empyreumatic oil, containing a crystalline principle possessed of Narcotic properties.

The leaves of Foxglove are apt to be intermixed with those of *Verbascum Thapsus*, also with those of *Symphitum officinale*, and sometimes with those of *Conyza squarrosa*, but they may be distinguished by attending to the description, or by comparison with genuine leaves.

Action. Uses. Indirectly Sedative, that is, first exciting and then greatly diminishing the force and frequency of the heart's action. The intestinal canal is apt to be disordered by large doses, as well as the brain and organs of the senses affected by vertigo, &c. The kidneys are often acted on, and the secretion of urine increased. It is cumulative in its effects; therefore, when nausea or intermission of the pulse occurs, its use should be discontinued for a time, and the patient should not rise from the recumbent position when under its influence. It has been used to control the circulation, in diseases of the Heart, in Fever, in Inflammations, and in Pulmonary affections after the acute symptoms have subsided, and is useful in excitement from nervous irritability. It is much prescribed as a Diuretic in Dropsies of all kinds, but is most useful in those associated with a debilitated and generally diseased state of the constitution.

Source: Royle, J. Forbes. *Materia Medica: Including the Preparation of Phamacopias.* London, Edinburgh, Dublin and Philadelphia. 1847, pp. 491–493.

29 Rāzī: A Treatise on the Smallpox (1848)

Rāzī, Abū Bakr Muḥammad ibn Zakarīyā (865?–925?), also known in Latin as Rhazes or Rasis was a renown Persian (Iranian) physician and scholar of early Islam. He translated ancient Greek and Roman science, medicine, and philosophy manuscripts that kept the information of antiquity alive in the West. He advanced medicine in the middle ages by writing case histories of patents and took clinical notes about the progress and symptoms of different illnesses. His works became standard texts for both Islamic and European medical students for centuries. His writings also brought the use of the ancient, but inaccurate, idea of personal temperaments used in the West into the 19th century as a means of diagnosis and treatment of disease. Based upon earlier writings of Greek physicians, and his own observations, Rāzī discovered that smallpox and measles were two different diseases, which are described in this entry along with temperaments. This passage is important as it illustrates the beginnings of keen observation to distinguish diseases. The beginning rashes of these two diseases had led other physicians to believe they were the same diseases in different forms with different people at different ages or temperaments.

Now the Small-Pox arises when the blood putrefies and ferments, so that the superfluous vapours are thrown out of it, and it is changed from the blood of infants, which is like must, into the blood of young men, which is like wine perfectly ripened: and the Small-Pox itself may be compared to the fermentation and the hissing noise which take place in must at that time. And this is the reason why children, especially males, rarely escape being seized with this disease, because it is impossible to prevent the blood's changing from this state into its second state, just as it is impossible to prevent must (whose nature it is to make a hissing noise and to ferment), from changing into the state which happens to it after its making a hissing noise and its fermentation. And the temperament of an infant or child is seldom such that it is possible for its blood to be changed from the first state into the second by little and little, and orderly, and slowly, so that this fermentation and hissing noise should not show itself in the blood. . .

As to young men, whereas their blood is already passed into the second state, its maturation is established, and the superfluous particles of moisture which necessarily cause putrefaction are now exhaled; hence it follows that this disease only happens to a few individuals among them, that is, to those whose vascular system abounds with too much moisture, or is corrupt in quality with a violent inflammation; or who in their childhood have had the Chicken-Pox, whereby the transition of the blood from the first into the second state has not been perfected. It takes place also in those who have a slight heat, or whose moisture is not copious; and to those who had the Chicken-Pox in their childhood, and are of a dry, lean habit of body, with slight and gentle heat; and who when they became young men, used a diet to strengthen and fatten their body, or a diet which corrupted their blood.

And as for old men, the Small-Pox seldom happens to them, except in pestilential, putrid, and malignant constitutions of the air, in which this disease is chiefly prevalent. For a putrid air, which has an undue proportion of heat and moisture, and also an inflamed air, promotes the eruption of this disease, by converting the spirit in the two ventricles of the heart to its own temperament, and then by means of the heart converting the whole of the blood in the arteries into a state of corruption like itself. . . .

The bodies most disposed to the Small-Pox are in general such as are moist, pale, and fleshy; the well-coloured also, and ruddy, as likewise the swarthy when they are loaded with flesh; those who are frequently attacked by acute and continued fevers, bleeding at the nose, inflammation of the eyes, and white and red pustules, and vesicles; those that are very fond of sweet things, especially, dates, honey, figs, and grapes, and all those kinds of sweets in which there is a thick and dense substance, as thick gruel, and honey-cakes, or a great quantity of wine and milk.

Bodies that are lean, bilious, hot, and dry, are more disposed to the Measles than to the Small-Pox; and if they are seized with the Small-Pox, the pustules are necessarily either few in number, distinct, and favorable, or, on the contrary, very bad, numerous, sterile, and dry, with putrefaction, and no maturation.

Lastly, those bodies that are lean and dry, and of a cold temperament, are neither disposed to the Small-Pox nor to the Measles; and if they are seized with the Small-Pox, the pustules are few, favorable, moderate, mild, without danger, and with a moderate light fever from first to last, because such constitutions extinguish the disease.

Source: Rāzī, Abū Bakr Muḥammad ibn Zakarīyā. *A Treatise on the Small-Pox and Measles*. Translated by William Alexander Greenhill. London: Sydenham Society, 1848, pp. 29–32.

30 John Snow: Mode of Communication of Cholera (1855)

British physician John Snow (1813–1858) is one of the fathers of modern epidemiology. His work, On the Mode of Communication of Cholera *(1855), is an epidemiology classic and is studied even in current times by medical and public health students. He compared the difference in the number of people who came down with the disease by water supplied by two water companies. Snow recorded his observations and developed basic epidemiological methods using charts and graphs. He hypothesized that cholera could be spread by contaminated water or food. In 1854 a cholera outbreak occurred in London, which gave Snow the opportunity to test his hypothesis. Snow recorded the location of deaths related to cholera on a map and was able to show that the majority were clustered around one particular public water pump on Broad Street, in the Soho district. After much debate, he eventually convinced London officials to remove the handle to the pump. Curiously by the time the water supply had been shut off, the epidemic was already in decline. Besides contaminated water and foods, touching soiled linen and then not washing hands can also transmit the disease. Snow's discovery led to the change in water supply and sewage systems in London along with other cities, which ended cholera epidemics in developed nations by the beginning of the 20th century.*

Instances of the Communication of Cholera through the Medium of Polluted Water in the Neighborhood of Broad Street, Golden Square

The most terrible outbreak of cholera which ever occurred in this kingdom, is probably that which took place in Broad Street, Golden Square, and the adjoining streets, a few weeks ago. Within two hundred and fifty yards of the spot where Cambridge Street joins Broad Street, there were upwards of five hundred fatal attacks of cholera in ten days. The mortality in this limited area probably equals any that was ever caused in this country, even by the plague; and it was much more sudden, as the greater number of cases terminated in a few hours. The mortality would undoubtedly have been much greater had it not been for the flight of the population. Persons in furnished lodgings left first, then other lodgers went away, leaving their furniture to be sent for when they could meet with a place to put it in. Many houses were closed altogether, owing to the death of the proprietors; and, in a great number of instances, the tradesmen who remained had sent away their families: so that in less than six days from the commencement of the outbreak, the most afflicted streets were deserted by more than three-quarters of their inhabitants.

There were a few cases of cholera in the neighborhood of Broad Street, Golden Square, in the latter part of August; and the so-called outbreak, which commenced in the night between the 31st August and the 1st September, was, as in all similar instances, only a violent increase of the malady. As soon as I became acquainted with the situation and extent of this irruption of cholera, I suspected some contamination of the water of the much-frequented street-pump in Broad Street, near the end of Cambridge Street; but on examining the water, on the evening of the 3rd September, I found so little impurity in it of an organic nature, that I hesitated to come to a conclusion. Further inquiry, however, showed me that there was no other circumstance or agent common to the circumscribed locality in which this sudden increase of cholera occurred, and not extending beyond it, except the water of the above mentioned pump. I found, moreover, that the water varied, during the next two days, in the amount of organic impurity, visible to the naked eye, on close inspection, in the form of small white, flocculent particles; and I concluded that, at the commencement of the outbreak, it might possibly have been still more impure. I requested permission, therefore, to take a list, at the General Register Office, of the deaths from cholera, registered during the week ending 2nd September, in the subdistricts of Golden Square, Berwick Street, and St. Ann's, Soho, which was kindly granted. Eighty-nine deaths from cholera were registered, during the week, in the three subdistricts. Of these, only six occurred in the four first days of the week; four occurred on Thursday, the 31st August; and the remaining seventy-nine on Friday and Saturday. I considered, therefore, that the outbreak commenced on the Thursday; and I made inquiry, in detail, respecting the eighty-three deaths registered as having taken place during the last three days of the week.

On proceeding to the spot, I found that nearly all the deaths had taken place within a short distance of the pump. There were only ten deaths in houses situated decidedly nearer to another street pump. In five of these cases the families of the deceased persons informed me that they always sent to the pump in Broad Street, as they preferred the water to that of the pump which was nearer. In three other cases, the deceased were children who went to school near the pump in Broad Street. Two of them were known to drink the water; and the parents of the third think it probable that it did so. The other two deaths, beyond the district which this pump supplies, represent only the amount of mortality from cholera that was occurring before the irruption took place [. . .].

The result of the inquiry then was, that there had been no particular outbreak or increase of cholera, in this part of London, except among the persons who were in the habit of drinking the water of the above-mentioned pump-well.

Source: Snow, John. "Instances of the Communication of Cholera through the Medium of Polluted Water in the Neighborhood of Broad Street, Golden Square." In *On the Mode of Communication of Cholera: Part 2.* London: John Churchill, New Burlington Street, England, 1855.

31 Henri Dunant: History of the Red Cross (1862)

Swiss businessman and social activist Henri Dunant (1828–1910) wrote Un Souvenir de Solférino *in 1862. It was first translated into English by American Anna B. Heylin Wright (1865–1916) in 1911 as* The Origins of the Red Cross. *In 1859, Dunant had witnessed suffering in the aftermath of the Battle of Solférino, Italy. Out of compassion, he organized aid for the wounded and formed an Aid Committee in Geneva. In his* A Souvenir of Solférino, *he described his memories and experiences of the battle. In this work, Dunant also laid out the principles behind the formation of a group that eventually became the International Red Cross in 1963 and later in 1919 the Red Cross Red Crescent movement. Dunant believed that in times of war or disaster, a corps of ready volunteers could aid and help nurse the wounded on all sides of a conflict. Napoleon III (1808–1873) became interested in his project and ordered his army to no longer make prisoners of the enemy's physicians and nurses. The 1864 Geneva Convention, which established the humanitarian treatment of prisoners of war and rules of war, were based on Dunant's ideas. The excerpt describes the initial meetings that led to the formation of the idea of the Red Cross.*

During the grand maneuvers at Cologne, in 1861, King William of Prussia invited to dinner, in Benrath Castle, near Dusseldorf, the officers of the different nations, who were sent there by their governments. Before going to the table the King took by the hand General Forey and General Baumgarten: "Now that you are friends," he said to them, smiling, "sit there, beside one another, and chat." Forey was the victor of Montebello, and Baumgarten was his adversary.

On extraordinary occasions, such as those which assembled at Cologne, at Chalons, or elsewhere, eminent men of the military art of different nations, is it not to be desired that they will profit by this kind of congress to formulate some international, sacred, and accepted principle which, once agreed upon and ratified, would serve as the foundation for societies for aid for the wounded in the different countries of Europe? It is still more important to agree upon and adopt in advance these measures, because when hostilities have commenced, the belligerents are ill-disposed one towards the other, and will not consider these questions, except from the exclusive point of view of their own interests.

Are not small congresses called together of scientists, jurists, medical men, agriculturists, statisticians, and economists, who meet expressly in order to consider questions of much less importance? Are there not international societies which are occupied with questions of charity and public utility? Cannot men, in like manner, meet to solve a problem as important as that of caring for the victims of war?

Humanity and civilization surely demand the accomplishment of such a work. It is a duty, to the fulfilment of which every good man, and every person possessing any influence owes his assistance.

What prince, what ruler, would refuse his support to these societies, and would not be glad to give the soldiers of his army the full assurance that they will be immediately and properly nursed in case they should be wounded?

With permanent societies, such as I propose, the chance of waste and the injudicious distribution of money and supplies would often be avoided. During the war in the East an enormous quantity of lint, prepared by Russian ladies, was sent from St. Petersburg to the Crimea; but the packages, instead of reaching the hospitals to which they were sent, arrived at paper mills which used it all for their own industry.

By perfecting the means of transportation, by preventing the accidents during the journey from the battle-field to the hospital, many amputations will be avoided, and the burden of the governments, which pension the injured will be proportionately lessened.

These societies, by their permanent existence, could also render great service at the time of epidemics, floods, great fires, and other unexpected catastrophies; the humane motive which would have created them would instigate them to act on all occasions in which their labors could be exercised.

This work will necessitate the devotion of a certain number of persons, but it will never lack money in time of war. Each one will bring his offering or his compassion in response to the appeals which will be made by the committee. A nation will not remain indifferent when its children are fighting for its defense. The difficulty is not there; but the problem rests entirely in the serious preparation, in all countries, of a work of this kind, that is, in the creation of these societies.

In order to establish these committees at the head of the societies, all that is necessary is a little good-will on the part of some honorable and persevering persons. The committees, animated by an international spirit of charity, would create corps of nurses in a latent state, a sort of staff. The committees of the different nations, although independent of one another, will know how to understand and correspond with each other, to convene in congress and, in event of war, to act for the good of all.

If the terrible instruments of destruction now possessed by the nations seem to shorten wars, will not, on the other hand, the battles be more deadly? And in this century, when the unexpected plays such an important role, may not war bring about the most sudden and unforeseen results?

Are there not, in these considerations alone, more than sufficient reasons for us not to allow ourselves to be taken unawares?

Source: Dunant, Henri. *The Origin of the Red Cross*. Translated from the French by Mrs. [Anna] David H. Wright, Philadelphia, Pa., John C. Winston Co., 1911, pp. 87–90.

32 Louisa May Alcott: Experience as a Civil War Nurse (1863)

American Louisa May Alcott (1832–1888), author of Little Women, *wrote letters home about her service as a nurse during the American Civil War. She served in the Union Hospital at Georgetown, DC, for about six weeks until she contracted typhoid fever. She was treated with calomel—mercurous chloride—a purgative, which may have contributed to her sickliness for the rest of her life. Alcott revised and published her letters home as* Hospital Sketches. *In this work, she discusses hospital mismanagement, the resilience of dying young men, the many amputations, and unfeeling physicians who often did not take the time to use ether to ease pain. In this excerpt, with humor and satire she discussed disfigurement and death of solders, their food, unsympathetic chaplains, and a heartless physician who probed a wound without much regard for the pain of his patient. This excerpt gives a graphic portrait of the massive injuries that war produces.*

See also: Document 72; Document 73

Another, with a gun-shot wound through the cheek, asked for a looking-glass, and when I brought one, regarded his swollen face with a dolorous expression, as he muttered—

I vow to gosh, that's, too bad! I warn't a bad looking chap before, and now I'm done for; won't there be a thunderin' scar? and what on earth will Josephine Skinner say?" [. . .]

The next scrubbee was a nice looking lad, with a curly brown mane, and a budding trace of gingerbread over the lip, which he called his beard, and defended stoutly, when the barber jocosely suggested its immolation. He lay on a bed, with one leg gone, and the right arm so shattered that it must evidently follow; yet the little Sergeant was as merry as if his afflictions were not worth lamenting over, and when a drop or two of salt water mingled with my suds at the sight of this strong young body, so marred and maimed, the boy looked up, with a brave smile, though there was a little quiver of the lips, as he said,

"Now don't you fret yourself about me, miss; I'm first rate here, for it's nuts to lie still on this bed, after knocking about in those confounded ambulances, that shake what there is left of a fellow to jelly. I never was in one of these places before, and think this cleaning up a jolly thing for us, though I'm afraid it isn't for you ladies."

"Is this your first battle, Sergeant?"

"No, miss; I've been in six scrimmages, and never got a scratch till this last one; but it's done the business pretty thoroughly for me, I should say. Lord! what a scramble there'll be for arms and legs, when we old boys come out of our graves, on the Judgment Day: wonder if we shall get our own again ? If we do, my leg will have to tramp from Fredericksburg, my arm from here, I suppose, and meet my body, wherever it may be."

The fancy seemed to tickle him mightily, for he laughed blithely, and so did I; which, no doubt, caused the new nurse to be regarded as a light-minded sinner by the Chaplain, who roamed vaguely about, informing the men that they were all worms, corrupt of heart, with perishable bodies, and souls only to be saved by a diligent perusal of certain tracts, and other equally cheering bits of spiritual consolation, when spirituous ditto would have been preferred. [. . .]

Having done up our human wash, and laid it out to dry, the second syllable of our version of the word war-fare was enacted with much success. Great trays of bread, meat, soup and coffee appeared; and both nurses and attendants turned waiters, serving bountiful rations to all who could eat. I can call my pinafore to testify to my good will in the work, for in ten minutes it was reduced to a perambulating bill of fare, presenting samples of all the refreshments going or gone. It was a lively scene; the long room lined with rows of beds, each filled by an occupant, whom water, shears, and clean raiment had transformed from a dismal ragamuffin into a recumbent hero, with a cropped head. To and fro rushed matrons, maids, and convalescent "boys," skirmishing with knives and forks; retreating with empty plates; marching and counter-marching, with unvaried success, while the clash of busy spoons made most inspiring music for the charge of our Light Brigade [. . .]

I laid a sheet over the quiet sleeper, whom no noise could now disturb; and, half an hour later, the bed was empty. It seemed a poor requital for all he had sacrificed and suffered,—that hospital bed, lonely even in a crowd; for there was no familiar face for him to look his last upon; no friendly voice to say, Good bye; no hand to lead him gently down into the Valley of the Shadow; and he vanished, like a drop in that red sea upon whose shores so many women stand lamenting. For a moment I felt bitterly indignant at this seeming carelessness of the value of life, the sanctity of death; then consoled myself with the thought that, when the great muster roll was called, these nameless men might be promoted above many whose tall monuments record the barren honors they have won.

All having eaten, drank, and rested, the surgeons began their rounds; and I took my first lesson in the art of dressing wounds. It wasn't a festive scene, by any means; for Dr. P., whose Aid I constituted myself, fell to work with a vigor which soon convinced me that I was a weaker vessel, though nothing would have induced me to confess it then. He had served in the Crimea, and seemed to regard a dilapidated body very much as I should have regarded a damaged garment; and, turning up his cuffs, whipped out a very unpleasant looking housewife, cutting, sawing, patching and piecing, with the enthusiasm of an accomplished surgical seamstress; explaining the process, in scientific terms, to the patient, meantime; which, of course, was immensely cheering and comfortable. There was an uncanny sort of fascination in watching him, as he peered and probed into the mechanism of those wonderful bodies, whose mysteries he understood so well. The more intricate the wound, the better he liked it. A poor private, with both legs off, and shot through the lungs, possessed more attractions for him than a dozen generals, slightly scratched in some "masterly retreat;" and had anyone appeared in small pieces, requesting to be put together again, he would have considered it a special dispensation.

The amputations were reserved till the morrow, and the merciful magic of ether was not thought necessary that day, so the poor souls had to bear their pains as best they might. It is all very well to talk of the patience of woman; and far be it from me to pluck that feather from her cap, for, heaven knows, she isn't allowed to wear many; but the patient endurance of these men, under trials of the flesh, was truly wonderful. Their fortitude seemed contagious, and scarcely a cry escaped them, though I often longed to groan for them, when pride kept their white lips shut, while great drops stood upon their foreheads, and the bed shook with the irrepressible tremor of their tortured bodies.

Source: Alcott, Louisa May. *Hospital Sketches.* Boston: J. Redpath, 1863, pp. 36–37, 39, 41–43.

33 Gray's Anatomy: Muscles of the Head (1867)

British anatomist and physician Henry Gray (1827–1861) wrote the classic anatomy book, Gray's Anatomy. *It was illustrated by English surgeon and anatomist Henry Vandyke Carter (1831–1897) and was first entitled* Anatomy, Descriptive and Surgical. *The second edition, from which the following illustration is taken, was published in 1867. As it was commonly called "Gray's Anatomy," it was later given this title. However, there was controversy as to credit for its authors as Carter did all of the illustrations, for which the book was noted, but did not get as much credit as Gray. A factor may have been Carter's student status at the time. He also spent most of his career in India. The book is widely regarded as an extremely influential work on anatomy of humans and has continued to be revised and republished from its initial 1858 publication for many generations of medical students around the world. In terms of illustrations, it rivals that of Eduard Pernkopf's* Atlas, *which is controversial due to its Nazi connection. Carter's illustration from* Gray's Anatomy *was one of first drawings to show great details of the muscles of the head and is still in used today.*

See also: Document 71

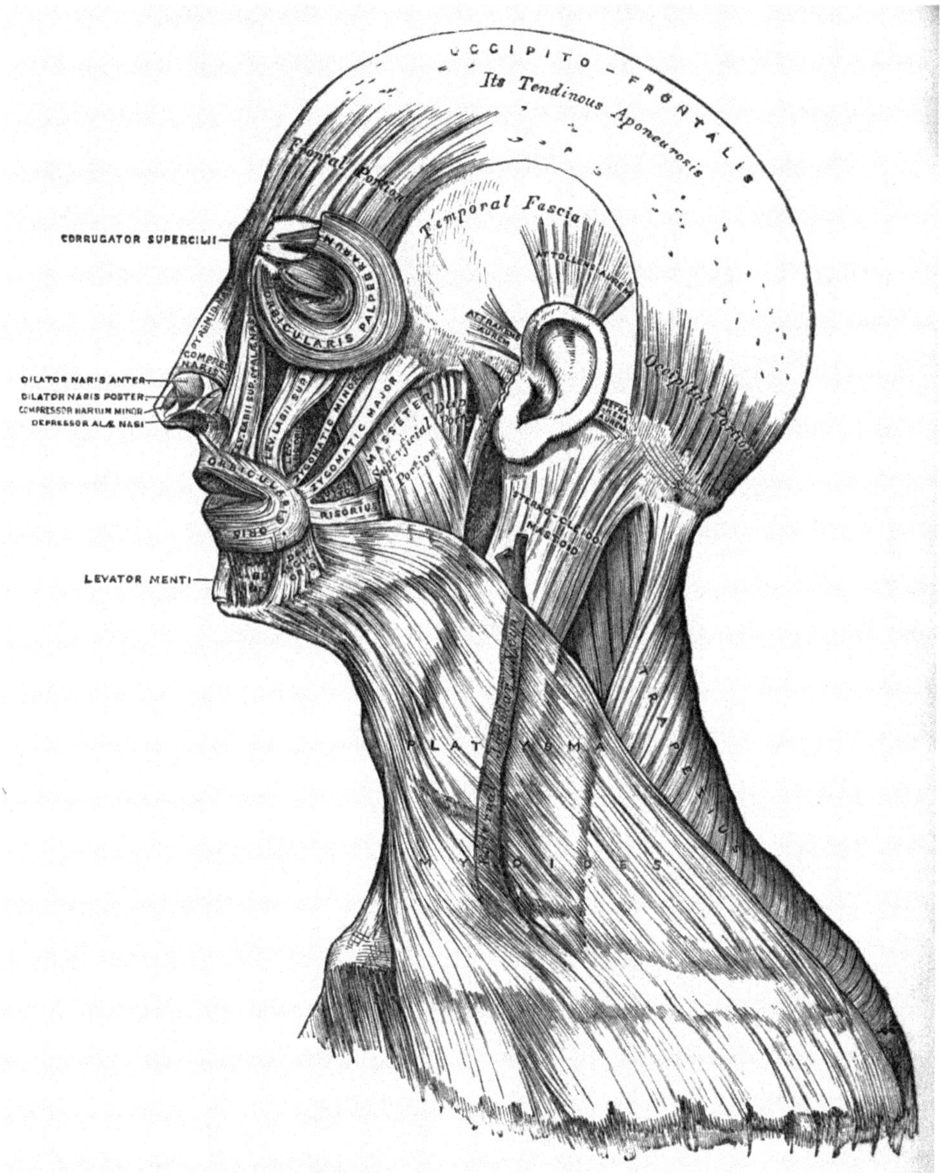

Muscles of the head, face, and neck

Source: Gray, Henry. *Anatomy, Descriptive and Surgical. 2nd American, from the rev. and enl.* London ed. Philadelphia: Henry C. Lea, 1867, p. 240.

34 Seventh-Day Adventist View of Alcohol and Tobacco (1870)

This anti-alcohol and tobacco excerpt is from a Seventh-Day Adventist health publication about obtaining good health in 1870. Its purpose was to educate people of the potential dangers of alcohol and tobacco use. Abstaining from these substances, along with eating a vegetarian diet, drinking pure water, and exercising were basic beliefs of Adventist religion. One of the most famous Adventist reformers was American physician John Harvey Kellogg (1852–1943) who ran a sanitarium, or health resort, based upon these health reform principles to cure diseases such as depression, obesity, and alcoholism. Moreover, the Adventists reflected the thoughts of other reformers of the time who felt alcohol and tobacco were harmful to the individual and society. During this era, alcohol was used as a medication for many ills, but Adventist and some temperance reformers felt that no alcohol should be consumed for any reason. Sentiments found in this article eventually led to a prohibition movement in late 19th century that culminated in the Eighteenth Amendment (National Prohibition) to the Constitution of the United States in 1920. During this same era, an anti-tobacco movement also arose as there was concern about young boys smoking. This concern led to tobacco bans in several states in the first decade of the 20th century.

Health Reform and Temperance

We have long been convinced that health reform is the true basis of the temperance reformation, and the only basis on which its success can ever be achieved. Believing this with a conviction that grows stronger with each year's observation and experience, we occasionally call the attention of the advocates of the temperance cause to this subject. The fundamental principle of the health reform is, the proper use of food and drink, and the disuse of all poisons. We discard poisons, both as regards the preservation of health and the treatment of disease.

We are, therefore, teetotalers in the teetotal sense. We reject alcohol as a beverage, because it is a poison, and its relations to the vital organism are abnormal; and we eschew it as a medicine, for the same reason. We believe that poisons which produce disease in well persons, are not proper remedies for sick persons. We deny the absurd dogma of medical systems, that poisons which are devitalizing in health maybe vitalizing in disease. Our temperance pledge is the "long one, and the strong one." It is, "Touch not, taste not, handle not," the accursed thing, neither as drink, nor as food, nor as medicine. Who doubts the efficacy of this pledge? [. . .]

It agrees with physiology, which teaches that alcohol is devitalizing to all living structures, animal or vegetable. It accords with psychology, which shows us that its effect on the mind is delirium, mania, and insanity. It accords with pathology and toxicology, in explaining that all of the effects of alcohol, whether termed exhilaration, intoxication, stimulation, fever, or inflammation, are disease-producing and poisonous. And it coincides with that common sense, and that

Christian charity, and that practical philanthropy, which put away the evil thing altogether. When will the professed friends of temperance learn the fallacy and the folly of doing with one hand and undoing with the other; of denouncing alcohol as a beverage, while applauding it as a medicine; of serving the cause of total abstinence with their well-meaning hearts, and proving the rumseller's most efficient allies with their misguided heads?

A Narcotized Conscience

NO OBSERVING person can walk the streets of our large cities . . . without noticing the deplorable fact that tobacco-using is rapidly leading our young men and boys to ruin. On this subject, a writer, who signs himself "Tobacconist," responds to an article in the *Philadelphia Star*:

> The article in your estimable paper of yesterday, signed "Friend to Boys," attracted my attention, and is a step in the right direction for reform. I am engaged in the tobacco business, and no one, save those directly engaged therein, has any idea of the multitude of young lads, hardly as high as a counter, who continually come in during the day and evening to buy a "cent's worth of ends," or address you with, "Say, mister, give me a light," to the stumps which they pick up on the street.
>
> I am obliged to sell to these lads, as I am a clerk, and act under instructions; but I know if I had my own way in the matter, I would certainly switch every boy out of the store, who wished to purchase. I am inclined to believe, and I think with good cause, that tobacco is the first cause which, in the majority of cases, creates a craving or desire for liquors, as a continual expectoration of saliva causes a corresponding degree of weakness in the system, which as a natural result desires again to be invigorated, and vile alcoholic stimulants are resorted to, until at last the habit becomes second nature, and ends in drunkenness and its attendant evils.
>
> A law should he made prohibiting any vender of tobacco from selling to minors under a heavy penalty, even if he should call to make a purchase under the pretense that it is for an adult.

This "clerk" has sad ideas of moral obligation and most unfortunate views of reform; but we fear there are too many like him. He is evidently "a man of the world." Being a clerk, he justifies himself in dealing out destruction to these lads. Is he obliged to be a clerk in such business? If he had a proper moral sense, he would starve first.

He, and thousands like him, ought to be instructed that he is not excusable on the ground of being a mere clerk. It is a sound maxim in morals, as well as in law, that "a partaker is as bad as a thief." The person who voluntarily hires himself to prosecute any vicious vocation is, in the sight of high Heaven, every whit as guilty as is the one who employs him. Both are pursuing a nefarious business; both know it to be wrong; and both are equally blameworthy. The relation of principal and agent, or merchant and clerk, will not bear examination in the day of final reckoning. And then, what muddled ideas of reform this man of narcotized conscience entertains! He would have the boys switched, and a law passed prohibiting the sale of cigars to boys. Better than switches and laws, Mr. clerk would be simple honesty. How can boys be expected not to crave the poison, when they see older persons continually using and apparently enjoying it; when the infection of it pervades all the atmosphere they breathe; and when it is, so far as they are taught or can see, regarded as an elegant accomplishment in the best society? We suggest that a better way of managing these young lads, than "switching them out of the store," is to close the store, set them better examples, and "lead them not into temptation."

Source: Good Health Publishing Company. "The Health Reformer," *Good Health* 5, no. 1 (July 1870): pp. 1–2.

35 International Sanitary Conference to Establish Quarantine and to Study Epidemics (1874)

Due to the fact that cholera was so devastating in the early through late 19th century in Europe, an international conference to establish quarantine standards and form a committee to study epidemics and how to prevent them was organized in Vienna in 1874. This was one of the first international committees to study an epidemic on an international level. However, interest in the disease only began when it spread from Asia into Europe. Although the committee came to the conclusion that cholera was passed by humans, they did not appear to recognize the 1855 thesis of British physician John Snow and the Broad Street pump observation that suggested that cholera was passed through water contaminated with sewage. Recommendations of the committee for ships coming into ports to prevent the spread of disease into another nation were put forth. They included medical inspection of everyone and disinfection of the ship if cholera had broken out. The British disinfected everyone and their effects while the other nations disinfected only the sick, their possessions, and the ship. This excerpt was published as part of the conference proceedings, its appendix suggesting methods of prevention.

See also: Document 30

The following summary is taken from the "Times" of the 1st of January, 1875, regarding the work of the Vienna International Sanitary Congress of 1874 :—

The subjects submitted to the Conference were divided into three categories. The first category related to certain preliminary scientific questions concerning the development and propagation of cholera; the second to the question for the discussion of which the Conference had especially been called together—namely, quarantine in relation to cholera; and the third to the formation of an International Commission for the study of epidemics.

The proceedings of the Conference on the preliminary scientific questions were remarkable for the unanimity which existed among the members regarding the primary doctrines of the origin and propagation of Asiatic cholera. The propositions submitted to the Conference on these questions were founded on the conclusions of the Conference of 1866, and the unanimity of opinion which existed as to the more important was so complete that they were accepted without discussion. It was affirmed that Asiatic cholera, susceptible of spreading epidemically, is developed spontaneously in India alone, and that the disease is transmissible by man. The first of these conclusions, it is necessary to remark, is not inconsistent with the opinion that epidemics of cholera may take their start from other countries than India, as in the European epidemics of

1854—56, and of 1869—71, which began, the former in Silesia, the latter in South Russia. These epidemics were developed, it is believed, from previously existing cholera, originally introduced from India, and which, having already undergone one period of epidemic diffusion, had remained some time dormant without wholly dying out. The Conference maintains that cholera susceptible of undergoing epidemic extension is of Indian origin, but it does not express the opinion that the manifestation of this quality of delusiveness is limited to India alone. The common accord of the members on the transmissibility of cholera by man proves not only that medical observation in Europe on this important question has everywhere led to the same conclusion, but also at recent official medical observations in India which have been held to throw discredit upon this conclusion have not been accepted as trustworthy. Indeed, although the observations referred to were brought under the consideration of the Conference by Professor Pettenkofer and Dr. Schleisner, they were not regarded otherwise than as suggestive of the direction in which certain further researches should be made as to the conditions under which the effective transmission of cholera occurs. The Conference, while affirming that man is the active agent in the transmission of cholera, further held that this transmission is inoperative without certain conditions of locality, some of which are well known, others, more obscure, have yet to be determined [. . .]

After active discussion, the recommendations of the committee were accepted by the delegates of twelve States, all of which were maritime, namely, Austria, Hungary, Germany, Great Britain, Russia, Italy, Belgium, Holland, Denmark, Sweden, Norway, and Persia; and rejected by the

delegates of eight States, five of which were maritime, namely, Egypt, France, Greece, Portugal, and Turkey, and three were non-maritime, namely, Luxembourg, Switzerland, and Servia.

The objections of the minority were of two kinds: first, it was argued that the conclusions of the committee were illogical, that is to say, inconsistent with the preliminary scientific conclusions adopted by the Conference. As Professor Sigmund, however, remarked, "There was no question as to the principle of quarantine as a means of arresting the progress of certain pestilences, including cholera, but the committee denied the possibility of carrying into execution real measures of quarantine in Europe, and in those parts of Asia and Africa where the means of incommunication were numerous and increasing." [. . .]

The committee prepared a second Report, which, in addition to suggested regulations for a system of medical inspection, as distinguished from quarantine, contained also recommendations for the amendment of the practice of quarantine in European ports. This Report formed the basis of the recommendations on maritime quarantine subsequently adopted by the delegates of all States, with the exception of Spain, the delegates of which State abstained from voting.

The system of medical inspection recommended by the Conference is in principle similar to that carried out in this country, in Denmark, Norway, and Sweden. It provides for the medical examination of ships arriving from suspected or infected ports, but it imposes no detention upon them unless there has been sickness on board during the voyage, or sickness exists at the time of examination. In the event of cholera existing on board at the time of arrival, or of suspicion of the disease having occurred in the course of the voyage, the shi [*sic*], passengers, and crew will be detained until they have been subjected to disinfection, the sick having previously been removed to a proper place for their reception, after which the vessel and those on board will be released. The recommendations differ from the English regulations in that the healthy and their personal effects are to be detained and disinfected; while here the healthy are permitted to go free with their personal effects, the ship only, with the personal effects of the sick, being detained for disinfection. Again, the recommendations (in this respect also differing from the English regulations) require the disinfection of rags and other so-called "susceptible" articles of merchandise, such as skins, hides, feathers, &c.

Source: Macnamara, Nottidge Charles. *Asiatic Cholera: History Up To July 15, 1892, Causes and Treatment.* New York: Macmillan, 1892, pp. 65, 68–69.

36 Military Field Hospitals and Amputations (1887)

American surgeon and noted medical librarian John Shaw Billings (1838–1913) wrote Hardtack and Coffee *in 1887, a little over 20 years after his experiences in the Civil War (sometimes called the War Between the States). The book is a memoir of the daily life of soldiers during the war and Billings' experience in a field hospital. Billings was a Union officer of the Army of the Potomac. He wrote a series of sketches about the life of a soldier for the descendants of those who had fought in the war. One of the sketches includes the lives of battlefield surgeons and their wounded patients in a field hospital. It examines the surgeons' attitudes toward amputations of limbs and discusses their disregard for patients' wishes. This excerpt mentions the many amputations—many likely unnecessary—during the war. It establishes the fact that surgeons often amputated limbs, even if a soldier only had flesh wounds, as it saved time on the battle field.*

See also: Document 32; Document 69

Then, there were in each of these division hospitals three surgeons, selected from the whole division, " without regard to rank, but solely on account of their known prudence, judgment, and skill," whose duty it was to perform all important operations, or, at least, be responsible for their performance. Three other medical officers were detailed to assist these three. Nor was this all, for the remaining medical officers of the division, except one to a regiment, were also required to report at once to the hospital, to act as dressers of wounds and assistants generally. In addition to these, a proper number of nurses and attendants were detailed to be on hand.

The medical officers left with regiments were required to establish themselves during the fighting in the rear of their respective organizations, at such a distance as not to unnecessarily expose themselves, where they could give such temporary aid to the wounded as they should stand in need of.

I have said that these hospitals were to be located out of all danger. That statement needs a little modifying. In case the tide of battle turned against our army and it was compelled to retreat, what was before a safe place might at once be converted into a place of great danger. But a hospital could not be struck and its patients moved at a moment's or even a day's warning, as a rule, and so it was made the duty of the medical director of a corps to select a sufficient number of medical officers, who, in case a retreat was found necessary, should remain in charge of the wounded. When the Rebels captured such a hospital, it was their general practice to parole all the inmates—that is, require them to give their word of honor that they would not bear arms again until they had been properly exchanged as prisoners of war. Our government established what were known as parole camps, where such prisoners were required to remain until duly exchanged.

I think it can now be readily understood, from even this fragmentary sketch, how the establishment of these field hospitals facilitated the care of the wounded, and, by their systematic workings, saved hundreds of lives. With a skilful, energetic man as medical director of the army, giving his orders to medical directors of corps, and these carefully superintending surgeons-in-chief of divisions, who, in turn, held the surgeons and assistant surgeons and officers of ambulance corps to a strict accountability for a careful performance of their duties, while the latter fortified themselves by judicious oversight of their subordinates, the result was to place this department of the army on a footing which endured, with the most profitable of results to the service, till the close of the war.

I vividly remember my first look into one of these field hospitals. It was, I think, on the 27th of November, 1863 [. . . near a] tavern the field hospital of Warren's Second Division had been located, and into this I peered while my battery stood in park not far away, awaiting orders. The surgeon had just completed an operation. It was the amputation of an arm about five inches below the shoulder, the stump being now carefully dressed and bandaged. As soon as the patient recovered from the effects of the ether, the attendants raised him to a sitting posture on the operating-table. At that moment the thought of his wounded arm returned to him, and, turning his eyes towards it, they met only the projecting stub. The awful reality dawned upon him for the first time. An arm had gone forever, and he dropped backwards on the table in a swoon. Many a poor fellow like him brought to the operator's table came to consciousness only to miss an arm or a leg which perhaps he had begged in his last conscious moments to have spared. But the medical officers first mentioned decided all such cases, and the patient had only to submit. At Peach-Tree Creek, Col. Thomas Reynolds of the Western army was shot in the leg, and, while the surgeons were debating the propriety of amputating it, the colonel, who was of Irish birth, begged them to spare it, as it was very valuable, being an *imported leg*,—a piece of wit which saved the gallant officer his leg, although he became so much of a cripple that he was compelled to leave the service.

It has been charged that limbs and arms were often uselessly sacrificed by the operators; that they were especially fond of amputating, and. just as likely to amputate for a flesh-wound as for a fractured bone, on the ground that they could do it more quickly than they could dress the wound; that it made a neater job, thus gratifying professional pride: but how the victim might feel about it or be affected by it then or thereafter did not seem to enter their thoughts. It was undoubtedly true that many flesh-wounds were so ugly the only safety for the patient lay in amputation. A fine fellow, both as a man and soldier, belonging to my company, lost his arm from a flesh-wound—needlessly, as he and his friends always asserted and believed.

Source: Billings, John Davis. *Hardtack and Coffee, or, The Unwritten Story of Army Life, Including Chapters on Enlisting, Life in Tents and Log Huts. . . etc.* Boston: George M. Smith & Co., 1889 [c1887], pp. 306–309.

37 Emil Kraepelin Characterizes Psychoses (1887)

Emile Kraepelin (1856–1926), a German psychiatrist, developed a system to classify symptoms of mental illness. Kraepelin, who focused on psychoses, separated "manic depression" and "dementia praecox"—now called bipolar or affective disorders and schizophrenia respectively—into separate conditions. Until this time, these diseases were considered different forms of the same illness. Kraepelin published Ein Lehrbuch der Psychiatrie *in the 1880s explaining the details of the different psychotic diseases. American psychiatric lecturer A. Ross Diefendorf (1871–1943) translated the work into English as* Clinical Psychiatry: A Text-Book for Students and Physicians *in 1902. The purpose of the translation and condensation of Kraepelin's work was to give these new classifications to American medical students and general practitioners as a concise textbook. In this excerpt, Kraepelin clearly defines details concerning dementia praecox.*

See also: Document 61

DEMENTIA PRECOX

Dementia praecox is the name first applied by A. Pick, in 1891, to a group of cases including the hebephrenia of Hecker and Kahlbaum, characterized by maniacal symptoms followed by melancholia and rapid deterioration.

Since then the meaning of the term has been extended so as to include a larger group of cases appearing in earlier life, characterized by a progressively chronic course with certain fundamental symptoms, of which progressive mental deterioration is the most prominent. Some psychiatrists, especially the Italian, use the name primary dementia, because it enables them to include a few cases characterized by similar symptoms which appear in patients long past the period of pubescence. The group of cases as understood by us is a large one, and includes, besides hebephrenia, the catatonia of Kahlbaum and certain forms of paranoia which undergo early deterioration.

Etiology.—The disease is one of the most prominent, compromising from fourteen to twenty per cent of all admissions to institutions. As the name indicates, it is a disease of early life. More than sixty per cent of the cases appear before the twenty-fifth year. There is, however, a difference in the various forms; in hebephrenia almost three-fourths of the cases appear before the twenty-fifth year, in catatonia sixty-eight per cent, and in the paranoid only forty per cent. In the hebephrenic form sixty-four per cent of the cases are men, in catatonia, and paranoid forms women slightly predominate. Defective heredity is a prominent factor, as it appears in about seventy per cent of cases. It varies somewhat in the different forms, being more prominent in the paranoid and catatonic, and least in hebephrenic forms. Acute diseases, especially typhoid and scarlet fever, act as the exciting causes in a small percentage of cases (ten per cent). Head injuries precede a still smaller number of cases. A number of patients present mental peculiarities from youth up, such as seclusiveness, precocious piety, impulsive actions and great susceptibility to alcohol, and at least seven per cent have always been weak-minded.

Various physical stigmata are occasionally encountered, such as asymmetries, malformation of the ears and palate, puerile expression, and strabismus.

Pathology.—It seems probable, judging from the clinical course, and especially in those cases where there has been rapid deterioration, that there is a definite disease process in the brain, involving the cortical neurones. In a few cases this is a reparable lesion, but in most cases the impairment of function is permanent and progressive. This pathological basis finds clinical expression in the few cases that recover and the larger number that show a permanent mental defect. The means by which these assumed changes are brought about in the nervous system is unknown. In consideration of the close relationship with the age of puberty, the presence of disturbances of menstruation, and the frequent appearance of the disease for the first time during pregnancy and puerperium, further assumption is made that it is the result of autointoxication. It is also to be noticed that many cases of imbecility develop a psychosis different in no essential particular from dementia praecox at the age of sexual development, and furthermore that epileptics and idiots at the same age show a tendency to undergo a decided mental deterioration. The total absence of any definite external cause, except in isolated cases, adds weight to this belief. As yet no one with the present methods of research has been able to demonstrate an anatomical pathological basis for the disease. Defective heredity, as well as imprisonment and acute diseases, is presumed to act by lessening the power of resistance to autointoxication.

Symptomatology.—The disease picture appears so varied that upon superficial observation the fundamental symptoms are not recognized. These symptoms, however, permit of an early recognition of the disease process and become more and more marked as the disease progresses.

In the field of apprehension there is usually very little disturbance. External impressions are correctly perceived, the patients being able to recognize their environment and to comprehend most of what takes place about them. This explains the fact that they remain quite well oriented, as to time, place, and person. During the acute or subacute onset of the disease, apprehension is affected, and there is some disorientation. This may also appear during transitory stupor or excitement; but even in these conditions, and especially in the apparent stupidity and indifference which characterize the later stages of the disease, it is surprising to see how many things in the environment are perceived. It is not unusual to find that they notice changes in the physician's apparel, in the furniture, or in the landscape. Nevertheless, as the disease advances and deterioration appears, apprehension, as well as other mental phenomena, becomes perceptibly impaired.

Occasionally delusions entertained by the patient lead to a misinterpretation of some of their surroundings. They may be days or years ahead of the correct time, their nurses may be called by fictitious names, or the hospital may be regarded as a nunnery, while in other respects the orientation is correct.

Apprehension is always more or less distorted by *hallucinations*, especially in acute and subacute development of the disease. These usually disappear later in the course of the disease, but may persist into the end stages. Hallucinations of hearing are most prominent, next come hallucinations of sight, and at rare intervals we find those of touch. Hallucinations at first are distressing, resulting in fear; but later in the course of the disease they do not excite much interest, and the patients when questioned are unable to give much information about them. Some patients seem to take pleasure in listening to the voices, whose communications are both incoherent and silly. During exacerbations of the disease the hallucinations may induce the former fear and distress [. . .].

Source: Kraepelin, Emil. A. Ross Diefendorf, Translator. *Clinical Psychiatry: A Text-Book for Students and Physicians; Abstracted and Adapted From the Sixth German Edition of Kraepelin's "Lehrbuch der Psychiatrie"* New York; London: 1902, pp. 152–155.

38 Florence Nightingale's Advice to Nurses (1888)

English social reformer and first professional nurse, Florence Nightingale (1820–1910) was the founder of modern nursing as a professional career that required education and training. During the Crimean War in the 1850s, Nightingale organized care for wounded soldiers. She cleaned up, sanitized, and organized the hospitals. In 1860, she established the first secular nursing school at St Thomas' Hospital in London. Most nurses before her reforms were sponsored by religious orders and were often poorly trained. Perhaps her most important reform was that she increased the reputation of nursing as an honorable vocation for women. Before her reform of the profession, nurses generally had low social status, little respect, and little to no training. Nightingale advocated rigorous education and training along with continuing education. She required that nurses be intelligent, had high moral character, and were honest and trustworthy. She also instituted examinations and certification for nurses. These basic tenets and requirements of nurses and nursing are discussed in this letter of 1888 to graduating nurses. They still form the basis of the nursing profession today in all nations.

London, May 16, 1888.

MY DEAR FRIENDS,—Here, one year more, is my very best love and heart-felt "good speed " to the work.

To each and to all I wish the very highest success, in the widest meaning of the word, in the life's work you have chosen.

And I am more sorry than for anything else that my illness, more than usually serious, has let me know personally so little of you, except through our dear Matron and dear Home Sister.

You are going steadily and devotedly on in preparing yourselves for future work. Accept my heartiest sympathy and thanks [. . .].

Every Nurse must grow. No Nurse can stand still. She must go forward or she will go backward every year.

And how can a Certificate or public Register show this? Rather, she ought to have a moral "Clinical" Thermometer in herself. Our stature does not grow every year after we are "grown up." Neither does it grow down. It is otherwise with our moral stature and our Nursing stature. We grow down, if we don't grow up, every year. [. . .]

I must be trustworthy, to carry out directions intelligently and perfectly, *unseen* as well as seen; "unto the Lord" *as well as* unto men; no mere eye service. (How can this be if she is a mere Association Nurse, and not an individual Nurse?)

I must have moral influence over my Patients. And I *can* only have this by *being* what I appear, especially now that everybody is educated, so that Patients become my keen critics and judges. My Patients are watching me. They know what my profession, my calling is: to devote myself to the good of the sick. They are asking themselves: does that Nurse act up to her profession? This is no supposition. It is a fact. It is a call to us, to each individual Nurse, to act up to her profession.

We hear a good deal nowadays about Nursing being made a "profession." Rather, is it not the question for me: am I living up to my "profession"?

But I must not crave for the Patient to be always recognizing my services. On the contrary: the best service I can give is that the Patient shall scarcely be aware of any—shall recognize my presence most by recognizing that he has no wants. (Shakespeare tells me that to be "nurse like" is to be to the Patient—

> So kind, so duteous, diligent,
> So tender over his occasions, true,
> So feat.)

I must be thorough—a work, not a word—a Nurse, not a book, not an answer, not a certificate, not a mechanism, a mere piece of a mechanism or Association. [. . .]

Do you remember Tennyson's farmer, who says of the clergyman:

> I 'eard 'um a bummin' away . . . ower my 'ead, . . .
> An' I thowt a said whot a owt to 'a said an' I coom'd away.

We laugh at that. But is the Parasite much better than that ?

Now the Ambulance Classes, the Registration, the Certificates of Nursing and of Nurses (and of midwifery), especially any which may demand the minimum of *practice*, which may *substitute* for *personal* progress in active proficiency, mere literary or word progress, instead of making it the material for growth in correct knowledge and practice, all such like things may tend this way.

It is not the certificate which makes the Nurse or the Midwife. It may *un-make* her. The danger is lest she let the certificate be *instead of* herself, *instead of* her own never ceasing going up higher as a woman and a Nurse.

This is the "day" of Examinations in the turn that Education—Elementary, the Higher Education, Professional Education—seems taking. And it is a great step which has substituted this for what used to be called "interest." Only let us never allow it to encroach upon what cannot be tested by examinations. Only let the "day" of *Practice*, the development of each individual's thought and practice, character and dutifulness, keep up, through the materials given us for growth and for correct knowledge, with the "day of examinations" in the Nurse's life, which is above all a moral and practical life, a life not of show, but of faithful action.

But above all, dear comrades, let each one of us, each individual of us, not only bid "God speed" in her heart to this, our own School (or Association—call it so if you will), but *strive* to *speed* it with all the best that is in her, even as your "Association" and its dear heads strive to speed each one of you.

Let each one of us take the abundant and excellent food for the mind which is offered us, in our training, our classes, our lectures, our examinations and reading—not as "Parasites," no, none of you will ever do that—but as bright and vigorous fellow-workers, working out the better way every day to the end of life.

Once more, my heartiest sympathy, my dearest love to each and to all of you,

from your ever faithful old comrade,

FLORENCE NIGHTINGALE.

Source: *Florence Nightingale to her Nurses. A Selection from Miss Nightingale's Addresses to Probationers and Nurses of the Nightingale School at St. Thomas's Hospital* London. Macmillan and Co., Ltd. 1914, pp. 139–147.

39 South African Mountains as Health Resorts for Tuberculosis (1888)

British tuberculosis physician Edmund Symes Thompson (1837–1906) presented a paper in 1888 at the Royal Colonial Institute about a region in South Africa being a good place for a tuberculosis sanatorium because of its climate. This institute focused on providing information and educating its members about various parts of the British Empire and provided a meeting place and library and held seminars on a range of issues. In his paper, Symes-Thompson makes a case that the best tuberculosis care needs to be in a suitable climate both in the Northern and Southern Hemispheres, which was about 43 degrees from the equator. This latitude, he argues, has a warm but not too hot climate in the winter. Before the development of antibiotics in the 1940s, clean air generally in the mountains, rest, exercise, and good nutrition were the standard treatments for tuberculosis. Symes Thompson proposed that a region near Cape Town, South Africa, was a suitable place for treatment as it enabled rest and exercise especially in the winter for English patients living in cold wet climate, which was thought to make the condition worse. This excerpt focuses upon the prevailing treatment of the time of getting fresh air away from urban areas and pollution.

See also: Document 44

When the request was made to me that I should read a paper on the climate of South Africa, before the Fellows of the Royal Colonial Institute, at the opening meeting of a new session, I could not but feel gratified by the honour conferred upon me. I am fully aware that some of my hearers may have spent half a lifetime in Africa; but it is one thing to live in a vast country, and another to collect particulars as to its climate and capabilities from the standpoint of a physician anxious to search into every region of earth and sea which may suit his purpose of giving or restoring health.

Fifteen years ago, when I published my first contribution on the subject, I was able to record, as the basis of my work, the details of some twenty cases of disease, treated for the most part in Natal and the Orange Free State [former Dutch provinces in South Africa].

Experience since gained, supplemented as it has been by information acquired during a recent visit, is my justification for venturing to address you on the subject.

On comparing the Southern with the Northern Hemisphere, the first point to which our attention is called is this, that Sydney, Melbourne, Adelaide, and Cape Town, only distant about 34° from the equator, have a corresponding mean annual temperature—namely, about 63°—with Naples, Nice, and the Riviera in from 41° to 43° north.

At this latitude in the Northern Hemisphere we are accustomed to regard an elevation of from 5,000 to 6,000 feet as necessary to secure immunity from consumption. But the elevation above the sea at which such immunity is secured in South Africa is remarkably low.

In the district of the "Karoo" we find a region characterized by excessive dryness of air and soil, where, at a level of less than 3,000 feet above the sea, remarkable purity and coolness of air are secured, with an almost complete absence of floating matter; together with great intensity of light and solar influence; great stillness in winter; a large amount of ozone, and a degree of rarefaction of proved value in cases of phthisis [TB].

In winter these conditions prevail in greater or less perfection in various places; in summer, however, the heat is apt to prove excessive, the winds hot and dust-laden, and it becomes difficult to take the amount of out-door exercise necessary for recovery. A physician who is brought into daily contact with those who are seeking relief from climate treatment, is accustomed to arrange his patients into various classes.

First, those who require "change of air" to complete their convalescence from acute illness.

Second, those who need to be sheltered from the vicissitudes of our English winter.

And third, those for whom health can alone be anticipated if they are content to be separated for years, or perhaps for life, from the conditions under which their disease originated.

Our European health resorts supply us with varied means by which we may successfully meet the requirements of the first and second group; but our Colonies must be searched to supply what is wanted for the third.

As regards the first, however, a sea voyage with a short sojourn in a sunnier clime may accomplish more completely what is often sought in a too hurried rush across Europe.

As to the second, shelter from the dangers of a northern winter may be sought and found in the Southern Hemisphere as readily as in the South of Europe, and with less risk of renewed illness during early spring.

The public mind is slowly awakening to the knowledge that the British Empire has climates adapted for every form of constitutional defect. Those in this room may do much to emphasize and to impress the fact that health and life may be secured and maintained at a higher level, and for a longer time, if we select with care and forethought the home for which we are fitted.

Source: Thompson, Symes. Royal Commonwealth Society. "South Africa as a Health Resort." *Proceedings of the Royal Colonial Institute* XX. London: Sampson Low, Marston, Searle & Rivington, 1888, pp. 4–6.

40 Sanitation in India (1891)

At the Seventh International Congress of Hygiene and Demography held during August 10–17, 1891, in London, various topics were presented concerning the health of India—at that time a British Colony. Sanitary engineer Baldwin Latham (1836–1917) discusses in "Sanitation in India" the dire problems of inadequate sanitation leading to a high mortality rate. The primary reason for increased life span in developed nations was sanitation and access to clean water. In this excerpt from his paper, he implies the poor hygiene habits of the majority of the native Indian population led to pollution of the air, ground, and all unprotected sources of water supply. He argues it is not the heat or rain that is causing high mortality but poor sanitation in large urban areas. He points out systems used to destroy waste, many of which contribute to the pollution problems. This excerpt implies that population pressure in urban environments, poverty, unhygienic personal habits, and primitive refuse collection and processing lead to serious health issues and early death. Issues of lower life expectancy due to poor sanitation are still found in the late-2010s in some urban areas of developing nations.

The most unhealthy periods in India are certainly not the hottest periods of the year. The high temperature of the ground is unfavourable to health in all those places in which the refuse from the population is stored in receptacles below the ground level. The favourable health statistics of large towns like Bombay and Calcutta show that it is not climate that causes the frightful mortality in many parts of India, but that this is due to the downright neglect of the simplest sanitary precautions.

The fixed wet and dry seasons of most parts of India can be depended upon with a degree of certainty. The excessive rainfalls of one period, compared with the long absence of rainfall in other periods, tend to show that the separate system of sewerage is one which is the most proper for certain places in India, and that the rainfall in these districts should, as far as possible, be completely segregated from the sewage proper. The rainfalls in some of the larger cities are excessive, for in Bombay falls exceeding 4 inches per hour have been recorded, while in a single day over 16 inches of rain have fallen. The average of the heavy falls of rain in Bombay exceeds 2 inches per hour, whilst the average of the daily heavy falls exceeds 7 inches per day. In Calcutta, the rains are not so heavy as in Bombay, but occasionally heavy falls exceeding the rate of 3 inches per hour have been recorded, but on an average rainfalls exceeding 5 inches per day are only recorded once in three years.

The sanitary appliances in use in India are of an extremely varied character. In many cases conservancy is unknown, and the refuse of the population rots at each man's door. In the cities, for the most part, the Halalcore system is adopted, a system by which the solid nightsoil is collected in a basket placed below the closet seat, an arrangement which allows the liquid parts, including the water of ablution, to flow away, usually to the street gutters. Under this system the stercoraceous matters are collected by men and women every day and then carried in baskets on their heads to some central point where they are deposited in a barrel on wheels and are then carted to some place for disposal. In the cities where they have sewers, these matters are mixed with water and flushed into the sewers; where they have not sewers, the matters are either trenched or buried in the ground or manufactured into poudrette [human manure].

The trenching of nightsoil cannot go on in the time of the monsoon, and at this period the material is generally buried in deep pits, to be sometimes resuscitated and manufactured into poudrette. As a rule, the effect of burying this matter in deep pits in the hot soil of India causes a violent fermentation to take place, and an indescribable nuisance to be created. The trenching grounds, too, are extremely obnoxious, and the position of these trenching grounds is ordinarily fixed as a matter of convenience, and often pollutes the underground water, the soil, and the atmosphere of the neighbourhood of a town to a most injurious extent. At Poonah an attempt has been made to manufacture the material into poudrette by admixture with wood ashes and drying in the sun, and under sheds in the monsoon; and it is found that a manure very valuable for some crops can be produced, but that the sale of the manufactured article does not return more than one half of the coat of its collection and manufacture.

In most cities privies are of common occurrence, and the author has seen a structure of this kind in Calcutta, in which the excreta drops into the basement of a many-storeyed building of considerable altitude, where it accumulates to a considerable depth and from whence it is removed in semi-liquid condition by the Sanitary Department. Cesspools constructed in brick, stone, and other materials are in common use, and large earthenware jars sunk into the ground are also used as cesspools, and are emptied at periods more or less remote. The surface of the street in most cities is the receptacle for a large part of the sewage of every city.

Source: Latham, Baldwin. "Sanitation in India" in *Transactions of the Seventh International Congress of Hygiene and Demography, August 10th-17th, 1891. Indian Hygiene and Demography* XI edited by Charles Edward Shelly. London: Eyre and Spottiswoode, 1892–93, pp. 198–200.

41 Asiatic Cholera in India Since Antiquity (1892)

British surgeon-general Nottidge Charles MacNamara (1833–1918) of the Indian Medical Service wrote the report from an international conference on cholera and other diseases. Cholera was transported into Europe in the early 1800s and was a frightening deadly epidemic with no obvious cure. Although British physician John Snow (1813–1858) in 1855 had demonstrated that it was caused by a bacterium in contaminated water, better sewage and access to clean water supplies were slow in being implemented. MacNamara's history of cholera points out that it was not a new disease but had been found in India for centuries. From his years in India, he also noticed that it appeared to have been primarily located in the Bengal region. He hypothesized that more recent outbreaks were due to the advancements in transportation, movement of soldiers, human migration, and global trade from this area in India into other regions of the world. This excerpt is important inasmuch as it pinpoints the origins of the disease and led to quarantine of ships into Europe and North America with suspected cholera cases in the late 1800s.

See also: Document 30; Document 35

We learn, from the description given by Sanskrit authors writing some 400 B.C., that Asiatic cholera existed in India in their day. They have described the symptoms of the disease, which are precisely similar to those met with at the present time. In spite, however, of repeated inroads of warlike races from the north-west into India, cholera does not appear to have spread with them beyond the confines of that country. Probably few of these conquering races overran Lower Bengal; which we may, therefore, suppose, was, as it now is, the home of cholera. As we pass from the study of these ancient records to comparatively recent history, we learn that, in the year 1438, Ahmed Shah, was compelled to raise the siege of Mando, in Mehwah, in consequence of an outbreak of a disease which is said to have destroyed some thousands of his troops in the course of a few days; the disease is described as "waba," a word still employed to designate Asiatic cholera. In 1490, Vasco de Gama visited the Malabar coast, and has left us a full account of the symptoms of cholera as it affected the natives and his own sailors. For centuries past, in the Gangetic Delta, the "Oolee Beebe," or Goddess of Cholera, has been worshipped, and temples still exist in that part of India containing emblems of this goddess.

In 1781—82 cholera was very deadly in Calcutta, and the government reported to the home authorities that it had "pursued its course northwards." During this year epidemic cholera visited Ganja'm; it attacked a division of our troops passing through that district, and in the course of a few days no less than 1,143 sepoys, out of a force of 5,000 men, were down with cholera. Colonel Pearce remarks that, "death raged in the camp with horrors not to be described, and all expected to be devoured by this pestilence."

In 1782—83 the whole of Madras and Ceylon were under the influence of Asiatic cholera; at the same time the disease broke out in Burma, and we hear of it in the north of India at Hurdwar, where it was reported to have destroyed 20,000 pilgrims. It seems, therefore, certain that, within twenty years of the Battle of Plassey, imperfect as our knowledge then was of many parts of India, that a vast area of the country was under the influence of a virulent form of Asiatic cholera. In fact, from the year 1438 to 1817, we have references, by sixty-six independent observers, as to the occurrence of Asiatic cholera in India, and of these authorities ten refer to epidemic outbursts of the disease.

Source: Macnamara, Nottidge Charles. *Asiatic Cholera: History Up To July 15, 1892, Causes and Treatment.* New York: Macmillan, 1892, pp. 1–2.

42 Worldwide Cholera in the Mid-19th Century (1892)

In 1892, British surgeon-general Nottidge Charles MacNamara (1833–1918) wrote a detailed report that included the history of the spread of cholera from 1817 to mid-1892. In this work, he discusses the cause of the disease, where it is found, how it is transmitted, and its symptoms, along with its prevention and treatment. Cholera was a frightening, often fatal, illness of 19th century Europe, the Americas, and Asia. The following excerpt from MacNamara's report discusses the cholera epidemic of the mid-1800s. It includes the transmission of the disease to New Orleans by German immigrants and then throughout the United States and Canada. It reviews the spread of cholera from India into the Middle East and Eastern Europe. The excerpt is an example of how fast an epidemic can spread by travelers. Efforts to eliminate the disease were carried out, particularly in the developed nations, through better hygiene, sanitation, and access to clean water by the 1890s based upon British physician John Snow's work.

See also: Document 30; Document 35

At New Orleans cholera was imported at the same time by German emigrants, who sailed in a vessel from Havre on the 3rd of November. Cases of cholera were brought into the hospital in New Orleans from this vessel; the disease rapidly spread through the city. "The weather was very warm and damp, the streets were as muddy as possible, and heavy fog overhung the city." The disease extended from town to town along the Mississippi, and covered the United States and Canada during the following year.

This, probably the most fatal epidemic of cholera that has ever spread from India throughout Europe, Asia, and America had almost completely died out by the end of 1851. In England alone it killed no less than 53,293 men, women, and children. In a report drawn up by the Royal College of Physicians, London, regarding this epidemic, they observe, "it is not probable that in the case of cholera the influence of water will ever be shown to consist in its serving as a vehicle for the poison generated in the bodies of those who had suffered from the disease."

The Indo-European Epidemic of 1848–53.

India was, unless in its endemic area, free of cholera in 1847, the epidemic of the previous years having died out, but in 1848 the accounts of cholera at Dinapore, Cawnpore, and Agra were bad. Throughout 1849 we have a repetition of the old story—cholera of a virulent type in the Mirzapore district, "the devastation of the disease was terribly fearful, the inhabitants fled for refuge to other districts, forsaking their habitations, cattle, and property." Central India was subjected to a most awful visitation of cholera, and Dr. Leith reported, that "cholera made its approach to Bombay from the east towards the end of the rains of 1849, in spite of the south-west monsoon which blew during the same week with a force varying from 1 1/2 to 5 lbs., or on an average of 3 1/2 lbs. on the square foot, which is equivalent to a velocity of more than 15 miles an hour, in a direction contrary to that in which the cholera advanced."

Throughout 1850 the disease was reproduced over the Bengal, Madras, and the Bombay Presidencies; in the town of Bombay, for instance, the number of deaths from this disease in 1848 had amounted to 69, in 1850 to 4,729, and in 1851 to 4,020. In 1851 cholera broke out in the port of Bassorah, having direct communication with Bombay, and from thence extended by two routes, the one towards the west to Hillah, the other east to Mohammera. That pilgrims spread the disease seems more than probable, for it was reported that from the 1st of December, 1849, to 1st December, 1850, there passed through the station of Khaneguin 52,053 pilgrims with 64,138 beasts of burden, 4,504 muleteers, and 2,837 leads of human corpses, which, giving three dead bodies to a load, would amount to 8,000 corpses to be buried at Kerbela." In 1852 cholera spread from Persia into Russia, along the borders of the Caspian Sea, when, as in previous years, it met with a stream of the disease extending from the Punjab through Cabul and Meshed to Teheran. In 1853 the disease broke out over the whole of Persia and Asiatic Turkey, Russia, and the north of Europe. It appeared in England first at Gateshead, afterwards in London, during the months of August and September. New York and New Orleans were both visited by cholera in 1853; Mexico and the whole of the West India Islands were during the year under the influence of the disease. In 1854 Asia, Europe, and America were covered by the epidemic which had originated in Bengal during the year 1848–49, and travelled thence to Bombay and to Cabul, and so to Persia and westward, as in previous years, in its progress causing untold misery and death. The disease died out of Europe and America in 1856–57.

Source: MacNamara, Nottidge Charles. *Asiatic Cholera: History Up To July 15, 1892, Causes and Treatment.* New York: Macmillan, 1892, pp. 9–11.

43 On Wine Drinking and Its Terrible Consequences (1893)

Thakur Mukand Singh, a Hindu Indian city official, published a book in 1893 on customs and practices of the Hinduism, Jainism, and Islam that resulted in health, social, and environmental problems that needed to be addressed. One entry is from a lecture by Lala Ram Dyal, a Hindu physician, who discusses the many dangers of alcohol consumption on the human body and its effects upon family and society. He views alcohol like opium and arsenic, which are both used in medicines to cure disease but should not be used on an ongoing basis as they are poisons. He details the signs of alcoholism and exhorts his audience and others to avoid it and not to follow the Western tradition of drinking because of its consequences. Dyal mentions that children—based upon the prevalent theory of the era of Lamarckian inheritance of acquired characteristics—also suffer brain damage due to alcohol having caused brain damage to their father from drinking. Dyal's lecture points out that concerns about alcohol abuse were worldwide in the late 19th century and not just confined to Western nations.

See also: Document 26

On Wine Drinking and Its Terrible Consequences.

Lala Ram Dyal, Assistant Surgeon, Lahore.

President and Gentlemen.

Permit me to spend a few minutes of precious time, in pointing out to you the evil effects of alcohol. The palpable ill-results of alcohol drinking are well known to those who read the newspapers, and are evident to those who see intoxicated people lying in the streets. The sight of a drunken man, in his senseless condition, is a good example to other men of the evils of the spiritshop.

The essential spirit of the liquor which brings about this condition is called alcohol. It is a kind of narcotic irritant poison, and is as prejudicial to the human system as arsenic or opium. Just as arsenic and opium are prescribed by Medical men, alcohol also is properly administered from time to time as a medicine in cases of sickness; but just as the two before-mentioned poisons, when taken at improper times its action is injurious. In the same way the drinking of spirituous liquor God has formed the human body like a machine, which must be kept in order if it is intended to be useful and to last for any length of time. It is a matter of great regret that people take care to keep in order such trivial things as a watch, but neglect their own bodily machinery, the construction of which is beyond the power of man. As a consequence they suffer many ills and inconveniences themselves, and impart diseases to their offspring.

The poison of alcohol injures the stomach, the liver, the brain, the heart, and the kidneys; which are the principal parts of the human body. At the first alcohol causes a kind of irritation in the stomach, which causes a derangement of its functions. You are probably aware that the special function of the stomach is to digest the food. If the food itself be not properly digested, can you suppose that the machine which depends entirely on the food will remain for any length of time his good order? Certainly not. Drunkards themselves say that they cannot relish their food without alcohol, but they also know that by the use of alcohol their food becomes daily less and less. It is deeply to be regretted that they knowing full well the disastrous effects of alcohols do not abstain from it.

Secondly. The greater portion of the food passes from the stomach to the liver in the liquid form; and the liver, digesting the food for the second time, produces the bile and forms blood. But wine irritates the liver to such an extent that its excessively minute particles are speedily destroyed. The liver contracts, is greatly reduced in bulk, and rendered entirely unfit for its office; as a consequence, the drunkard suffers from bile, inflammation of the liver, jaundice, and other painful diseases, which ultimately terminate his life.

Thirdly. Alcohol has an effect upon the brain, which is the chief organ of the system, by direction of which all man's sacred and secular duties are performed. By a continued indulgence in alcohol, blood accumulates in the brain, from the effects of intoxication, and causes the drunkard's death. Indulgence in wine weakens the brain to such an extent that a drunkard cannot perform his ordinary duties properly; his health fails, and tremors, congestion, palsy, imbecility, and lunacy supervene, under the accumulation of which diseases, he too often commits suicide. The chief of the causes of madness is drunkenness, and this may be proved by the statistics of lunatic asylums. The injury to the brain is not confined to the drunkard himself, but is passed on to his offspring, and this is why his children are generally weak, emaciated, and low-spirited, and incapable of any great mental exertion. O Brethren! by indulgence in alcohol you are not alone playing with your own lives, but you are injuring your families and your country also. What a Misfortune it is that our countrymen should take to Western liquors with such zest, and be disinclined to adopt the measures which Western scholars have devised for checking the evil! Should any such devices be brought to their notice, they consciously turn a deaf ear to them. O drunkards! if you will only open your eyes to the Work of the English Temperance Society, and see how they have successfully indicated the evil consequences of indulgence in alcohol, you will surely abandon the use of the dangerous poison.

Fourthly. Alcohol deranges the action of the heart, which is the special apparatus for the circulation of the blood. If the blood does not circulate properly in the body, the body becomes like a tree in which the sap does not properly circulate.

Fifthly. Alcohol affects the kidneys. These organs are the guardians of the body's purity, and carry off offensive matters through their minute passages. Should any obstruction occur in the kidneys or their ducts, you can easily imagine the consequences. You know what happens when the sanitary officer of a town becomes negligent, and allows the filth to accumulate in the sewage system. Foul smells fill the air, and the inhabitants are infected with various disorders; and alcohol drinking occasions just such disorders in the kidneys of a human being. Drunkards say that a moderate use of alcohol cheers the heart, freshens the brain, improves the thinking-powers; and enables ordinary business to be transacted with much greater ease; but they fail to think of condition of the drunkard after the intoxication has passed off, They are then seen to be in a wretched condition [. . . .]

Source: Singh, Mukand. *An Inquiry into the Truth, etc.* Translated by Frederic Pincott. Aligarh, India: Lala Ram Dyal, Manager of the Jagat Binod Press, 1893, 94–96.

44 Trembling Mountain (A TB Education Tract) (1895)

Tuberculosis (TB) was one of the leading causes of death in the late 19th century. Although some felt it was a hereditary disease, the realization, based upon scientific research, that it was a bacterial infection was emerging. This report by physician Camille Laviolette—who operated a TB sanatorium in the mountains of Canada in 1895—discusses how TB is spread and the conditions where the disease was most prevalent. It had been noticed that individuals who worked in closed environments were more likely to contract TB compared to those who worked outside. Based upon the principles of Koch Postulates and the identification of the TB bacillus, it was concluded that TB was transmitted by an infected person to others in closed environments. Out of this information, sanitariums were suggested in rural areas where treatment was largely rest outdoors in fresh air and good nutrition. Public health promotion to prevent the spread of the disease, such as coughing in disposable handkerchiefs, not spitting, and keeping windows open, were advocated. This document is important not only for discussing the cause of TB but also as an early example of a patient education and a marketing tract for a TB treatment center.

See also: Document 39

Some of the grandest discoveries ever made in the field of medical science, have been effected in the present day. One of the most important is the discovery demonstrating the contagious character of certain diseases—of pulmonary phthisis, for instance, and the mode of treatment necessary for its cure.

It had long been established that one-seventh of the deaths that took place throughout the world, were caused by tuberculosis, the ravages of which were growing worse and worse, whilst no adequate remedy was as yet known to stay its progress. But thanks to the genius of Robert Koch, the true nature of this fell malady has been laid bare, and the best means of crushing it, have been satisfactorily explained. Now that it has proved to be a contagious disease, its prevention and cure, are possible of accomplishment.

The existence of tuberculosis is universal; it is no respecter of man or brute. It preys alike on all the organs and tissues of the body, but most frequently attacks the lungs—hence, it is commonly termed pulmonary phthisis.

There seems, however, to be an impression abroad, that tuberculosis is not contagious, owing to the opposition to such a doctrine of certain practitioners, and that its germs, so far as propagation is concerned, only exist in the diseased imagination of bacteriologists.

Such an impression is both erroneous and mischievous . . .

By means of carefully conducted experiments, all physicians of any note, are now conversant with the origin of consumption and its mode of propagation. It is proved that the bacilli of the disease are always present in the affected parts of men and animals suffering from tuberculosis.

This germ can be readily distinguished, by its morphological characteristics and its reaction to staining fluids, from all other micro-organisms; it is never present in any disease except tuberculosis; it has been grown or cultivated in proper substances outside the living body for long periods of time; and when the growths or cultures suspended in distilled water are used for the inoculation of susceptible animals, the same disease, tuberculosis, is produced, with the same changes in the tissues; and in these diseased tissues the same germ is present with the same morphological appearances, and the same staining reactions. Finally, it has been shown that no other kind of living or dead thing can or does produce this disease, when used for such inoculations. . . .

But, for the bacilli to be contagious, the conditions must be favorable—the constitution must be feeble and sickly. The more the constitution is undermined by defective hygiene, insufficient nourishment, un-healthy surroundings, from hereditary causes, inflammation of a broncho-pulmonary nature, etc., the more favorable will it be found for the pernicious operations of the bacilli. But, as stated before, all the conditions here mentioned merely favor the reception of tuberculosis; no one of them, nor the whole of them together, could generate tuberculosis without, the active presence of its germs.

It may here be remarked that consumption is more prevalent amongst people of sedentary habits, than amongst those engaged in outdoor pursuits. The following statistics prove this contention: Out of 1000 who died from all causes, it was found that, of the number who died of pulmonary phthisis, 103 were farm laborers, 108 fishermen. 121 gardeners, 122 farmers, 167 grocers; whilst the mortality amongst tailors was 290, and amongst drapers 301. The death rate for printers was 411 out of a, thousand, or close on 50 per cent. This havoc of human life is even worse in the mines of Cornwall, where the miners fall victims to this grim malady at the rate of 600 per thousand. Those whose occupation compels them to work in confined, dusty quarters show the highest mortality. The vitiated atmosphere tends to breed bronchial and pulmonary affections, thus paving the way for the inroads of consumption. To live in close company with a person who has the disease, is to court the infection. The stuffy atmosphere of mills and manufactories of all kinds, is fatal to the lungs. Arthaud found 32 out of 38 workmen, employed in an electric factory in Paris, affected by tuberculosis, the disease having been propagated by four of their number, the only ones in the factory originally infected by it. [. . .]

As previously mentioned, (one-seventh of the deaths that occur throughout the world are caused by tuberculosis. Take France as an instance—the accuracy of whose statistics is admitted. There we see that small-pox annually claims 10,000 victims, measles 15,000. Scarlatina [scarlet fever caused by toxin from a streptococcal throat infection] 6,000, diphtheria 8,000. Typhoid fever 15,000—at total of 64,000 whereas tuberculosis alone claims 160,000 victims every year. These figures show that the latter disease is far more deadly than all the other infectious diseases combined.

Source: Laviolette, Camille. *Trembling Mountain, Laurentides, (Canada), (3,000 feet), A High-Level Sanitarium for the Treatment of Tuberculosis: Cures Operated Winter and Summer* Montreal?: s.n., 1895, pp. 3–5, 9–10.

45 Anesthesia in the 19th Century (1895)

American surgeon and noted medical librarian John Shaw Billings (1838–1913) oversaw the improvement of the Surgeon General's Library of Medicine and was a cofounder of index medicus*—a medical and biomedical science bibliographical database. This paper database was used until 2004, when it merged with* Medline*, an online resource. In his 1895 excerpt from "The History and Literature of Surgery," a chapter in* System of Surgery*, he discusses the history of anesthesia and its use in the mid-19th century, which not only allowed painless surgery but also enabled surgeons to cut into a patient in order to make a diagnosis. The importance of asepsis and antisepsis was mentioned in the excerpt, which points out the recognition of the importance of sterile environments and the acceptance of the germ theory of disease by the late 19th century. Billings also presents surgical advances by American medical personnel, which were often influenced by study in Europe. One innovation was the use of traction for fractures of the thigh.*

See also: Document 8

We now come to an epoch in the history of surgery. On November 3, 1846, Dr. Henry J. Bigelow read before the American Academy of Arts and Sciences an abstract of a paper which was published in full in the *Boston Medical and Surgical Journal* of November 18, 1846, under the title "Insensibility during surgical operations produced by inhalation," which was the first definite account of the method of production of satisfactory anaesthesia in surgical operations. Writers of the thirteenth and fourteenth centuries had described the inhalation of narcotic vapors from certain plants for this purpose. Sir Humphry Davy had suggested in 1800 that "nitrous oxide may probably be used with advantage in surgical operations." Mr. Hickman, a London surgeon, had written in 1828 a letter to King Charles X (which letter was laid before the Academy of Medicine of Paris), in which he said that he had discovered the means of performing the most troublesome operations without pain by producing insensibility by the introduction of certain gases into the lungs. Dr. Crawford W. Long of Athens, Ga., had produced anaesthesia by ether in 1842 for the operation of removing small tumors, but had not published the results, when Dr. Warren allowed a dentist, Dr. Morton, to give ether to produce insensibility while he performed a small operation in the Massachusetts General Hospital.

It is to Warren, Hayward, and Bigelow that the surgical world is indebted mainly for a sufficient, general, and safe method of anaesthesia. Morton wanted to patent his method, which was not a thoroughly safe one until modified by Bigelow, and little credit is due to him or to Wells or Jackson for the part which they then played in the business. The statements of Dr. Bigelow were readily accepted by surgeons, and early in 1847 anaesthesia was in general use throughout the civilized world.

Nothing like it had been known before, and there has been little improvement in it since, for chloroform, though more convenient for use, is decidedly more dangerous than ether in many cases. Most of the great operations had been devised and performed by a few skilled operators before the introduction of anaesthesia, but the performance was not in the deliberate, careful manner which is now well recognized as characterizing the best surgery, especially in these days of asepsis and anti-sepsis. The influence of anaesthesia upon surgical diagnosis has been almost as great as upon methods of operation, for with its aid it is possible to explore the interior of the body in ways that would be impossible without it. With its aid the recent graduate undertakes operations which he would not dream of trying without it: it has done away with the need for some of the most special qualifications which formerly were thought to be, if not indispensable, at least of great importance to the operator [. . .]

The number of American surgeons who have become known as inventors, teachers, or writers since 1850 is very large, and only a brief notice can be given of the most prominent. In New York we have had William H. Van Buren (1819–83), who studied in Paris, was an assistant surgeon in the army for four years, in 1845 joined Mott in clinical teaching, became professor of anatomy in 1852, and professor of surgery in the Bellevue Medical College in 1868. His Contributions to practical surgery appeared in 1865, and his work on Diseases of the genito-urinary system in 1874.

Gurdon Buck (1807–77), surgeon of the New York Hospital in 1837, and of St. Luke's in 1858, made valuable contributions to surgery in the method of treating fractures of the thigh by weight and pulley, in the plastic surgery of the face, and in the treatment of ankylosis of the knee.

James R. Wood (1816–82), the first to introduce clinical teaching in Bellevue Hospital, and one of the founders of Bellevue Medical College, was a bold operator and a very popular teacher. He removed the entire lower jaw in a case of phosphorus-necrosis, leaving the periosteum from which a new jaw was formed; excised Meckel's ganglion with the superior maxillary branch of the fifth pair; and was one of the first in America to perform excision of the shoulder- and elbow-joints.

Frank H. Hamilton (1813–66), a native of Vermont, graduated in Philadelphia in 1833; became professor of surgery in Buffalo in 1844, and in the Bellevue Medical College in New York in 1862. He published his Practical treatise on fractures and dislocations and his Practical treatise on military surgery.

Alden March (1795–1869) settled in Albany in 1820 after graduating at Brown University, Rhode Island, and commenced lecturing on anatomy in 1821, being the first lecturer in that city. He was professor of surgery in the Albany Medical College in 1838, and gave one of the first surgical clinics in this country. He made valuable investigations in hip-joint disease, and performed a large number of surgical operations, including sixty-five amputations through the thigh and eleven excisions of the lower jaw.

Henry Berton Sands (1830–88) graduated from the College of Physicians and Surgeons in New York in 1854; studied in Paris; and on his return became professor of anatomy, and then of surgery. He was surgeon to the Bellevue and New York

Hospitals and to the Roosevelt Hospital, and in the latter part of his life was the leading surgeon in New York City. He was the first to operate in peritonitis due to perforation of the appendix.

Source: Billings, John S. "The History and Literature of Surgery" in *System of Surgery*, edited by Frederic S. Dennis. Philadelphia, Lea Brothers & Co., 1895, 137–139.

46 Scottish Foundations of Modern Surgery (1895)

American surgeon and noted medical librarian John Shaw Billings (1838–1913) coedited System of Surgery *with American physician Frederick S. Dennis (1850–1934), who introduced Lister's antiseptic methods in operations in the United States. The book examines the advancement of surgery and contributions of surgeons. Its purpose was to educate practicing surgeons not only of the history of surgery but also to introduce the latest surgical developments. In this excerpt, Billings describes the beginnings of more modern surgical techniques from the Middle Ages until the late 19th century in Scotland. Scotland had become one of the centers for medical and surgical innovations by the mid-19th century. The excerpt shows that some techniques developed by earlier surgeons were still being used in the 2010s. For example, Billings remarks that in the mid-17th century, a Dr. Edwards was marking the skin with ink where he planned to make the incision for an operation, which is still standard practice. This surgeon also added wine to the surgical wound to prevent infection. Although wine is not put into surgical wounds today, antibiotics often are. Note: The older English spelling has been kept in this excerpt.*

See also: Document 45

In Scotland the University of Aberdeen was founded in 1494, and in 1505 had a professor of medicine [. . .]

The first charter of the Royal College of Surgeons of Edinburgh is dated July 1, 1505. It directs that no person shall make use of the craft of surgery or of barber craft within this burgh unless he is freeman and burgess of the same, and that he must be examined by the masters of the same craft upon the following points—namely: The anatomy, nature, and complexion of every member in man's body, and all the veins of the same. Every year one executed criminal was to be given to the college for anatomical purposes. No master of the craft shall take any apprentice who cannot write and read. Probably the most important provision was, that no person within the burgh shall make or sell any aqua vite except the masters, members, and freemen of the corporation.

By 1589 it had become the custom to admit barbers at a lower rate, but they had only the right to act as barbers, being specially forbidden to practice surgery, and were to have "na signe of chirurgie in their bughts or houses oppenlie or privatlie."

In the early part of the seventeenth century the leading British surgeons were Clowes and Lowe . . . and John Woodall (156?-164?), who had served as an army surgeon, and about 1612 was elected surgeon to St. Bartholomew's Hospital and likewise surgeon-general to the East India Company, which last gave him the appointing of surgeons and mates to all the company's ships. In 1617 he published a work entitled *The Surgeons Mate* or *Military & Domestique Surgery*. Discoursing faithfully & plainly the method and order of the Surgeons chest, the uses of the instruments, the vertues and Operations of the Medicines, and the exact Cures of

Wounds made by Gun-shott, etc. In 1628 he published a work entitled Viaticum, Being the Path-Way to The Surgeons Chest. Containing, Chirurgical Instructions for the yonger sort of Surgeons, imployed in the Service of his Majestic, or for the Common-Wealth upon any occasion whatsoever. Intended chiefly for the better curing of Wounds made by Gunshot. His works are not specially instructive but are in parts very good reading. In amputation he recommends tying large vessels, especially those of the thigh, if it can be done, but he seems to think that the surgeon will often fail, in which case, as well as for the smaller vessels, he recommends buttons of astringent and caustic powders.

In gangrene Woodall urged amputation in the mortified instead of the sound part—an old treatment which had then fallen into disuse. He also suggests amputating as low as the ankle for disease of the foot, instead of just below the knee, as was usually the case. He had never seen the actual cautery used in amputation [. . .].

The greatest English surgeon of the seventeenth century was Richard Wiseman (1622–76) [. . .].

Wiseman used the complex dressings of the period, but knew that simple measures produced equally good results. He used styptics and cauteries, and not the ligature, but he included the end of the cut vessel in one of the stitches through the lips of the wound. Being a personal friend of the king, he used his influence with him to promote the interests of the Barber Surgeon's Company. His works were never translated, and were very little known on the Continent, but they had a decided influence on the improvement of the art in England.

James Yonge (or Young) (1646–1721), a native of Plymouth and a naval surgeon, published in 1679 a little book of 120 pages entitled *Currus Triumphalis, é Terebintho. Or an account of the many admirable Vertues of Oleum Terebinthinae. More particularly, of the good effects produced by its application to recent Wounds." . . . And. lastly, A new Way of Amputation, etc.* He objected to Paré's method of ligatures in amputations, saying that it is "a way always tedious, often successless; and whatever vaunts the Author makes of it, it cannot be so secure as he pretends ; it being liable (sometimes from the slackness, otherwise from the too great straightness of the thred; sometimes from its smallness, cutting through, or from its weakness, giving way) to a new flux when not so tolerable to the Patient, or so easily cured by the Artist as at first; moreover, where two Vessels or more bleed in one Wound (which is very frequent), the one must be neglected, while the Ligature is making on the other." [. . .]

Some curious illustrations of the English surgery of the middle of the seventeenth century are to be found in the *Diary of the Rev. John Ward, Vicar of Stratford-upon-Avon, extending from 1648 to 1679*, edited by Charles Severn (London, 1839, 8vo). For example: "A cancer in Mrs. Townsend's breast, of Alverston, taken off by two surgeons. First they cutt the skin cross and laid itt back, then they workt their hands in ytt, one above and the other below, and so till their hands mett, and so brought itt out There came out a gush of a great quantitie of waterish substance, as much as would fill a flaggon. They put in a glass of wine and some lint, and so let itt alone till the next day; then they opened itt again, and injected myrrhe, aloes, and such things, as resisted putrefaction, and so bound itt up againe. The way how and where itt should be cutt was markt with ink by one Dr. Edwards."

Source: Billings, John S. "The History and Literature of Surgery" in *System of Surgery* edited by Frederic S. Dennis. Philadelphia, Lea brothers & co., 1895, pp. 65–67.

47 *Charaka Samhita*: Ancient Indian Medical System (1896)

The Indian Charaka Samhita *is based on a myth of a celestial deity giving medical knowledge and healing techniques to a wise person. Three Sanskrit books known as the "Great Trilogy" written in antiquity are the main texts of Ayurvedic medicine—*Caraka Samhita, Sushruta Samhita, *and* Astanga Hridaya. *According to legend, the chief Hindu deity gave the text to a sage who founded six schools of Indian medicine. The text from one school was considered the best and it was reedited by Charaka. However, modern researchers suggest that Charaka does not refer to one person but to many individuals. Also in Sanskrit, "charaka" is a term for a wanderer. It is often used in the context of the ancient tradition of wandering, or itinerate, physicians who took their medical practices and religious rites from village to village. The* Charaka Samhita *is still the basis of traditional Ayurveda medicine into the 21st century. The excerpt from this late 19th century translation explains some principles of the practice, reflects the medical knowledge of this time period, and stresses hygiene and cleanliness that was a developing concern of Western medical practitioners.*

See also: Document 10; Document 12

THOSE who have enquired into the subject know that the medical literature of ancient and mediaeval India is exceedingly voluminous. All the works, if capable of being collected together, would fill a fairly large library. Besides a respectable number of works that profess to be comprehensive treatises on the causes of disease and its cure and the normal conditions of health, the number of abridgments is almost unlimited. The reason of this is not far to seek. In the absence of Colleges and Universities established and conducted under royal patronage and thronged with students from every part of the country, individual practitioners, whose professional success became marked or whose learning was generally admitted, attracted a fairly large number of pupils around them. Like the professors of other branches of knowledge, medical practitioners also, in conformity with the excellent custom of the country, had to teach their pupils gratis . . . These teachers very frequently compiled abridgments of their own, drawing largely upon the larger standard works, and incorporating with the abstracted matter the results of their own experience . . . Sometimes teachers of greater ambition, who desired to address the whole profession instead of their immediate pupils, made more pretentious compilations or wrote excellent commentaries on works or abridgments of acknowledged authority. In this way the medical literature of ancient and mediaeval India increased and swelled into almost gigantic proportions.

Of all these works, however, the most ancient one that is still extant and universally studied by the profession is "Charaka Samahita." Professor Wilson supposed "that from Charaka and Susruta being mentioned in the Purānas, the ninth or tenth century is the most modern limit of our conjecture; while the style of the authors, as well as their having become the heroes of fable, indicate a long anterior date." . . . Professor Wilson is of opinion that the Arabians of the eighth century cultivated the Hindu Works on Medicine before those of the Greeks; and that Charaka and Susruta, and the treatise called Nidāna, and others, were translated and studied by the Arabians in the days of Harun and Mansur (A. D. 775) . . . An older work called "Ayurveda," and supposed to have formed a part of the *Atharvan*, is frequently mentioned. But no trace can be had of it in any form however mutilated. It is believed to have been of divine or at best of inspired origin . . .

In the introduction of Charaka's great work it is stated that Bharadwaja, a learned sage, obtained the sacred *Ayurveda* (Science of Life) from Indra the chief of the celestials . . . [Legendary figures transcribed it and] Agniveca's treatise was edited and corrected by Charaka whose name it now bears.

The work of Charaka abounds with weighty aphorisms about disease and its causes as also about the way of avoiding disease, the truth and beauty of which, considering the age in which they were composed, will extort the admiration of the modern reader . . . " Speaking, for example, of the causes of disease, the following aphorism, as laid down by the author, may be cited as an instance of the wisdom the reader may expect in the following pages :-

"Correlation, adverse or absent or excessive, between time, mental faculties, and objects of the senses, constitutes in brief the threefold causes of disease affecting either the body or the mind." Time, in the above, is regarded to be of two kinds; first, the different states or periods of life, as childhood, youth, manhood, old age, and secondly, the seasons of the year. That which is done or borne by a person at a certain period of his life and in a certain season of the year, may not be suitable to him at another period of life and in another season. Then again the relation, adverse or friendly, of mental faculties with both time and objects of the senses, is another fruitful cause of disease or a condition of health . . . Without doubt, they were arrived at after careful observation for centuries. Omitting all reference to those portions of the work that deal with pathogenic conditions, the portions that are purely hygienic and treat of how best to keep health, are invaluable to all classes and races of men. The reader will find that some of the highest and latest discoveries of hygienic science were well known to the ancient medical authorities of India. A life of purity, of cleanliness, and freedom from stirring emotions, is recommended in language that often rises to the dignity of poetry and is unquestionably ennobling throughout.

As a system of cure, Charaka is still regarded to be of very high authority. That system is professed and practiced by a very large number of persons in India, and if it were all empiricism and quackery, it could never have survived so many centuries. The effects of medical treatment are visible and addressed to the commonest understanding. Real quackery in the treatment of disease and human suffering has very little chance of going undetected. Many persons who have enquired into the matter, without yielding to the prejudices fostered by Western culture, are of opinion that many diseases peculiar to India can be cured more effectually, cheaply, and quickly, by the aid of the intelligent native practitioner relying on Charaka than by pursuing Western systems of cure.

Source: Caraka, and Avinash Chunder Kaviratna. *Charaka-samhita: Translated Into English. Published by Avinash Chandra Kaviratna.* Calcutta: G. C. Chakravarti [etc.], 1896, 1913, pp. i–iv.

48 Letters from a Missionary Nurse in East Africa (1896)

British missionary nurse Gertrude Ward published letters she had written to a friend describing her experience living in, and providing health care, at a rural east-African mission station from 1895–1897. The station was located in the small village of Magila. From the mid-through the early 20th century, it was common for health care missionaries from several European and North American Christian denominations to go to poor developing nations, not only to convert the native populations but also to provide medical care and education. However, this colonial rule was not always welcomed by native populations. In this excerpt, Ward describes fevers among fellow workers. People took quinine along with tea to prevent malaria, so the fevers she describes could have been other tropical illness such as dengue, scrub typhus, or typhoid. Smallpox was also found among the unvaccinated. Ward also observes locus devouring crops leading to famine. This excerpt from 1896 points out that Western medicine was provided by health care missionaries in rural areas of Africa and is still the case in the late 2010s in some rural areas of Africa.

See also: Document 73

To M. A. W.

MAGILA, February 7, 1896.— . . . The first and most important news I have to tell you is that I am quite well, and have been so all along. As for prudence and precautions, you would not recognize me in my present character. Not that I was ever careless at home, but I believe you fancied me so. Now I am Medical Officer of Health, and Sanitary Inspector, and Hygiene Lecturer, besides being Physician, Surgeon, and Nurse; so it behoves me to practice what I preach, and keep myself well, as an object lesson to the rest of the European world. So far the results have been satisfactory, and I have been able to be of some little use to the Mission instead of being a troublesome sick burden. The men are on the whole very good, both when well and ill; and we have not any of the rash and foolhardy sort amongst us, which is a great comfort. I have had a few days' complete holiday from sick-rooms, and have spent three nights up on a salubrious hill 1,500 feet high—a lovely spot, which I have described in my letter to A.

To-day, unluckily, my companion of the hill-top has taken to her bed with fever; but she is not very bad, and I hope she will soon throw it off. I am getting quite experienced now in the different forms of this mysterious malady, which is so unlike anything we have at home, and is so full of unexpected surprises even to the experienced. It does seem odd that people, after all these years, have not discovered really either the cause, prevention, or remedy thereof.

Our day here is rather differently planned from the days in Zanzibar; generally it is as follows:—the waking-bell rings a little before 6, and church is at 6.30. If I have patients to see to, I sometimes cannot get to church, as they have to have a cup of tea and quinine, and other etceteras, as soon as I am up.

At 7 we have a first breakfast of porridge and coffee, and between that and lunch, at 10, I am generally quite occupied with patients up here or down at the dispensary. The rest of the morning varies. One cannot make a plan of campaign because the unexpected is always turning up; but if I am not busy with nursing,

February 8.—This is written in scraps, and I had quite forgotten to continue about the day's routine. After our lesson we always, if we possibly can, go for a walk; but as this is the hot time of year, and we cannot start till 5, it leaves very little time, for sunset is at 6. At 6.30 we have church, and then dinner at 7, after which we write, or work, or gossip, or, if I have patients, I am generally looking after them.

Sometimes I go down late to the native hospital, if there is any one specially needing attention. We go early to bed, of course, and are generally quite ready for sleep. Since I began this letter Miss B., the other English lady, has been sent to bed with fever, so now I have them both on my hands, together with the ordering of the house . . . and we have only to walk into the dining-room to be fed. Schools and classes look after themselves on these occasions; they are quite accustomed to all their teachers disappearing simultaneously, and take it calmly.

The locusts have been rather troublesome here of late, and it is sad to see many trees and plants entirely stripped of their green. Last year there was a disastrous famine amongst the natives for miles round from this same cause, and we much hope things will not be so bad again. The first time I saw locusts in any number was when I came here from Zanzibar and the train passed through a cloud of them. Now they are as familiar as flies at home, and I scarcely notice them; but it is very depressing to watch vast swarms of them sweeping over the country in one ceaseless cloud for hours and hours, only stopping at sunset, when they settle into the foliage and rest till next day. They are pretty creatures in themselves, looking like small hummingbirds fluttering in the sunshine, and when near, shining in various shades of pink, green and brown. They are really like very large grasshoppers. I often catch one and examine it, and wish that science would invent some means of exterminating the whole devastating tribe [. . .]

February 11.—However, every now and then these things come to a complete standstill, as, for instance, now, when I have my hands so full with sick folk that I scarcely think of church. This is a typical "Magila week." Last Friday Miss D. took to her bed with fever; the next day Miss B. . . . next day Mr. R. succumbed with fever; the same afternoon a native boy was sent over from Mkuzi very ill with pneumonia; and in the evening Mr. B. was carried over from Mkuzi in the hammock! If that is not enough for one nurse single-handed, without a doctor or any help, I wonder what is? However, they are managing to recover somehow, and we jog along merrily till next time.

. . . I am keeping very well indeed, and do not feel the least tired; so pray don't let anyone feel anxious. At the same time, send a few more nurses out!

Source: Ward, Gertrude. *Letters from East Africa, 1895–1897.* London: Office of the Universities' Mission to Central Africa, 1899, pp. 73–76.

49 Medical Testimony against the Use of Tobacco (1896)

This article by American physician health crusader and sanitarium health spa director, John Harvey Kellogg (1852–1943), was one of the first to point out the potential dangers of tobacco use based upon some research in the late 19th century. Although anti-alcohol and tobacco crusaders campaigned against the use of these "stimulants," their arguments against their use had been based upon moral and religious reasons. Kellogg, in this 1896 article from a health journal Modern Medicine and Bacteriological World *published out of his Battle Creek Sanitarium, reports on some research studies that purported to show that smokers were less healthy compared to nonsmokers among a sample of college students. This was in terms of weight gain, height, chest girth, and larger lung capacity. He mentions reports of other physicians who had observed that tobacco could cause inflammation of the throat. He also points out that anti-tobacco education programs had been started on college and university campuses and that some institutions had strictly forbade any tobacco use at their colleges.*

Medical Testimony against the Use of Tobacco

Dr. Mulhall, of St. Louis, Mo., recently read before a medical society a paper on cigarette-smoking, a practise which he heartily condemned, especially in young persons. Dr. Ingalls, of Chicago, was outspoken in his condemnation of tobacco in all forms, especially in the form of cigars and cigarettes. He declared that he had seen many persons whose nervous system was seriously affected by indulgence in tobacco, and had also seen chronic inflammation of the throat produced by smoking. Dr. Langmade had so long been accustomed to recognize the ill effects of tobacco-smoking upon the throat, that he was able to tell by examination of the throat alone whether or not an individual was a smoker, and also whether he had abstained for a few days. He called attention to the interesting fact that the best singers abstain from smoking before a public appearance, and that, in some cases, singers have been obliged to abstain from smoking for several weeks before some special effort. He also complained of cigarette-smoking because of the narcotic effect produced by it, to which the smoker becomes readily addicted.

As an evidence of the poisonous effects of tobacco, he referred to a case in which he had applied a solution of nicotin to the throat of a patient for the relief of a condition which was supposed to be benefited by smoking, but with the most disastrous results, the patient fainting at once, and being revived only with much difficulty.

Dr. Mulhall, who was somewhat of an apologist for tobacco, admitted that "tobacco leads, in a certain degree, to the use of stimulants, . . . owing to the temporary depression produced by smoking, which could be relieved by alcohol." But he held that the combined effect of alcohol and tobacco was very bad in the end. It is thus that the use of one poison leads to that of another. Smoking is only a stepping-stone to alcoholic intemperance.

Tobacco and Education

A crusade against the use of tobacco has recently been started in a number of our American universities. It is a recognized fact that tobacco, when taken into the system in any form, is injurious not only to the physical health, but to the intellectual development as well. The results obtained in schools where the use of tobacco has been discarded are very encouraging, and show clearly the harmful effect which this obnoxious weed has upon the system. It is gratifying to note that some of the best colleges of our country have taken a decided stand against its use by their students. The Boston University has issued an ordinance that those students who are unwilling to forego the use of tobacco while within the precincts of the university will have their fees returned, and their names taken from the books. The Ohio Wesleyan University has made a rule forbidding its students to use tobacco in any form, and other universities have made similar ordinances.

In some of the higher educational institutions of this country attempts have been made to obtain statistics as to the effects of tobacco on the academic youth. In 1891 the official physician of Yale published the results of observations on the under-graduates of that university. In a class of one hundred and forty-seven students, he found that in four years seventy-seven who did not use tobacco surpassed the seventy who did use it to the extent of 10.4 per cent in increase of weight, twenty-four per cent in increase of height, and 26.7 per cent in increase of chest girth. The most marked difference was, however, in point of lung capacity, the abstainers showing an average gain of 77.5 per cent, more than smokers or chewers. Among the undergraduates at Amherst it was found that during the four years the abstainers from tobacco gained twenty-four per cent in weight, thirty-seven per cent in height, forty-two per cent in chest girth, and seventy-five per cent in lung capacity, over those who used tobacco.

Source: Kellogg, John Harvey, editor. *Modern Medicine and Bacteriological World* 5, (May 1896), pp. 110–111, 305.

50 Hot Water in Surgery (1896)

American physician, surgeon, and health reformer, John Harvey Kellogg (1852–1943) wrote a brief report in a medical journal edited by him on an international surgery convention in 1896. Kellogg discusses a method of preventing infection introduced by French physician M. Reclus, who recommended the use of hot water to disinfect and clean the wound during surgery. Hot water was also recommended to prevent wound infections in antiquity but appeared to have been lost or not practiced by physicians centuries later. It is not known if the idea presented by Reclus were based upon these procedures offered by Celsus that had been translated into English and reprinted earlier in the century or if the author arrived at this procedure on his own. During the late 19th century, information about disease-carrying bacteria and aseptic environments for surgery was slowly being accepted by the medical establishment.

See also: Document 8

At the last Surgical Congress, M. Reclus *(La Presse Medicale*) stated that he never amputates a crushed limb, no matter how great may be the extent of the injury. He envelops the limb with antiseptic gauze, and allows nature to separate the living from the dead tissues. But this method is possible only by the aid of hot water, which may be employed in the following manner:—

After disinfection of the injured part, the patient, who is nearly always in a state of traumatic shock, is surrounded by hot blankets, and the wound is laved with hot water at 60° to 62°C. (140° to 144°F.) An irrigator is employed, the vessel containing the water being at such an elevation as to produce a strong jet. A jet of hot water should fall upon every portion of the injured surface. It is only by this means that all clots, micro-organ-isms, and foreign particles can be removed. The hot water has a triple advantage :—

1. The high temperature is truly antiseptic.
2. It is hemostatic, and under its influence the hemorrhage is arrested.
3. It antagonizes the traumatic shock resulting from loss of blood.

Another indication for the employment of hot water in surgery is in cases of hemorrhoids in which a radical operation is declined. Whenever an acute attack occurs, there should be applied to the anal region compresses of tarlatan or cheesecloth moistened in water at 55° C. (131° F.). The compress rapidly cools, and should be renewed every minute, being applied as quickly as possible after heating by dipping in hot water. The patient should take, every morning, an enema of hot water at the same temperature. If the hemorrhoids are of recent development, and small in size, with no marked contraction of the sphincter or varicose masses of appreciable size, the hot water will relieve these attacks to such a degree that the amelioration will amount to a cure.

Hot water, according to M. Reclus, is truly a sovereign remedy in the treatment of acute prostatitis. The technique is as simple as possible. An irrigating-tube is carefully and slowly introduced into the anus so as not to injure the swollen prostate which obstructs the rectum, and water is applied at a temperature of 55° to 60° C. (131° to 140° F.). The water should be admitted very slowly. This application should be made twice a day until a cure is effected. The relief is almost immediate, and nine cases are given by M. Reclus in which there has been no suppuration.

[I have made use of a special form of irrigator for application of hot water to the rectum for many years, which I find much more convenient than the ordinary rectal tube. It consists of a tube furnished with a bulbous extremity perforated with small openings through which the water passes into the rectum. This tube is placed inside a larger tube, or sleeve, through which the water escapes from the rectum. This irrigator is made of hard rubber . . . —J. H. K.]

The same treatment also gives excellent results in prostatic congestion, and M. Reclus has seen a hot enema relieve the retention of urine which is brought on in patients suffering from enlarged prostate by the slightest excess of fatigue or exposure to cold.

In salpingo-ovaritis, M. Reclus proceeds as follows: "The uterine cavity is disinfected and thoroughly drained, and enemata of hot water are daily administered. The best time for the enema is in the morning half an hour after rising." M. Reclus has seen many cases of peri-metro-salpingitis recover under this treatment.

Source: Kellogg, John Harvey, editor. "Hot Water in Surgery." *Modern Medicine and Bacteriological World* 5, May 1896,, p. 62.

51 Osler's Medical Textbook and Typhus (1898)

Canadian physician William Osler (1849–1919), the author of The Principles and Practice of Medicine *([1898] 1903), was one of the four founding professors of Johns Hopkins Hospital and is sometimes considered one of the "fathers of modern medicine." Osler is noted for creating the first residency program for physician specialty training. He was also the first to introduce bedside clinical training rather than just studying medicine in lecture halls. His medical text was a beginning in the reform of medical education in the early 20th century in North America as it gave students a more scientific basis for medical practice. The extract on typhus points out that the speculation as to its cause was not accurate at this point. As medical knowledge advanced, its cause was finally discovered in 1909. The body louse was identified as the vector for the disease. This epidemic typhus, caused by* Rickettsia prowazekii, *was associated with poverty, jails, battlefields, and those living in unhygienic and war-torn conditions. Encouragement of overall hygiene, including frequent bathing and washing of clothing in hot water, was fostered as a general public health practice.*

II. TYPHUS FEVER.

Definition.—An acute infectious disease of unknown origin, highly contagious, characterized by sudden onset, maculated rash, marked nervous symptoms, and a cyclical course terminating by crisis, usually about the end of the second week. Post-mortem there are no special lesions other than those associated with fever.

The disease is known by the names of hospital fever, spotted fever, jail fever, camp fever, and ship fever, and in Germany is called *exanthematic* typhus, in contradistinction to *abdominal* typhus.

Etiology.—Typhus fever has been one of the great epidemics of the world. Until the middle of the nineteenth century it prevailed extensively in all the larger cities of Europe, and at times extended to widespread, outbreaks. As Hirsch has remarked, "The history of typhus is written in those dark pages of the world's story which tell of the grievous visitations of mankind by war, famine, and misery of every kind." Few countries have suffered more than Ireland, particularly between the years 1817 and 1819 and in 1846. In England the disease has progressively diminished in intensity. In 1875 there were 1,499 deaths, in 1895 only 58 deaths. In 1897 there were only 3 cases of typhus fever in the London Fever Hospitals. The last really great epidemic was in the Turko-Russian War in 1877-'78.

The gradual disappearance of typhus fever is one of the great triumphs of modern medicine. At present the disease lurks in only a few centers in Great Britain and on the Continent, and every few years slight outbreaks occur in larger cities, and sporadic cases appear from time to time. In the United States typhus fever has not prevailed as an extensive epidemic for many years. There were small outbreaks in New York in 1881-'82 and in 1892-'93, and in 1883 in Philadelphia. A remarkable feature is the occurrence of a few cases at long intervals of time from any other outbreaks and at great distances from any known foci of the disease. This was one of the points which led Murchison to the belief that under favorable conditions the disorder might originate spontaneously. But although it is sometimes impossible to explain satisfactorily its importation, such negative evidence can not be regarded as conclusive. Certainly, the analogy of the other infectious diseases is against this view.

In 1877 there occurred a local outbreak of typhus at the House of Refuge, in Montreal, a city in which the disease had not existed for many years. The overcrowding was so great in the basement rooms of the refuge that at night there were not more than 88 cubic feet of space to each person. Eleven individuals were affected. It was not possible to trace the source of infection.

In the spring of 1901 from one house three cases of fever were admitted to my wards, which were regarded at first as typhoid fever, but the features were so anomalous that our suspicions were aroused. The rash was perfectly characteristic of typhus, the Widal reaction was negative, blood cultures were negative, and a post-mortem on one fatal case showed no typhoid lesions, and no cultures were obtained from the spleen or the blood post-mortem. The other two cases terminated by crisis, so that I think there can be no question that the cases were typhus fever. The disease has not prevailed in Baltimore for more than a quarter of a century. The patients were Lithuanians, they lived under most unsanitary conditions, and were workers at a suburb frequented by a great many foreigners from the eastern parts of Europe. The origin of the outbreak could not be traced, nor did any other cases occur.

Typhus is one of the most highly contagious of febrile affections. In epidemics nurses and doctors in attendance upon the sick are almost invariably attacked. There is no disease which has so many victims in the profession. It is stated that in a period of twenty-five years, among 1,230 physicians attached to institutions in Ireland, 550 succumbed to this disease. Casual attendance upon cases in limited epidemics does not appear to be very risky, but when the sick are aggregated in wards the poison appears concentrated and the danger of infection is much enhanced. Bedding and clothes retain the poison for a long time. Murchison thought that the virus was thrown off from the lungs and from the skin. It attaches itself particularly to the clothing and linen and to the furniture of the room, and appears to retain its activity for a remarkably long time. To catch the disease there apparently must be fairly intimate contact with the patient, more particularly contact with a large number of patients. Thus in mild outbreaks of only a few cases physicians and nurses are rarely affected, while in severe epidemics all in attendance may be attacked in succession [. . .]

Morbid Anatomy.—The anatomical changes are those which result from intense fever. The blood is dark and fluid; the muscles are of a deep red color, and often show a granular degeneration, particularly in the heart; the liver is enlarged and soft and may have a dull clay-like lustre; the kidneys are swollen; there is moderate enlargement of the spleen, and a general hyperplasia of the lymph-follicles. . . . The skin shows the petechial rash.

Symptoms.—Incubation.—This is placed at about twelve days, but it may be less. There may be ill-defined feelings of discomfort. As a rule, however, the *invasion* is abrupt and marked by chills or a single rigor, followed by fever. The chills may recur during the first few days, and there is headache with pains in the back and legs. There is early prostration, and the patient is glad to take to his bed at once. The temperature is high at first, and may attain its maximum on the second or third day. The pulse is full, rapid, and not so frequently dicrotic as in typhoid. [. . .]

Source: Osler, William. *The Principles and Practice of Medicine, Designed for the Use of Practitioners and Students of Medicine.* New York, D. Appleton and company [1898] 1903, pp. 49–51.

52 Digitalis (or Foxglove) Illustration (1900)

American pharmacology professor David M. R. Culbreath (1856–1943) wrote a pharmacology textbook, materia medica, *in 1900 in order to help medical and pharmacological personnel to identify various plants, minerals, and other materials that were contained in the* United States Pharmacopoeia *(publication of approved drugs to be used by American physicians). Foxglove, the source of digitalis, was used for centuries in Europe. Other names for the plant include Fairy Gloves, Folks or Ladies' Glove, Dog's Finger (thus the name "digitalis" from the Latin for fingers). The digitalis extracted from the leaves was used for congestive heart failure to give the heart rate more strength and to treat cardiac arrhythmias. The plant grows in sandy soil, and at the edges of woods and thickets. It is a beautiful flower in various white, pinks and purple shades that was, and is, now common in gardens from many parts of the world. This illustration aided the physician and pharmacist in identifying the plant to be collected and used in their practice at the turn of the 20th century.*

See also: Document 28

Digitalis purpurea

Source: Culbreth, David M. R. *A Manual of Materia Medica and Pharmacology: Comprising All Organic and Inorganic Drugs Which are and Have Been Official in the United States Pharmacopoeia . . . as well as for druggists, pharmacists, and physicians*. Philadelphia: Lea, 1900, p. 512.

53 Causes of Summer Diarrhea, A Major Killer of Infants (1902)

Summer diarrhea was a major killer of infants through the late 1930s in many developed nations and is still a major cause of infant mortality in some developing regions, in particular sub-Saharan Africa. This report written in 1902 was one of the first to supply scientific evidence to suggest the cause of diarrhea in infants was likely a pathogenic bacterium. Different kinds of bacteria had been noticed in the stool, but it was difficult to identify the bacterium that might be causing problems due to the many different ones found in the intestine. The diarrhea causing pathogen, Shigella, *was first discovered around the turn of the 20th century by a Japanese bacteriologist using a new serological testing method. This report was one of the first to study a pathogenic bacterium based upon this new test in infants. This study led to public health promotion of basic hygiene, such as hand washing, and public policies for the pasteurization of milk and access to clean water, which greatly reduced infant mortality from summer diarrhea.*

The successful studies of Japanese dysentery by Shiga in 1898, which led to the isolation of *B. dysenteriae* and its demonstration as the cause of acute endemic dysentery were followed by the studies of acute tropical dysentery in Manila by Flexner in 1900 and epidemic dysentery in Germany by Kruse in 1901 with results confirming the observations of Shiga. Since that time a considerable number of observations bearing upon and extending the studies just mentioned have been carried out both in the United States and elsewhere. Inasmuch as the organism has also been obtained from cases of dysentery in troops returning from China, in Constantinople, in Italy and other European countries its wide diffusion in nature as well as its pathogenicity are clearly evident.

That the summer diarrheas of infants have an infectious origin has long been believed by clinicians and pathologists. Indeed, within the last ten or fifteen years notable contributions to the bacteriology of the dejecta, intestinal contents, and intestinal mucosa in the disease have been made by Escherich and his pupils in Germany and by Booker in this country. The valuable studies of these investigators have been less conclusive than might have been expected by reason of the multiplicity of bacteria in the intestine and the absence of satisfactory criteria of distinction between the saprophytic and parasitic varieties. Notwithstanding these drawbacks some facts have been established. But no success has attended the efforts to prove the action of a specific organism as the cause of infantile summer diarrheas. Indeed, no pathogenic organism was constantly present in the discharges.

The nomenclature of summer diarrhea is by no means clear. The various names given and the divergent views held as to its nature well illustrate the confusion that purely symptomatic and anatomical conceptions bring into the classification of disease.

The original problem set before us the past summer (1902), was the investigation of the intestinal bacteria of infants suffering from different forms of summer diarrhea, especially as to the presence of the Bacillus dysenteriae (Shiga). Subsequently, as a control, the stools of healthy infants were also studied. Following the method of investigation employed by Shiga in adult dysentery it was our intention to make use of the agglutination reaction of the blood of the patients with the organisms, in isolating the pathogenic organisms from the dejecta. Prof. Flexner drew our attention to this method of approaching the problem, and suggested the lines of special study.

The present unsatisfactory, state of our knowledge of the etiology of the intestinal inflammations of children may be gathered from the statements regarding it to be found in any of the recent authoritative textbooks upon the diseases of children. [. . .]

The conclusion that the bacillus of dysentery is an important, if not the most important, cause of the summer diarrheas of children seems, therefore, justifiable. In how far the presence of the bacillus may account for the general diarrheal diseases among children, both in the summer and winter larger study, embracing a wide range of cases of intestinal disturbances and distributed over a wide area, alone can determine.

Source: Duval, Charles W. and Victor H. Bassett, "The Etiology of Summer Diarrhea in Infants" in Simon Flexner and L. Emmet Holt [eds.], *Bacteriological and Clinical Studies of the Diarrheal Diseases of Infancy with Reference to the Bacillus Dysenteriae (Shiga): From the Rockefeller Institute for Medical Research.* New York: Rooney and Otten Printing Co, 1904, pp. 7–8, 24–25.

54 Developing Dementia from Syphilis (1902)

American physician and longtime director of a mental hospital, Robert Howland Chase (1845–1921), wrote General Paresis, Practical and Clinical. *Its purpose was to educate physicians and medical students about the signs and symptoms of general paresis—the term used for mental disorders caused by tertiary syphilis—in the prodromal (early), second, and final stages of dementia. The disease, caused by the* Treponema pallidum *spirochete, went through three phases. In the first, a chancre (painless ulcer), and in the second, rashes and swollen glands, occurred. However, syphilis was called the great imitator as it resembled many other conditions in this secondary phase. The final or tertiary phase of syphilis in untreated patients could cause brain damage that results in signs and symptoms of dementia. This generally occurs a few decades after initial infection. A blood test for the disease was not developed until 1906; mercury and mercury vapor were used for treatment in the early phases. However, the disease was difficult to cure until the mid-20th century when antibiotics were discovered and became widely used. Until this time, general paresis was common.*

See also: Document 17

A CASE OF GENERAL PARESIS IN THE PRODROMAL STAGE.

A man forty-five years old, vigorous, married, of a healthy family. . . . An extraordinary salesman with a salary of $4,500 per year; he lost his position, because he had lost his faculty of making ready sales. His wife found that he had not saved any money, that he could not tell what had become of it, and that he could not be depended upon to earn anything. He became indifferent rather than idle; therefore, he could not get a position. He performed the ordinary duties of the house. Subsequently, he went to the door inadequately dressed, and in other respects he showed a lack of a sense of delicacy, but he did not realize it. . . . [He was] somewhat sluggish in speech; a lack of animation; a failure in quickness of memory and intellectual promptness . . . On this account, he went to an asylum, where marked intellectual impairment soon appeared.

ILLUSTRATIVE CASES IN THE SECOND STAGE.

R. J. B., admitted to Philadelphia Hospital February, 1895, age 51, salesman. Family history negative as to mental and nervous diseases. Patient had a severe blow on the back of the head in 1876, which left him with a headache for several years. He had been a hard drinker. In 1887, after a drinking bout, his friends say that he "acted crazy" for a week or ten days. Recently, he has been indifferent to the wants of his family; developed delusions as to wealth, money-getting, etc . . . signed his mother's name to checks on a bank, where some years ago he had an account; abandoned his religious belief and joined the new order of the "third Christians." On admission, when asked what was his business, he replied: "I have been a manufacturer of the first character of ladies' shoes for twenty-five years . . . We do a business of $600,000 a year, the profits being 28 to 30 per cent. . . . He said he had not accumulated much money because his brothers needed so much of it. “However, I have been left $6,000,000 in the following way: In January, 1877, I caught the runaway horses of a gentleman and no doubt saved his life. He took my name and address, and four months ago when he died he left me $3,000,000, and there was a codicil which said that if not satisfied I should ask for more, and so I asked for $6,000,000 more. . . . The patient says that he was “Governor of the State; in 1873 Mayor; at the present time he is United States Senator.”. . . In another minute he says he is a graduate in medicine at Harvard, in Berlin, in Paris; that he has practiced medicine for eighteen years; that he has been an “elegant singer and player.” He is sleepy-looking, nervous in action, calm in mind; hardly recognizes his surroundings; calls the hospital the “Hughes Academy.” He seemed to believe exactly what he said. February 12, 1895, his delusions of grandeur are growing greater; he sleeps and eats well. February 15, at 5:45 last evening he was determined to leave the hospital and broke a pane of glass with a chair, and when the attendant tried to quiet him he attacked the latter. March 5, transferred to acute ward and placed in bed; he has been perfectly tractable and in one week was allowed to get up. . . . he is not cognizant of his surroundings; shows no discontent. His face is expressionless and pale; eyes, partial ptosis; pupils small, unequal, the right larger; reaction to light imperfect; accommodation normal; tongue slightly tremulous; knee-jerk exaggerated . . .

ILLUSTRATIVE CASE IN THE THIRD STAGE.

J. E. J., age 44, now presents the conditions of the final stage, the previous stages having been typical. He cannot walk or stand, but lies in bed in the position in which he may be placed, barely able to turn his body unassisted. He is now unable to articulate more than a word or two at a time. His flesh is fast wasting, swallows with difficulty, and is fed chiefly with liquid food. His dejections pass unconsciously in bed. But the expression of good feeling still lingers on his face and he never complains. When addressed he sometimes tries to reply and even to smile a recognition, but does not succeed and the semi-flaccid muscles of the mouth and face fail in their effort of movement. Bed-sores are hard to prevent. He will become even thinner than at present unless the drama ends by a paralysis of the muscles of deglutition.

Source: Chase, Robert Howland. *General Paresis, Practical and Clinical*. Philadelphia: P. Blakiston’s Son, 1902 , pp. 35–36, 59–60, 66.

55 Upton Sinclair: *The Jungle* (1906)

American novelist, social commentator, and health reformer, Upton Sinclair (1878–1968), published The Jungle *in 1906. The book investigates the terrible conditions in the Chicago meatpacking industry. He writes about poverty, family illnesses, and terrible working conditions among the recent Lithuanian immigrants who worked in the packing industry. Although Sinclair was attempting to show the plight of slaughterhouse workers to gain sympathy for socialism, the book caused revulsion against the meat industry. President Theodore Roosevelt (1858–1919) had Sinclair's claims investigated and found them accurate.* The Jungle *was highly controversial, and Sinclair was classified as a "muckraker," a writer who delighted in digging up dirt, a term coined by Roosevelt. The book became a major factor in the passage of the Pure Food and Drug Laws and The Meat Inspection Act of 1906. The following excerpt shows the making of hams and sausages in a most unsanitary and unhealthy way that turns the stomach of most readers—past and present.*

See also: Document 63

CHAPTER XIV

With one member trimming beef in a cannery, and another working in a sausage factory, the family had first-hand knowledge of the great majority of Packingtown swindles. For it was the custom, as they found, whenever meat was so spoiled that it could not be used for anything else, either to can it or else to chop it up into sausage. With what had been told them by Jonas, who had worked in the pickle-rooms, they could now study the whole of the spoiled-meat industry on the inside, and read a new and grim meaning into that old Packingtown jest,—that they use everything of the pig except the squeal.

Jonas had told them how the meat that was taken out of pickle would often be found sour, and how they would rub it up with soda to take away the smell, and sell it to be eaten on free-lunch counters; also of all the miracles of chemistry which they performed, giving to any sort of meat, fresh or salted, whole or chopped, any color and any flavor and any odor they chose. In the pickling of hams they had an ingenious apparatus, by which they saved time and increased the capacity of the plant—a machine consisting of a hollow needle attached to a pump; by plunging this needle into the meat and working with his foot, a man could fill a ham with pickle in a few seconds. And yet, in spite of this, there would be hams found spoiled, some of them with an odor so bad that a man could hardly bear to be in the room with them.

To pump into these the packers had a second and much stronger pickle which destroyed the odor—a process known to the workers as "giving them thirty per cent." Also, after the hams had been smoked, there would be found some that had gone to the bad. Formerly these had been sold as "Number Three Grade," but later on some ingenious person had hit upon a new device, and now they would extract the bone, about which the bad part generally lay, and insert in the hole a white-hot iron.

After this invention there was no longer Number One, Two, and Three Grade—there was only Number One Grade. The packers were always originating such schemes—they had what they called "boneless hams," which were all the odds and ends of pork stuffed into casings; and "California hams," which were the shoulders, with big knuckle-joints, and nearly all the meat cut out; and fancy "skinned hams," which were made of the oldest hogs, whose skins were so heavy and coarse that no one would buy them—that is, until they had been cooked and chopped fine and labelled "head cheese"!

It was only when the whole ham was spoiled that it came into the department of Elzbieta. Cut up by the two-thousand-revolutions-a-minute flyers, and mixed with half a ton of other meat, no odor that ever was in a ham could make any difference. There was never the least attention paid to what was cut up for sausage; there would come all the way back from Europe old sausage that had been rejected, and that was moldy and white—it would be dosed with borax and glycerin, and dumped into the hoppers, and made over again for home consumption. There would be meat that had tumbled out on the floor, in the dirt and sawdust, where the workers had tramped and spit uncounted billions of consumption germs. There would be meat stored in great piles in rooms; and the water from leaky roofs would drip over it, and thousands of rats would race about on it. It was too dark in these storage places to see well, but a man could run his hand over these piles of meat and sweep off handfuls of the dried dung of rats. These rats were nuisances, and the packers would put poisoned bread out for them; they would die, and then rats, bread, and meat would go into the hoppers together. This is no fairy story and no joke; the meat would be shovelled into carts, and the man who did the shoveling would not trouble to lift out a rat even when he saw one—there were things that went into the sausage in comparison with which a poisoned rat was a tidbit. There was no place for the men to wash their hands before they ate their dinner, and so they made a practice of washing them in the water that was to be ladled into the sausage. There were the butt-ends of smoked meat, and the scraps of corned beef, and all the odds and ends of the waste of the plants, that would be dumped into old barrels in the cellar and left there. Under the system of rigid economy which the packers enforced, there were some jobs that it only paid to do once in a long time, and among these was the cleaning out of the waste-barrels. Every spring they did it; and in the barrels would be dirt and rust and old nails and stale water—and cart load after cart load of it would be taken up and dumped into the hoppers with fresh meat, and sent out to the public's breakfast. Some of it they would make into "smoked" sausage—but as the smoking took time, and was therefore expensive, they would call upon their chemistry department, and preserve it with borax and color it with gelatine to make it brown. All of their sausage came out of the same bowl, but when they came to wrap it they would stamp some of it "special," and for this they would charge two cents more a pound.

Source: Sinclair, Upton. *The Jungle.* New York: Doubleday, Page & Company, 1906, pp. 160–162.

56 Clifford Beers: The Horrors of Mental Institutions (1906)

Conditions in most "insane asylums" were deplorable in the late 19th and early 20th centuries. Patients were locked up and also shackled and thrown into cold damp cells. Wealthy Wall Street financier Clifford Beers (1876–1943), who had been in and out of mental institutions for bipolar affective disorder, wrote about his experiences in A Mind that Found Itself *in 1906. Beers's book had an immediate impact and launched a massive mental health reform movement not only in the United States but also in other Western countries. This excerpt is one of several that were pivotal in the change of mental health treatment for those with mental disorders as it shows the inhumane treatment of a patient. The book led to the organization of mental health associations to advocate for better treatment. These associations grew and also influenced mental health professionals to practice more humane treatment of the mentally ill. These associations still influenced research and treatment concerning mental disorders into the 21st century.*

FOR THIS PERIOD OF 3 WEEKS—from October 18th until November 8th, 1902, when I left this institution and was transferred to state hospital—I was continuously either under lock and key (in the padded cell or some other room) or under the eye of an attendant. Over half the time I was in the snug, but cruel embrace of a strait-jacket—about 3 hundred hours in all.

While being subjected to this terrific abuse I was held in exile. I was cut off from all direct and all honest indirect communication with my legally appointed conservator—my own brother—and also with all other relatives and friends [. . .].

When for the first time in 6 weeks I saw my conservator, did he learn of the treatment to which I had been subjected. From his office in New Haven he had telephoned several times to the assistant physician and inquired about my condition. Though Jekyll-Hyde [this physician] did tell him that I was highly excited and difficult to control, he did not even hint that I was being subjected to any unusual restraint [. . .].

How helpless, how at the mercy of his keepers, a patient may be is further illustrated by the conduct of this same man. Once, during the third week of my nights in a strait-jacket, I refused to take certain medicine which an attendant offered me. For some time I had been regularly taking this innocuous concoction without protest; but I now decided that, as the attendant refused most of my requests, I should no longer comply with all of his. He did not argue the point with me. He simply reported my refusal to Doctor Jekyll. A few minutes later Doctor Jekyll—Doctor Hyde—accompanied by 3 attendants, entered the padded cell. I was robed for the night—in a straight-jacket. Mr. Hyde held in his hand a rubber tube. An attendant stood near with the medicine. For over 2 years, the common threat had been that the "tube" would be resorted to if I refused medicine or food. I had begun to look upon it as a myth; but in presence in the hands of an oppressor now convinced me of its reality. I saw that the doctor and his bravos meant business; and as I had already endured torture enough, what seemed to be in store for me.

"What are you going to with that?" I asked, eyeing the tube.

"The attendant says you refuse to take your medicine. We are going to make you take it."

"I'll take your old medicine," was my reply.

"You have had your chance."

"All right," I said. "Put that medicine into me in any way you think best. But that time will come when you'll wish you hadn't. When that time does come it won't be easy to prove that you had the right to force a patient to take medicine he had offered to take. I know something about the ethics of your profession. You have no right to do anything to a patient except what's good for him. You know that. All you are trying to do is to punish me, and I give fair warning I'm going to camp on your trail till you are not only discharged from this institution, but expelled from the State Medical Society as well. You are a disgrace to your Profession, and that society will attend to your case fast enough when certain members of it, who are friends of mine, hear about this. . . .

Coming from one in my condition, this was rather straight talk. The doctor was visibly disconcerted. Had he not feared to lose caste with attendants who stood by, I think he would have given me another chance. But he had too much pride and too little manhood to recede from a false position already taken . . . I was [put] flat on my back, with simply a mattress between me and the floor. One attendant held me. Another stood by with the medicine and funnel through which, as soon as Mr. Hyde should insert the tube in one of my nostrils, the dose was to be poured . . . Though the insertion of the tube, when skillfully done, need not cause suffering, the operation as conducted by Mr. Hyde was painful. Try as he would, he was unable to insert the tube properly, though in no way did I attempt to balk him. . . . After what seemed ten minutes of bungling, though it was probably not half that, he gave up the attempt, but not until my nose had begun to bleed. He was plainly chagrined when he and his bravos retired. Intuitively I felt that they would soon return. That they did, armed with a new implement of war. This time the doctor inserted between my teeth a large wooden peg—to keep open a mouth which he usually wanted shut. He then forced down my throat a rubber tube, the attendant then adjusted the funnel, and the medicine, or rather liquid—for its medicinal properties were without effect upon me—was poured in.

As the scant reports sent to my conservator during these 3 weeks indicated that I was not improving as he had hoped, he made a special trip to the institution to investigate in person. On his arrival he was met by none other than Doctor Jekyll, who told him that I was in a highly excited condition, which, he intimated, would be aggravated by a personal interview. . . . Doctor Jekyll did tell him it had been found necessary to place me in "restraint" and "seclusion" (the professional euphemisms for "strait-jacket," "padded cell," etc.), but no hint was given that I had been roughly handled. Doctor Jekyll's politic dissuasion was no doubt inspired by knowledge that if ever I got within speaking distance of my conservator, nothing could prevent my giving him a circumstantial account of my sufferings—which account would have been corroborated by the blackened eye I happened to have at the time.

Source: Beers, Clifford Whittingham. *A Mind that Found Itself.* New York: Longmans, Green, and Co. 1906, pp. 136–139.

57 R. M. O'Reilly: Yellow Fever Commission Report (1906)

Robert Maitland O'Reilly (1845–1912), surgeon general of the United States, compiled many papers written about yellow fever around the turn of the 20th century for the United States Senate into one large report. In this excerpt, since Maj. Walter Reed (1851–1902), the head of the Yellow Fever Commission died of appendicitis, O'Reilly describes the experiments of the commission who were investigating the cause and prevention of yellow fever in Cuba. They tested the theory of Cuban epidemiologist Carlos Finlay (1833–1915) that the mosquito was the vector that transmitted yellow fever between humans. In the controlled experiment carried out by the commission, its members subjected themselves to bites of infected mosquitoes, received injections of blood from, and slept in bedding that had been used by, yellow-fever patients. The commission found that many of those bitten or injected with infected blood came down with the fever. They also determined that after three days, a yellow-fever patient could not transmit the disease to a mosquito. Some patients had mild cases of the disease with headache and fever. More severe cases had jaundice (yellowing) of the skin and eyes and delirium, and from 20 to 50 percent of these patients died. Later the infective agent transmitted by the Aedes aegypti *mosquito was found to be a virus, and in 1951 a vaccine to prevent infection was developed.*

See also: Document 24

Experiments Conducted For The Purpose of Coping With YELLOW FEVER.

[Senate Document No. 10, Fifty-ninth Congress, second session.]

To the Senate and House of Representatives:

The enclosed papers are transmitted to the Congress in the earnest hope that it will take suitable action in the matter. Maj. Reed's part in the experiments which resulted in teaching us how to cope with yellow fever was such as to render mankind his debtor, and this nation should in some proper fashion bear witness to this fact.

Theodore Roosevelt.

The White House, *December, 5, 1906.*

[Memorandum for the President, through The Military Secretary of the Army.]

War Department,

Office of the Surgeon General,

Washington, August 30, 1906.

The persons taking an important part in the investigations in Cuba, which resulted in the demonstration of the fact that yellow fever is transmitted by a species of mosquito, were three members of the board appointed to investigate epidemic diseases in Cuba—Walter Reed, James Carroll, and Jesse W. Lazear—and the individuals who submitted themselves for experimentation by receiving the bites of infected mosquitoes, by receiving injections of mood from yellow-fever patients, and by sleeping in bedding which had been used by yellow-fever patients.

When the Yellow Fever Commission, composed of Walter Reed, James Carroll, Jesse W. Lazear, and A. Agramonte, assembled in Habana they had no thought of investigating the connection of the mosquito with the spread of yellow fever. This idea came to Dr. Reed after the board had demonstrated that the claim of Sanarelli, concurred in by Wasdin and Geddins, that the *Bacillus icteroides* was the cause of yellow fever was without foundation. Dr. Reed then determined to investigate the theory of Dr. Carlos Finlay, that the mosquito was instrumental in conveying yellow fever, which theory Finlay had failed to demonstrate, and which was not then accepted by scientific men. This determination was reached for the reasons which are well stated in Dr. Kelly's biography, and was original with Reed, not being suggested to him by anyone. The final determination to investigate the mosquito theory was arrived at during an informal meeting of the board (Dr. Agramonte being absent) at Columbia Barracks on the evening before Dr. Reed's departure for the United States, early in August. 1901. It was agreed by these members of the board that in making the experiments on human beings, by which alone the demonstration could be made, that they should submit themselves as subjects for experimentation. To Dr. Lazear, who was familiar with mosquito work, was assigned the duty of breeding and infecting the mosquitoes; while Dr. Carroll was to continue the bacteriological work on which the board had been engaged.

On August 2, 1900, before the mosquitoes were ready for the experiment, Dr. Reed was called back to Washington to prepare for publication the abstract of the report of the board appointed in 1898 to investigate the spread of typhoid fever in the volunteer camps in the United States, of which board he was president. This vast work, of which the full report was published by special authority of Congress about a year after Dr. Reed's death, by the only surviving member of the board, Prof. Victor C. Vaughan, of the University of Michigan, was one of the most valuable contributions to science which has been made by the Surgeon General's Office. The work of preparation of the abstract report had been brought to a standstill by the sudden death of the third member of the board, Dr. Edward O. Shakespeare, of Philadelphia, and Dr. Reed's presence at this time was essential for its completion.

During Dr. Reed's absence the inoculations by means of the mosquito were begun. On August 11, Dr. Lazear made the first experiment, but nine distinct inoculations on persons, including himself and Acting Asst. Surg. A. S. Pinto, were unsuccessful. We know now that these failures were clue to two facts—first, that patients after the third day of the disease can not convey the infection to the mosquito, and second, that after having bitten a yellow-fever case the mosquito can not transmit the disease until after an interval of at least 12 days. On August 27 one mosquito was applied to Dr. Carroll, one which happened to fulfill both of these conditions.

The result was a very severe attack of yellow fever, in which for a time his life hung in the balance. This was thus the first experimental case. The fever developed on the 31st of August, on which day Dr. Lazear applied the same mosquito which bit Dr. Carroll with three others to another person. This man came down with a mild but well-marked case.

On September 13 Dr. Lazear, while on a visit to Las Animas Hospital (for the purpose of collecting blood from yellow-fever patients for study) was bitten by a mosquito of undetermined species, which he deliberately allowed to remain on the back of his hand until it had satisfied its hunger. Five days thereafter he came down, without other exposure, with yellow fever, which progressed steadily to a fatal termination. These three cases established in Reed's mind the proof of the mosquito theory and made it, in the opinion of his friends, an unnecessary and foolish risk for him, at his age, to submit himself to inoculation. These cases, with his deductions therefrom, were reported by the board in a paper called "The etiology of yellow fever—A preliminary note," read before the American Public Health Association at Buffalo, N. Y., October 22–26, 1900. He then immediately returned to Cuba to undertake a second and more elaborate series of experiments which were made possible by the promise made to him by Gen. Wood on October 12, when told by Reed of the experiments already made, to assist him with whatever money was necessary. [. . .]

R. M. O'REILLY,

Surgeon General, United States Army

Source: O'Reilly, R. M. Yellow Fever Commission report (1906) in *Yellow Fever: A Compilation of Various Publications . . .* , Senate Doc. 822, 61st Congress, 3d Session, edited by Robert L. Owen. Washington: Government Printing Office, 1911, pp. 17–23.

58 Why Brewers Think Prohibition Is Bad (1908)

Anti-alcohol forces in the early 20th century fought to make all forms of alcoholic beverages illegal in the United States. However, the United States Brewers Association fought against the trend. They published a booklet, Prohibition Makes "Drug Fiends," *in 1908 arguing that prohibition would increase drug problems. They asserted that if alcoholic beverages were not available, there would be an increase in use of cocaine, methyl alcohol, and opiates, thus creating many drug-dependent people and causing serious social and health problems. In this excerpt, they point out that since local option laws—prohibition in a community—had been passed, increased problems had occurred with other substances. This tract shows that manufacturers of alcohol beverages fought against the institutions of anti-alcohol laws. Based upon newspaper reports, the excerpt discusses an increase in cocaine abuse in Mississippi among the black population and how cocaine is readily sold by druggists to anyone. They point out that farm labors drinking deadly methyl alcohol from fermentation of silage led to illness, and that an increase in opium use in the Midwest had occurred under local option. However, this tract was not effective in preventing prohibition laws, particularly in rural areas, nor the passage of the Eighteenth Amendment to the Constitution, which prohibited the manufacture and distribution of alcoholic beverages.*

COCAINE EVIL IN MISSISSIPPI.

Prohibition under local option laws exists in the greater part of Mississippi. Since the adoption of this policy, an alarming growth of the use of cocaine as a stimulant is reported. So widespread and demoralizing has this become that earnest appeals for legislation to check it are coming from many sections of the State. While the evil has until recently been largely among the n—o, it is beginning to spread steadily among the whites, and is causing much apprehension.

The *Okolona* (Miss.) *Messenger*, of October 29th, 1902, said:,
"The alarming growth of the accursed use of cocaine among the n—o of Mississippi has caused the suggestion to be made that more radical laws should be enacted for the suppression of the evil. The cocaine habit is demoralizing the race in this State, and its growth in recent years has been phenomenal. Thousands of victims have been found among the n—o, and in the delta section the habit is almost general. The drug has a quick and demoralizing effect, and the n—o succumbs quicker to its seductions than a white man, and when the habit has fastened upon him, he rarely reforms.

"It has been suggested that a law should be passed making it a crime for any person to use cocaine except on a physician's certificate. In 1900 the Legislature passed an act forbidding the sale of the drug except upon a physician's certificate, but the law is ignored by nine-tenths of the druggists in the State and they sell cocaine to all customers.

THE SILO HABIT.

In some of the farming districts of Kansas and Iowa, where local sentiment had pronounced so strongly against any traffic in intoxicating liquors that they could only be brought in at the risk of subjecting the importer to prosecution and persecution, it was noticed that drunkenness of a particular violent and insanity-producing kind was largely on the increase among the farm laborers. Ultimately the explanation was found in the fact that the craving for stimulants, which was denied a more reasonable gratification, had led to the tapping of the vegetable juices of ensilage from the silos in which an alcoholic fermentation was produced in the vegetable masses. These juices contained poisonous qualities capable of causing a peculiarly maddening and destructive form of intoxication.

"For one young man," says the New York Times of October 12th, 1902, "who would have defied public opinion by over-indulgence in liquor obtainable by purchase, many were destroyed in mind and body by acquiring the unspeakable habit of drinking fermented poisons from the silos. Granted that the alternative presented a choice of evils, it can scarcely be questioned that well-conducted saloons would have done less harm than was created by their suppression."

OPIUM IN IOWA.

Following the adoption of prohibition in Iowa, the opium habit grew alarmingly in that State. So much so, that it attracted the attention of the State Board of Health, and it was stated officially that there were over 4,000 known opium-eaters in the State who had become confirmed in the habit.

All prohibition communities have experienced the same results in a greater or less degree. Habits of this kind are carefully concealed, as a rule, and it is difficult to ascertain with accuracy their true extent. Only the most pronounced cases become known to the community, while the insidious evil is secretly sapping the vitality of many. It is common knowledge that the people of Turkey and Mohammedan countries to whom liquor is prohibited by religious Inhibition are inveterate consumers of opiates of various kinds.

It has been the experience, without exception, that where one form of stimulant is denied, another, more secret and usually more harmful, is sought. It is the wise policy which permits the sales of stimulants under State regulation that insures purity, prevents excess or the use of insidious poisons, and the evils of the secret use of such poisons.

Source: United States Brewers Association. *Prohibition Makes "Drug Fiends": How the Morphine, Opium and Cocaine Dealers Flourish Under 'Dry Laws.'* New York: U.S.B.A., 1908, pp. 10–11, 12–14.

59 The Flexner Report on Medical Education (1910)

Medical Education in the United States and Canada, *a 1910 report by American Abraham Flexner (1866–1959), was considered the pivotal point for medical education in North America. This "Flexner Report" was so important that other nations soon embraced many of its conclusions. The report advocated increasing the standards of medical education in North America. This included teaching and research based upon mainstream science, medical schools being associated with universities, and stricter standards for student admission and graduation. Many North American medical education institutions fell short of these standards, as they tended to be stand-alone proprietary establishments based upon historic dogma. The report also concluded that there were too many medical schools and that too many physicians were being trained. After its publication, nearly half of the schools merged or were closed. A repercussion of the report due to closure or consolidation was male-only acceptance to accommodate a smaller admission pool. John Hopkins Medical School was considered a model of this new scientific medical education. Due to the limiting of the number of physicians and few new schools being built, an undersupply of physicians emerged later in the 20th century.*

For the past two decades there has been a marked tendency to set up some connection between universities and detached medical schools . . . Meanwhile the requirements of medical education have enormously increased. The fundamental sciences upon which medicine depends have been greatly extended.

The laboratory has come to furnish alike to the physician and to the surgeon a new means for diagnosing and combating disease. The education of the medical practitioner under these changed conditions makes entirely different demands in respect to both preliminary and professional training.

Under these conditions and in the face of the advancing standards of the best medical schools it was clear that the time had come when the relation of professional education in medicine to the general system of education should be clearly defined. The first step towards such a clear understanding was to ascertain the facts concerning medical education and the medical schools themselves at the present time. In accordance, therefore, with the recommendation of the president and the executive committee, the trustees of the Carnegie Foundation at their meeting in November, 1908, authorized a study and report upon the schools of medicine and law in the United States and appropriated the money necessary for this undertaking. The present report upon medical education, prepared, under the direction of the Foundation, by Mr. Abraham Flexner, is the first result of that action.

[. . .]

In making this study the schools of all medical sects have been included. It is clear that so long as a man is to practice medicine, the public is equally concerned in his right preparation for that profession, whatever he call himself,—allopath, homeopath, eclectic, osteopath, or whatnot. It is equally clear that he should be grounded in the fundamental sciences upon which medicine rests, whether he practices under one name or under another.

[The report recommends . . .]

Reduction of our 155 medical schools to 31 would deprive of a medical school no section that is now capable of maintaining one. It would threaten no scarcity of physicians until the country's development actually required more than 3500 physicians annually, that is to say, for a generation or two, at least. Meanwhile, the outline proposed involves no artificial standardization: it concedes a different standard to the south as long as local needs require; it concedes the small town university type where it is clearly of advantage to adhere to it; it varies the general ratio in thinly settled regions; and, finally, it provides a system capable without overstraining of producing twice as many doctors as we suppose the country now to need. In other words, we may be wholly mistaken in our figures without in the least impairing the feasibility of the kind of renovation that has been outlined; and every institution arranged for can be expected to make some useful contribution to knowledge and progress.

The right of the state to deal with the entire subject in its own interest can assuredly not be gainsaid. The physician is a social instrument. If there were no disease, there would be no doctors. And as disease has consequences that immediately go beyond the individual specifically affected, society is bound to protect itself against unnecessary spread of loss or danger. It matters not that the making of doctors has been to some extent left to private institutions. The state already makes certain regulations; it can by the same right make others. Practically the medical school is a public service corporation. It is chartered by the state; it utilizes public hospitals on the ground of the social nature of its service. The medical school cannot then escape social criticism and regulation. It was left to itself while society knew no better. But civilization consists in the legal registration of gains won by science and experience; and science and experience have together established the terms upon which medicine can be most useful. [. . .]

One should not train disciples but from observers: one must teach and work in the spirit of natural science. Scientific medicine therefore brushes aside all historic dogma. It gets down to details immediately. No man is asked in whose name he comes—whether that of Hahnemann, Rush, or of some more recent prophet. But all are required to undergo rigorous cross-examination. Whatsoever makes good is accepted, becomes in so far part, and organic part, of the permanent structure [. . .]. The logical position of medical sectarians to-day is self-contradictory. They have practically accepted the curriculum as it has been worked out on the scientific basis.

They teach pathology, bacteriology, clinical microscopy. They are thereby committed to the scientific method; for they aim to train the student to ascertain and interpret facts in the accepted scientific manner. He may even learn his sciences in the same laboratory as the non-sectarian. But scientific method cannot be limited to the first half of medical education. [. . .]

Source: Flexner, Abraham. *Medical Education in the United States and Canada: A Report to the Carnegie Foundation for the Advancement of Teaching. With an introduction by Henry S. Pritchett. Bulletin Number Four.* New York City: [s.n.], 1910, pp. viii, 154–155, 157.

60 Medical Education of Women in Early-20th-Century North America (1910)

The Flexner Report *dramatically changed medical education in North America. In one chapter, the report suggests that women had equal opportunity as men to enter the medical profession in the early 20th century in North America. However, this information is not borne out by later studies. With the closing and consolidation of medical schools after new standards were initiated based upon this report, institutions essentially became all male, and women were generally still only about 5 percent of admitted classes. This low percentage only began to change in 1972 with the passage of Title IX of the Education Amendments, which prohibited discrimination on the basis of sex for educational programs that received federal funding, including post-secondary programs. Flexner's chart of the number of women in medical school, including both coeducational and women's medical schools, appears to suggest that approximately 20 percent of the total number of women students graduated. This chart also shows that fewer were attending over the first decade of the 20th century. Although Abraham Flexner's (1866–1959)* Medical Education in the United States and Canada *(1910) was important for the improvement of North American medical education, this chapter shows the beginning of a decline in women in medical school.*

Medical education is now, in the United States and Canada, open to women upon practically the same terms as men. If all institutions do not receive women, so many do, that no woman desiring an education in medicine is under any disability in finding a school to which she may gain admittance. Her choice is free and varied. She will find schools of every grade accessible: the Johns Hopkins, if she has an academic degree; Cornell, if she has three-fourths of one; Rush and the state universities, if she prefers the combined six years' course; Toronto on the basis of a high school education; Meridian, Mississippi, if she has had no definable education at all.

Woman has so apparent a function in certain medical specialties and seemingly so assured a place in general medicine under some obvious limitations that the struggle for wider educational opportunities for the sex was predestined to an early success in medicine. It is singular to observe the use to which the victory has been put [. . .]

The number of medical schools, number of women students, and women graduates from 1904 to 1909

Year	Number of schools	Number of women students	Number of women graduates
1904	100	1129	254
1905	99	1073	219
1906	93	895	233
1907	89	928	211
1908	91	835	185
1909	94	921	162

Now that women are freely admitted to the medical profession, it is clear that they show a decreasing inclination to enter it. More schools in all sections are open to them; fewer attend and fewer graduate. True enough, medical schools generally have shrunk; but as the opportunities of women have increased, not decreased, and within a period during which entrance requirements have, so far as they are concerned, not materially altered, their enrolment should have augmented, if there is any strong demand for women physicians or any strong ungratified desire on the part of women to enter the profession. One or the other of these conditions is lacking,—perhaps both.

Whether it is either wise or necessary to endow separate medical schools for women is a problem on which the figures used throw light. In the first place, eighty per cent of women who have in the last six years studied medicine have attended coeducational institutions. None of the three women's medical colleges now existing can be sufficiently strengthened without an enormous outlay. The motives which elsewhere recommend separation of the sexes would appear to be without force, all possible allowance being made for the special and somewhat trying conditions involved. In the general need of more liberal support for medical schools, it would appear that large sums, as far as specially available for the medical education of women, would accomplish most if used to develop coeducational institutions, in which their benefits would be shared by men without loss to women students; but, it must be added, if separate medical schools and hospitals are not to be developed for women, interne privileges must be granted to women graduates on the same terms as to men.

Source: Flexner, Abraham. *Medical education in the United States and Canada: A report to the Carnegie Foundation for the Advancement of Teaching. With an introduction by Henry S. Pritchett.* Bulletin Number Four. New York City: [s.n.], 1910, pp. 178–179.

61 Eugen Bleuler: Theory of Schizophrenic Negativism (1912)

A major psychotic disorder, dementia praecox, was renamed "schizophrenia" in 1908 by Swiss psychiatrist Eugen Bleuler (1857–1939). This happened when Bleuler gave a lecture at a meeting of the German Psychiatric Association in Berlin. In 1911, the term "schizophrenia" first appeared in print in a paper, "Zur Theorie des schizophrenen Negativismus," as a more accurate description of the term "dementia praecox." The work was translated into English in 1912 by American psychiatrist William A. White (1870–1937) as "The Theory of Schizophrenic Negativism" as the introduction to a series of papers on mental illness and introduced the term to the English-speaking psychiatric community. Schizophrenia is a serious chronic mental illness characterized by auditory hallucinations, paranoia, delusions, and/or disorganized thinking, which Bleuler discovered by close observation of patients. It can impair functioning and the inability to earn a livelihood. The following excerpt outlines the various characteristics of schizophrenia worldwide.

See also: Document 37

The theories of negativism that have been advanced heretofore are incorrect or unsatisfying. Negativism is a complicated symptom, having in some cases, many cooperating causes.

The predisposing causes of negativistic phenomena are:

1. ***Ambitendency***, which sets free with every tendency a counter tendency.

2. ***Ambivalency,*** which gives to the same idea two contrary feeling tones and invests the same thought simultaneously with both a positive and a negative character.

3. ***The schizophrenic splitting of the psyche,*** which hinders the proper balancing of the opposing and cooperating psychisms, with the result that the most inappropriate impulse can be transferred into action just as well as the right impulse and that in addition to the right thought, or instead of it, its negative can be thought.

4. ***The lack of clearness and imperfect logic of the schizophrenic thoughts*** in general which makes a theoretical and practical adaptation to reality difficult or impossible.

On the ground of this disposition there may occur direct negativistic phenomena in such a manner that positive and negative psychisms replace one another indiscriminately, only the incorrect reactions standing out as pathological negativism.

As a rule, however, the negativistic reaction does not appear merely as accidental, but as actually preferred to the correct reaction.

In ordinary ***external negativism*** which consists in the negation of external influences (Ex. Command) and of what one would normally expect the patient to do (Ex. Defaecation in the closet instead of the bed), the following causes are at work:

(a) The autistic withdrawing of the patient into his phantasies, which makes every influence acting from without comparatively an intolerable interruption. This appears to be the most important factor. In severe cases it alone is sufficient to produce negativism.

(b) The existence of a hurt (negative complex, unfulfilled wish) which must be protected from contacts.

(c) The misunderstanding of the surroundings and their purpose.

(d) Direct hostile relations to the surroundings.

(e) The pathological irritability of the schizophrenic.

(f) The pressure of thought and other difficulties of action and of thought, through which every reaction becomes painful.

(g) The sexuality with its ambivalent feeling tones is also often one of the roots of negativistic reaction.

Inner negativism (contrary tendency opposed to the will, and intellectually opposed to the right thoughts) is accounted for, in large part, by ambitendency and ambivalency, which in view of the inner splitting of the thought renders intelligible a slight preference for the negativistic reaction. Very pronounced phenomena of inner negativism probably have other cooperating causes, which we, at the present time, do not know.

A conclusive explanation of all negativistic phenomena would be premature. It seems to me, however, that the falsity or unsatisfactory nature of the theories hitherto erected might be demonstrated. It is always possible to discover roots of negativism in other directions and to understand genetically, at least, a part of the symptoms grouped together under this name. A better attitude is gained in this way for further progress.

At this point we must first make clear that negativism is not a unitary symptom. The chief and predominating group is characterized throughout by the fact that the patient, by outside influences, by command, will not do precisely, what under normal conditions would be expected (passive negativism); or, that he does exactly the opposite (active negativism). A command is not executed, most often after am; repulsing mimik. If one tries to bring about a desired movement passively (raise the arm, sit up to slip on clothes) they show opposition, seek to get away, resist often with abuse and blows. The patients will not stand up, will not go to bed, if it is desired of them; they will not-sit at the place assigned to them, will not eat the food offered them, they take the soup with the spoon for the preserves, and the preserves with the soup spoon; they satisfy natural needs out of time and place.

Source: Bleuler, Eugen. Translated by William A. White. *The Theory of Schizophrenic Negativism*. New York: The Journal of Nervous and Mental Disease Publishing Company, 1912, pp. 1–3.

62 International Opium Convention at The Hague (1912)

At a 1909 conference in Shanghai, China, concerns about international opium trafficking and high use of opium in China laid the groundwork for the first major global effort to control drugs. Representatives from China, France, Germany, Italy, Iran (Persia), Japan, the Netherlands, Portugal, Russia, Thailand (Siam), the UK, and British territories, including India, met at The Hague in the Netherlands and signed the International Opium Convention on January 23, 1912. It became known as The Hague Convention. In addition to opium and morphine, heroin and cocaine were also included. This international opium convention consisted of six chapters and 25 articles. The treaty did not result in much change due to WWI. In fact, the war led to increased drug use among allied troops in France, which in turn resulted in increased control over the drugs as part of the wartime effort, particularly in Britain. This excerpt established rules for international trade and control of opiates and cocaine that are still in force in the early 21st century.

CHAPTER I: RAW OPIUM.

Definition.—By "raw opium" is understood:

The spontaneously coagulated juice obtained from the capsules of the *papaver somniferum* which has only been submitted to the necessary manipulations for packing and transport.

Article I.

The contracting Powers shall enact effective laws or regulations for the control of the production and distribution of raw opium, unless laws or regulations on the subject are already in existence.

Article 2.

Due regard being had to the differences in their commercial conditions, the contracting Powers shall limit the number of towns, ports, or other localities through which the export or import of raw opium shall be permitted.

Article 3.

The contracting Powers shall take measures—

(a) To prevent the export of raw opium to countries which shall have prohibited its entry, and

(b) To control the export of raw opium to countries which restrict its import, unless regulations on the subject are already in existence.

Article 4.

The contracting Powers shall make regulations requiring that every package containing raw opium intended for export shall be marked in such a way as to indicate its contents, provided that the consignment exceeds 5 kilog.

Article 5.

The contracting Powers shall not allow the import and export of raw opium except by duly authorised persons.

CHAPTER II: PREPARED OPIUM

Definition.—By "prepared opium" is understood:

The product of raw opium obtained by a series of special operations, especially by dissolving, boiling, roasting and fermentation, designed to transform it into an extract suitable for consumption.

Prepared opium includes dross and all other residues remaining when opium has been smoked.

Article 6.

The contracting Powers shall take measures for the gradual and effective suppression of the manufacture of, internal trade in, and use of prepared opium, with due regard to the varying circumstances of each country concerned, unless regulations on the subject are already in existence.

Article 7.

The contracting Powers shall prohibit the import and export of prepared opium; those Powers, however, which are not yet ready to prohibit immediately the export of prepared opium shall prohibit it as soon as possible.

Article 8.

The contracting Powers which are not yet ready to prohibit immediately the export of prepared opium—

(a) Shall restrict the number of towns, ports, or other localities through which prepared opium may be exported;

(b) Shall prohibit the export of prepared opium to countries which now forbid, or which may hereafter forbid, the import thereof;

(c) Shall, in the meanwhile, prohibit the consignment of prepared opium to a country which desires to restrict its entry, unless the exporter complies with the regulations of the importing country;

(d) Shall take measures to ensure that every package exported, containing prepared opium, bears a special mark indicating the nature of its contents;

(e) Shall not permit the export of prepared opium except by specially authorised persons.

CHAPTER III: MEDICINAL OPIUM, MORPHINE, COCAINE, ETC.

Definitions.—By "medicinal opium" is understood:

Raw opium which has been heated to 60° centigrade and contains not less than 10 per cent of morphine, whether or not it be powdered or granulated or mixed with indifferent materials.

By "morphine" is understood:

The principal alkaloid of opium, having the chemical formula $C_{17}H_{19}NO_3$.

By "cocaine" is understood:

The principal alkaloid of the leaves of *Erythroxylon Coca*, having the formula $C_{17}H_{21}NO_4$.

By "heroin" is understood:

Diacetyl-morphine, having the formula $C_{21}H_{23}NO_5$.

Article 9.

The contracting Powers shall enact pharmacy laws or regulations to confine to medical and legitimate purposes the manufacture, sale, and use of morphine, cocaine, and their respective salts unless laws or regulations on the subject are already in existence. They shall co-operate with one another to prevent the use of these drugs for any other purpose.

Article 10.

The contracting Powers shall use their best endeavours to control, or to cause to be controlled, all persons manufacturing, importing, selling, distributing, and exporting morphine, cocaine, and their respective salts, as well as the buildings in which these persons carry on such industry or trade.

With this object, the contracting Parties shall use their best endeavours to adopt, or cause to be adopted, the following measures, unless regulations on the subject are already in existence:—

(a) To confine the manufacture of morphine, cocaine, and their respective salts to those establishments and premises alone which have been licensed for the purpose, or to obtain information respecting the establishments and premises in which these drugs are manufactured and to keep a register of them;

(b) To require that all persons engaged in the manufacture, import, sale, distribution, or export of morphine, cocaine, and their respective salts shall be furnished with a licence or permit to engage in these operations, or shall make to the competent authorities and official declaration that they are so engaged;

(c) To require that such persons shall enter in their books the quantities manufactured, import sales, and all other distribution, and export of morphine, cocaine, and their respective salts. This rule shall not necessarily apply to medical prescription and to sales by duly authorised chemists.

Article 11

The contracting Powers shall take measures to prohibit, as regards their internal trade, the delivery of morphine, cocaine, and their respective salts to any unauthorised persons, unless regulations on the subject are already in existence.

Article 12

Due regard being had to the differences in their conditions, the contracting Powers shall use their best endeavours to restrict to authorised persons the import of morphine, cocaine, and their respective salts.

Article 13

The contracting Powers shall use their best endeavours to adopt, or cause to be adopted, measures to ensure that morphine, cocaine, and their respective salts shall not be exported from their countries, possessions, colonies, and leased territories to the countries, possessions, colonies and leased territories of the other contracting Powers, except when consigned to persons furnished with the licences or permits provided for by the laws or regulations of the importing country.

With this object, each Government may communicate from time to time to Governments of the exporting countries lists of the persons to whom licences or permits for the import of morphine, cocaine, and their respective salts have been granted.

Article 14.

The contracting Powers shall apply the laws and regulations respecting the manufacture, import, sale, or export of morphine, cocaine, and their respective salts—

(a) To medicinal opium;

(b) To all preparations (officinal and non-officinal, including the so-called anti-opium remedies) containing more than 0.2 per cent of morphine, or more than 0.1 per cent of cocaine;

(c) To heroin, its salts and preparations containing more than 0.1 per cent of heroin;

(d) To all new derivatives of morphine, of cocaine, or of their respective salts, and to every other alkaloid of opium, which may be shown by scientific research, generally recognised, to be liable to similar abuse and productive of like ill-effects.

Source: League of Nations, Treaty Series, vol 8. p. 187. Available online at http://www.worldlii.org/int/other/LNTSer/1922/29.html.

63 Upton Sinclair: Satire of Health Remedies (1912)

American novelist, social commentator, and health reformer, Upton Sinclair (1878–1968), noted for The Jungle *(1906), also wrote about health cures after experiencing methods to cure his "unruly stomach" from the stress of writing. In some of his works he presents fasting and vegetarianism as the cure for all ills, and in other works he satirized various cures of the day. In his novella,* Little Algernon *(1911–1912), a rich young man searches for treatments for all his aches and pains. He is fleeced of his money for quack medical devices and cures. These cures include "life-salt cure" (mixture of cocaine and magnesium), milk diet, anti-protein, cereal and vegetable/fruit diets along with extreme exercise. The excerpt from this novella was serialized in* Physical Cultures Magazine. *It also promotes Sinclair's own fasting cure and gives examples of the health fads of the Progressive Era in the early 20th century. It points out the quackery found in this era with abundant patent medicines, many with undisclosed drugs.*

See also: Document 55

Chapter 1. December 1911.

He was a very puny infant, and there were many anxious crises—it seemed that not all of the canopies of Valenciennes lace were able to protect little Algernon's twenty-million-dollar body from the onslaught of irreverent and plebian disease-germs. They called in the very highest-priced doctors, and paid them the very highest fees, so presumably they should have got the best possible advice on the subject of the care and feeding of a twenty-million-dollar infant [. . .].

It was not until the child was eight years old that they really got the problem solved, as they thought—it was about that time when they first heard of the wonderful Dr. Plumstone, the original inventor and discoverer of "Life Salts."

Chapter 2. Jan 1912

A bottle of life salts gives energy to guardian and little Algernon which contains cocaine, magnesium, salt

Mr. and Mrs. De Puyster [his guardians] had been getting along so well that they were moved by slow stages to increase the dose of the precious mixture. The more they took of it, the more noticeable became the good results; they yielded to the temptation almost without realizing it. Very soon they were taking double doses, and giving Little Algernon double doses as well. But then, to their great perplexity, they found that Little Algernon was not doing so well as before. He seemed to be nervous, cried very easily, and woke up a good deal at night.

Mrs. De Puyster did not want to tell about the wonderful remedy, for Dr. Plumstone had warned her that he was a much persecuted and misunderstood man. But the doctor insisted upon knowing [. . .]

Mr. de Puyster had found it impossible to break the cocaine-habit which he had acquired, was a secret known only to himself and the family physician, who wrestled with him in vain for a couple of years thereafter, and finally issued a certificate in which the cause of the old gentleman's death was certified to be cirrhosis of the liver [. . .].

Also, poor Algernon was bewildered about his health. Why was it that he could never be well like other people? That he was so much smaller and feebler, and needed to be continually having doctors, and was never able to eat any good things? Life confronted the poor boy as a dreadful Sphinx, propounding a riddle: Why is it that everything that tastes good is bad for you? Why is it that nothing can be delicious without also being indigestible?

Chapter 3. February 1912

He took it just as he took his ill health, one of the facts of Nature which it was not for human beings to complain of or to question.

Like dyspepsia, for instance! . . . About this time Algernon's old family physician contracted a disease which he did not know how to cure, and went to confront his numerous patients in the other world, and so Little Algernon was left alone, not merely parentless and friendless, but also doctorless. He sought out a new doctor, and he told the tale of all his symptoms.

"What do you eat nowadays?" inquired the doctor.

Algernon went over his diet-schedule which he had been following for nearly a year; zwieback and milk and poached eggs and apple sauce and chicken broth, and such like invalid concoctions. "And I can't digest even these!" added Algernon, mournfully.

"It is a matter of much research, you understand," said Dr. Pierce. "We shall have to take a sample of your stomach contents and make analyses of your secretions; also bacterial examinations, you see. There may be a thousand causes for a case of dyspepsia. It may be due to hyper-acidity or hypo-acidity, to hyper-chloronidity or hypo-chloronidity, to deficiency in peptic secretion" [. . .].

So our hero let himself in for a long course of treatment by Dr. Pierce. He ate various kinds of foods, according to orders, and then, an hour after eating them, he had his stomach pumped out and the contents analyzed and studied under the microscope. And when it was all over he was presented with a list of his intestinal deficiencies; also—the culmination of all the labors—a little bottle of magical pink liquid, the elaborate formula for which had been compiled by Dr. Pierce, containing all the elements necessary to make up for his deficiencies.

And so Algernon went on, and for the first time in his life he sat down at the table like any other human beings and ate a square meal. And after he had finished it, he took a teaspoonful of this pink liquid, and sat down in fear and trembling to wait results [. . .].

Truly, was not this a marvelous triumph of the mind of man, an illustration of the adjustment of means to ends? Here was his whole life made over again—all by a little pink liquid!

Source: Sinclair, Upton. "The Health of Little Algernon, being the story of a twenty-million-dollar quest for health." *Physical Culture* xxvi-xxvii. (Dec 1911, Jan–June 1912).

64 Harrison Narcotics Tax Act (1914)

Concern about opiates and coca products in patent medicines and drug addiction as a part of the Progressive Era of the United States to clean up America resulted in several laws. The Harrison Narcotics Tax Act in the United States, commonly called the Harrison Narcotic Act, was passed in 1914. It was a federal law that restricted the manufacture and sale of marijuana, cocaine, heroin, and morphine and provided regulations such as registration and taxes for the production, importation, and distribution of opiates and coca products. It allowed physicians to prescribe opiates to patients with medical conditions but not for the treatment or maintenance of addiction. Small amounts of opiates such as paregoric for diarrhea and codeine for pain and cough were allowed without a prescription until the 1990s. After the act, records needed to be kept of date, drug, dosage, and name and address of each person prescribed one of the controlled drugs. The Harrison Act is the foundation of the US drug policy. This excerpt gives the details of the law that were still used in the United States into the 21st century.

Chap 1.—

An Act To provide for the registration of, with collectors of internal revenue, and to impose a special tax on all persons who produce, import, manufacture, compound, deal in, dispense, sell, distribute, or give away opium or coca leaves, their salts, derivatives, or preparations, and for other purposes.[. . .]

It shall be unlawful for any person required to register under the terms of this Act to produce, import, manufacture, compound, deal in, dispense, sell, distribute, any of the aforesaid drugs without having registered and paid the special tax provided for in this section.

That the word "person" in this Act shall be construed to mean and include a partnership, association, company, or corporation, as well as a natural person; and all provisions of existing law relating to special taxes, so far as applicable, including the provisions of section thirty-two hundred and forty of the Revised Statutes of the United States are hereby extended to the special tax herein imposed.

That the Commissioner of Internal Revenue, with the approval of the Secretary of the Treasury, shall make all needful rules and regulations for carrying the provisions of this Act into effect.

Sec 2.—

That it shall be unlawful for any person to sell, barter, exchange, or give away any of the aforesaid drugs except in pursuance of a written order of the person to whom such article is sold, bartered, exchanged, or given, on a form to be issued in blank for that purpose by the Commissioner of Internal Revenue. Every person who shall accept any such order, and in pursuance thereof shall sell, barter, exchange, or give away any of the aforesaid drugs shall preserve such order for a period of two years in such a way as to be readily accessible to inspection by any officer, agent, or employee of the Treasury Department duly authorized for that purpose, and the State, Territorial, district, municipal and insular officials named in Section five of this Act. Every person who shall give an order as herein provided to any other person for any of the aforesaid drugs shall, at or before the time of giving of such order, make or cause to be made, a duplicate thereof on a form to be issued in blank for that purpose by the Commissioner of Internal Revenue, and in the case of the acceptance of such order , shall preserve such duplicate for said period of two years in such a way as to be readily accessible to inspection by the officers, agents, employees, and officials herein mentioned. Nothing contained in this section shall apply—

(a) To the dispensing or distribution of any of the aforesaid drugs to a patient by a physician, dentist, or veterinary surgeon registered under this Act in the course of his professional practice only: Provided, That such physician, dentist, or veterinary surgeon shall keep a record of all such drugs dispensed or distributed, showing the amount dispensed or distributed, the date, and the name and address of the person to whom such drugs are dispensed or distributed; except such as may be dispensed or distributed to a patient upon whom such physician, dentist, or veterinary surgeon shall personally attend; and such record shall be kept for a period of two years from the date of dispensing or distributing such drugs, subject to inspection, as provided in this Act.

(b) To the sale, dispensing, or distributing of any of the aforesaid drugs by a dealer to a consumer under and in pursuance of a written prescription issued by a physician, dentist, or veterinary surgeon registered under this Act. Provided, however, That such prescription shall be dated as of the day on which signed and shall be signed by the physician, dentist, or veterinary surgeon who shall have issued the same: And provided further, That such dealer shall preserve such prescription for a period of two years from the day on which such prescription is filled in such a way as to be readily accessible by the officers, agents, employees, and officials hereinbefore mentioned.

(c) To the sale, exportation, shipment, or delivery of any of the aforesaid drugs by any person within the United States or any Territory or the District of Columbia or any of the insular possessions of the United States to any person in any foreign country, regulating their entry in accordance with such regulations for importation thereof into such foreign country as are prescribed by said country, such regulations to be promulgated from time to time by the Secretary of State of the United States.

(d) To the sale, barter, exchange, or giving away of any of the aforesaid drugs to any officer of the United States Government, or any State, territorial, district, county, or municipal or insular government lawfully engaged in making purchases thereof for various departments of the Army and Navy, the Public Health Service, and for Government, State, territorial, district, county, or municipal, or insular hospitals and prisons.

Source: *Public Law No. 223, 63rd Cong.* Available at Schaffer Library of Drug Policy. http://druglibrary.org/schaffer/history/e1910/harrisonact.htm.

65 Ruth Fielding: Red Cross Nurse in France in WWI (1918)

Three authors wrote the Ruth Fielding *series under the pseudonym of Alice B. Emerson in the early 20th century. This series was written for adolescent girls in different settings with various adventures or mysteries to be solved and were popular in North America and Britain. Other writers also wrote books concerning young nurses and their adventures. The* Ruth Fielding *series of novels were popular among girls from 1910 to 1934. The thirteenth book of the series was* Ruth Fielding in the Red Cross *(1918), which describes her works as a nurse's aide on the battlefield in a sanitized version of the WWI. It mentions conditions of hospitals, battlefield medicine, shell shock, trench warfare, and the exhaustion of nurses and soldiers. The novel was an effort to encourage girls to go into nursing for the war effort. This excerpt depicts the anxiety and insomnia common in battlefield nursing and medicine when a friend is missing.*

See also: Document 32; Document 72; Document 73

"Your friend is from the hospital, Hetty?"

"Oh, yes, Madame!" Henriette hastened to say. "She is an *Americaine*. Of the Red Cross."

"I could imagine her nativity," said the countess, bowing to Ruth, and with cordiality. "I traveled much with the count—years ago. All over America. I deem all Americans my friends."

"Thank you, Madame," replied Ruth gravely.

[. . .]

Henriette ran her down to the town and to the hospital gate. Ruth was more than tired—she felt exhausted when she got out of the car. But she saw the matron before retiring to her own cell for a few hours' sleep.

"We shall need you, Mademoiselle," the Frenchwoman said distractedly. "Oh! So many poor men are here. They have been bringing them in all day. There is a lull on the front, or I do not know what we should do. The poor, poor men!"

Ruth had to rest for a while, however, although she did not sleep. Her mind was too painfully active.

Her thoughts drummed continually upon two subjects, the mystery regarding Tom Cameron [her boyfriend]—his letter to her found in another man's pocket.

. . . She hoped hourly to hear from Tom; but no word came. She wished, indeed, that she might even see Charlie Bragg again; but nobody seemed to have seen him about the hospital of late. The ambulance corps was shifted around so frequently that there was no knowing where he could be found, save at his headquarters up near the front. And Ruth Fielding felt that she was quite as near the front here at Clair as she ever wished to be!

She went on duty before midnight and remained at work until after supper the next evening. She had nothing to do with the severely wounded, of course; but there was plenty to do for those who had already been in the hospital some time, and whom she knew.

Ruth could aid them in simple matters, could read to them, write for them, quiet them if they were nervous or suffering from shell-shock. She tried to forget her personal anxieties in attending to the poor fellows and aiding them to forget their wounds, if for only a little while. [. . .]

About daylight, when she did fall into a more or less refreshing sleep, an orderly came to her door and knocked until she responded.

"Mademoiselle has waiting for her on the steps a visitor," he said, with a chuckle. "She should come down at once."

"A visitor, Henri?" she cried. "Who can it be?"

"One young *Americain*," he replied, and went away cheerfully humming a tune.

"What can that Charlie Bragg want at this hour in the morning?" Ruth murmured, yet hurrying her toilet. "Possibly he brings news of Tom!"

Down she ran to the court as soon as she was neat. A man was sitting on the steps, leaning against the doorpost. It was not Charlie, for he was in military uniform and she could see an officer's insignia. He was asleep.

She saw as she left the stairway and crossed the entrance hall that he wore his arm in a sling. She thought instantly of the unknown American in Lyse Hospital who had lost his forearm. Then—

"Tom Cameron!" she cried, and sprang to his side.

The soldier awoke with a start. He looked up at her and grinned.

"Hullo, Ruthie," he observed. "Excuse this early call, but I might not have another rest day for a long time. We're going into the trenches—going to take over a sector of the French line, they say, before long. So—

"Hullo! What's happened?"

"Your arm, Tom! You are wounded?" she gasped.

"Oh, shucks! Got a splinter of shell in it. Nothing much. Keeping it in splints so it will mend quicker," he said.

"But your letter, Tom!" she cried, and there, in the early morning, standing upon the hospital steps, she told him the story of the happening that had so disturbed and troubled her.

"Don't that beat all!" exclaimed Tom. "I wondered what had happened to that letter that I had just finished when I was called on duty. It was Sam Hines who had his arm torn off—poor fellow. We heard from him. He's getting all right, but, of course, he'll have to go home.

"He must have picked up my letter, maybe to give it to me, knowing I had forgotten it. Well, it's all right, Ruthie. I can tell you lots more than was in that letter—and you've got a lot to tell me."

So they sat down, side by side, and related each to the other all their adventures, while the great guns on the battle line boomed a rumbling accompaniment to what was said.

Source: Emerson, Alice B. *Ruth Fielding in the Red Cross: or, Doing her best for Uncle Sam.* New York: Cupples & Leon Co., 1918, pp. 181–186, 202–204.

66 Materia Medica for Nurses: Drugs Used for the Effect on the Blood (1920)

Physician A. S. (Aaron Samuel) Blumgarten (1884–1958), an admitting physicians and lecturer for nurses and other training at the German Hospital in New York City wrote this pharmacological, or materia medica *(1920), text book for nursing education, or "training" as it was then called. Most "trained nurses," now considered registered nurses, were educated in hospitals where they also worked in the hospital for room and board. This* materia medica *was a popular text and was updated in several editions during the early 20th century. It is representative of the type of texts used for nursing education in this time period. This third edition represented changes from before and after the Great War (WWI) in terms of new drugs and treatment. A sample chapter on medical preparations for circulatory and heart diseases problems is given. However, some of the physiological explanations for blood and the circulatory system would be considered simplistic or incorrect by the late 20th century. A large and heavy text, it was aimed at teachers and students in nursing courses and as a reference to be used on the "ward" when mixing various preparations.*

PART III—DRUGS USED PRINCIPALLY FOR THEIR EFFECTS UPON THE BLOOD AND CIRCULATION

CHAPTER XI

HAEMATINICS

BLOOD STIMULANTS OR TONICS

Physiology of the Blood

The blood is a thick red fluid, which supplies all the various tissues and organs of the body with nourishment and oxygen. It also takes away all the waste products, resulting from their various activities. These waste products are brought to the lungs, kidneys and intestines where they are excreted.

The blood consists of a straw colored fluid (plasma) in which float small round cells called corpuscles. The corpuscles are of two kinds: red corpuscles and white corpuscles, or lecucocytes.

The red corpuscles contain a protein substance, haemoglobin, which contains iron and which imparts the red color to them.

This haemoglobin of the red corpuscles takes up oxygen from the air in the lungs; and brings it to the various organs of the body where it is used up by their various activities.

The white corpuscles, together with the plasma act as cleansers of the blood. They destroy bacteria in the blood and help to neutralize their poisons by the formation of antidotes. The white corpuscles then bring these dead bacteria to the kidneys, intestines and other organs for excretion.

Formation of Blood

The plasma is formed from the digested food, which passes through the lining membrane of the intestines into the blood vessels. Some of the plasma formed from the digested food first enters the lymphatic vessels, from which it finally reaches the blood stream.

The red and white corpuscles are formed in the bone marrow and spleen. The haemoglobin is formed in the liver and spleen.

Effects of Drugs on the Blood

Drugs affect the blood in two ways:

1. They may increase the amount, or improve the quality, or both (stimulation.)
2. They may lessen the amount, or deteriorate the quality of the corpuscles and plasma (depression).

Stimulation of the blood occurs:

a. When drugs *increase the amount* of plasma and the number of red or white corpuscles, or both.
b. When they *improve the quality* of the corpuscles, for example, by increasing the amount of haemoglobin.

Depression of the blood occurs:

a. When drugs *lessen the amount of blood* by withdrawing some of the fluids.
b. When they *reduce the number of corpuscles.*
c. When they *combine with the haemoglobin* so that it is unable to take up oxygen from the air in the lungs.

In this chapter we shall consider only those substances which improve the condition of the blood (blood stimulants).

NORMAL SALT SOLUTION

In cases where a patient has lost a considerable amount of blood, life may be endangered, because there is not sufficient blood in the body for the heart to pump. The heart beats then become very weak, slow or rapid, and the pulse is weak, slow and soft.

To keep the heart beating, until new blood can be formed, to make up for the amount lost, salt solution of a definite strength is often injected into a vein, or into the muscles. This keeps the heart beating, thus maintaining the circulation of the blood.

The percentage of salt (sodium chloride) used, is a 0.9% solution, or 9 parts of salt to a thousand parts of water. Such a solution is called a normal salt solution.

A salt solution of this strength does not destroy the red corpuscles of the blood and is called an isotonic solution. If a fluid weaker than this percentage is injected into the blood, the red corpuscles are destroyed. Such a solution is called a hypotonic or anisotonic solution. If a stronger percentage of salt solution than 0.9% is used, the blood corpuscles are shrunk (crenated). Such a solution is called a hypertonic solution.

The strengths usually given for normal salt solution vary from 0.6–0.9%. Different percentages are often used for different purposes. We may readily understand the variation in the strengths usually given for normal salt solution, by reviewing the essential facts regarding the salts of the blood.

The blood contains various salts. Of these salts 0.6% is sodium chloride or table salt; and the others, which are principally potassium chloride and calcium chloride, comprise 0.3%. A solution which contains these salts in the percentages in which they occur in the blood best maintains the integrity of the corpuscles. Such a solution is called Ringer's solution, and is frequently used in laboratory work. It is now coming into use in practical medicine. The integrity of the corpuscles, however, may also be maintained by any salt solution which contains 0.9% of salt. For practical purposes we therefore use such a solution of sodium chloride or ordinary table salt. This may be prepared by adding 8.0 gms. or 3ii of sodium chloride to a quart of sterile water, thus preparing a normal salt solution.

Frequently we use a 0.6% solution of salt or sodium chloride, especially when other medicines are to be added to the solution which may tend to increase its isotonic power (the power of maintaining the integrity of the corpuscles). Since such a salt solution contains the exact physiological quantity of sodium chloride as the blood, it is better to call it a physiological salt solution.

Source: Blumgarten, A. S. *Materia Medica for Nurses, Third edition.* New York: Macmillan, 1920, pp. 187–189.

67 Sigmund Freud: On Psychoanalysis (1920)

Viennese psychiatrist and neurologist Sigmund Freud (1856–1939) developed psychoanalysis, or "talking therapy," in the early part of the 20th century. He also founded psychoanalysis theory for the causes and treatment of mental disorders. The publication, A General Introduction to Psychoanalysis, *was translated by an unknown author and was composed of 28 of his lectures for nonprofessionals on various topics of psychoanalysis. The excerpt here is from his chapter on nervousness. In this excerpt, Freud defends his theory of psychoanalysis as a science as other systems of the nature of mental illness and behavior began to challenge his theories. He explains the nature of psychoanalysis and the origins of neurosis—an outdated term by the 1990s—with a connection to sexual energies. He also discusses the types of neurosis and the difference between the true neuroses and the psychoneuroses, or psychotic illness. This classic Freud excerpt implies that most neurosis may at one time have had physical symptoms but because of sexual issues in early development that have not been resolved the neurotic behavior continues due to these items being buried in the unconscious.*

Psychoanalysis is characterized as a science, not by reason of the subject matter it handles but by the technique it employs. This can be employed in dealing with the history of civilization, the science of religion or mythology, as well as with the theory of neurosis, without altering its character. The revealing of the unconscious in psychic life is all it aims to accomplish. The problems of the true neuroses, whose symptoms probably originate in direct toxic damage, yield no point of attack to psychoanalysis. Psychoanalysis can do little for their elucidation, and must leave the task to biological-medical research. Perhaps you understand now why I did not choose to organize my material differently. If I had given to you an Introduction to the Theory of the Neuroses as you wished, it would unquestionably have been correct to proceed from the simple forms of the true neuroses to those complex illnesses caused by a disturbance of the libido. In discussing the true neuroses I would have had to brim; together the facts we have gleaned from various quarters and present what we think we know of them. Only later, under the psychoneuroses, would psychoanalysis have been discussed as the most important technical aid for insight into these conditions. I had, however, intended and announced A General Introduction to Psychoanalysis, and it seemed to me more important to give you an idea of psychoanalysis than to present certain positive facts about neuroses; and so I could not place the true neuroses into the foreground, for they prove sterile for the purposes of psychoanalysis. I believe that I have made the wiser choice for you, since psychoanalysis deserves the interest of every educated person because of its profound hypotheses and far-reaching connections. The theory of neurosis, on the other hand, is a chapter of medicine like any other.

You are, however, justified in expecting some interest on our part in the true neuroses. Because of their intimate connection with psychoneuroses we find this decidedly necessary. I shall tell you then that we distinguish three pure forms of true neuroses: neurasthenia, anxiety neurosis and hypochondria. Even this classification has not remained uncontradicted. The terms are all widely used, but their connotation is vague and uncertain. Besides, there are in this world of confusion physicians who object to any distinctions between manifestations, any emphasis of clinical detail, who do not even recognize the separation of true neuroses and psychoneuroses. I think they have gone too far and have not chosen the road which leads to progress. The types of neuroses we have mentioned occur occasionally in pure form; more often they are blended with one another or with a psychoneurotic condition. This need not discourage us to the extent of abandoning the task of distinction. Think of the difference between the study of minerals and that of ores in mineralogy. Minerals are described as individuals; frequently of course they occur as crystals, separated sharply from their surroundings. Ores consist of an aggregate of minerals which have coalesced not accidentally, but as a result of the conditions of their origin. We understand too little of the process of development of neuroses, to create anything similar to the study of ores. But we are surely working in the right direction when we isolate the known clinical factors, comparable to the separate minerals, from the great mass.

A noteworthy connection between the symptoms of the true neuroses and the psychoneuroses adds a valuable contribution to our knowledge of symptom formation in the latter. The symptom in the true neuroses is frequently the nucleus and incipient stage of development of the psychoneurotic symptom. Such a connection is most easily observed between neurasthenia and the transference neuroses, which are termed conversion hysteria, between anxiety neurosis and anxiety hysteria, but also between hypochondria and paraphrenia (dementia praecox and paranoia), forms of neuroses of which we shall speak subsequently. Let us take as an illustration the hysteric headache or backache.

Analysis shows that through elaboration and displacement this pain has become the gratification substitute for a whole series of libidinous phantasies or reminiscences. But once upon a time this pain was real, a direct sexual toxic symptom, the physical expression of libidinous excitation. We do not wish to assert, by any means, that all hysteric symptoms can be traced to such a nucleus, but it is true that this is frequently the case, and that all influences upon the body through libidinous excitation, whether normal or pathological, are especially significant for the symptom development in hysteria. They play the part of the grain of sand which the mollusk has enveloped in mother-of-pearl. In the same way passing signs of sexual excitation, which accompany the sexual act, are used by psychoneurosis as the most convenient and appropriate material for symptom formation.

A similar procedure is of diagnostic and therapeutic interest especially. Persons who are disposed to be neurotic, without suffering from a flourishing neurosis, frequently set in motion the work of symptom development as the result of an abnormal physical change—often an inflammation or an injury. This development rapidly makes the symptom given by reality the representative of the unconscious phantasies that had been lurking for an opportunity to seize upon a means of expression. In such a case the physician will try different ways of therapy. Either he will try to do away with the organic basis without bothering about its noisy neurotic elaboration, or he will struggle with the neurosis brought out by the occasion, and ignore its organic cause. The result will justify now one, now the other method of procedure; no general laws can be laid down for such mixed cases.

Source: Freud, Sigmund. *A General Introduction to Psychoanalysis by Prof. Sigmund Freud, LL.D.* Authorized translation, with a preface by G. Stanley Hall. New York: Boni and Liveright, c.1920, pp. 337–339.

68 Margaret Sanger: Strain of Children on Working Mothers (1922)

American nurse Margaret Sanger (1879–1966), author of The Pivot of Civilization *(1922), was the leader of the birth-control movement of the early 20th century. After encountering horrible health and social conditions of women overburdened with unwanted pregnancies, she advocated for contraception information, which she called "birth control," for all. However, it was illegal under the Comstock laws for information on contraception or sexually transmitted diseases (STD) to be openly discussed or sent through the mail. Sanger was arrested for distributing birth-control information but was later pardoned. She established the first birth-control clinic in 1916 for which she was arrested. But the publicity brought the birth-control movement to public attention. She embraced eugenics, as did most educated middle-class and professionals of this era, and considered birth control along with prenatal care and the prevention of STDs as eugenic measures. The law concerning sending contraception information and devices through the mail was finally overruled in 1936. Sanger's essay based upon governmental reports illustrates the plight of impoverished uneducated overworked immigrant women in the early 20th century who had no information on how to control their fertility, leading to numerous unwanted children. They also had little knowledge of how to properly feed their infants resulting in high infant mortality from summer diarrhea and malnutrition. The social burdens of having too many unwanted children are also pointed out.*

Every year I receive thousands of letters from women in all parts of America, desperate appeals to aid them to extricate themselves from the trap of compulsory maternity. Lest I be accused of bias and exaggeration in drawing my conclusions from these painful human documents, I prefer to present a number of typical cases recorded in the reports of the United States government, and in the evidence of trained and impartial investigators of social agencies more generally opposed to the doctrine of Birth Control than biased in favor of it.

A perusal of the reports on infant mortality in widely varying industrial centers of the United States, published during the past decade by the Children's Bureau of the United States Department of Labor, forces us to a realization of the immediate need of detailed statistics concerning the practice and results of uncontrolled breeding. Some such effort as this has been made by the Galton Laboratory of National Eugenics in Great Britain.

The Children's Bureau reports only incidentally present this impressive evidence. They fail to coordinate it. While there is always the danger of drawing giant conclusions from pigmy premises, here is overwhelming evidence concerning irresponsible parenthood that is ignored by governmental and social agencies.

I have chosen a small number of typical cases from these reports. Though drawn from widely varying sources, they all emphasize the greatest crime of modern civilization—that of permitting motherhood to be left to blind chance, and to be mainly a function of the most abysmally ignorant and irresponsible classes of the community.

Here is a fairly typical case from Johnstown, Pennsylvania. A woman of thirty-eight years had undergone thirteen pregnancies in seventeen years. Of eleven live-births and two premature stillbirths, only two children were alive at the time of the government agent's visit. The second to eighth, the eleventh and the thirteenth had died of bowel trouble, at ages ranging from three weeks to four months. The only cause of these deaths the mother could give was that "food did not agree with them." She confessed quite frankly that she believed in feeding babies, and gave them everything anybody told her to give them. She began to give them at the age of one month, bread, potatoes, egg, crackers, etc. For the last baby that died, this mother had bought a goat and gave its milk to the baby; the goat got sick, but the mother continued to give her baby its milk until the goat went dry. Moreover, she directed the feeding of her daughter's baby until it died at the age of three months. "On account of the many children she had had, the neighbors consider her an authority on baby care."

Lest this case be considered too tragically ridiculous to be accepted as typical, the reader may verify it with an almost interminable list of similar cases. Parental irresponsibility is significantly illustrated in another case:

A mother who had four live births and two stillbirths in twelve years lost all of her babies during their first year. She was so anxious that at least one child should live that she consulted a physician concerning the care of the last one. "Upon his advice" to quote the government report, "she gave up her twenty boarders immediately after the child's birth, and devoted all her time to it. Thinks she did not stop her hard work soon enough; says she has always worked too hard, keeping boarders in this country, and cutting wood and carrying it and water on her back in the old country. Also says the carrying of water and cases of beer in this country is a great strain on her." But the illuminating point in this case is that the father was furious because all the babies died. To show his disrespect for the wife who could only give birth to babies that died, he wore a red necktie to the funeral of the last. Yet this woman, the government agent reports, would follow and profit by any instruction that might be given her.

It is true that the cases reported from Johnstown, Pennsylvania, do not represent completely "Americanized" families. This lack does not prevent them, however, by their unceasing fertility from producing the Americans of to-morrow. Of the more immediate conditions surrounding child-birth, we are presented with this evidence, given by one woman concerning the birth of her last child:

On five o'clock on Wednesday evening she went to her sister's house to return a washboard, after finishing a day's washing. The baby was born while she was there. Her sister was too young to aid her in any way. She was not accustomed to a midwife, she confessed. She cut the cord herself, washed the new-born baby at her sister's house, walked home, cooked supper for her boarders, and went to bed by eight o'clock. The next day she got up and ironed. This tired her out, she said, so she stayed in bed for two whole days. She milked cows the day after the birth of the baby and sold the milk as well. Later in the week, when she became tired, she hired someone to do that portion of her work. This woman, we are further informed, kept cows, chickens, and lodgers, and earned additional money by doing laundry and charwork. At times her husband deserted her. His earnings amounted to $1.70 a day, while a fifteen-year-old son earned $1.10 in a coal mine.

One searches in vain for some picture of sacred motherhood, as depicted in popular plays and motion pictures, something more normal and encouraging. Then one comes to the bitter realization that these, in very truth, are the "normal" cases, not the exceptions. The exceptions are apt to indicate, instead, the close relationship of this irresponsible and chance parenthood to the great social problems of feeblemindedness, crime and syphilis.

Source: Sanger, Margaret. *The Pivot of Civilization.* New York: Brentano's, c. 1922, p. 30–35.

69 Care and Setting of Fractures in Ancient Egypt, with Commentary (1930)

The Edwin Smith Surgical Papyrus *is an ancient Egyptian medical text, named after the dealer who bought it in 1862. It is thought that the original manuscript was written sometime in the Pyramid Age (ca. 8000–2500* B.C.E.*), and this is a reproduction of the earliest manuscript. The papyrus is the oldest known surgical treatise on wound care, injuries, and trauma. One of its owners was Abraham Flexner (1866–1959), who wrote the report that changed medical education in North America based upon scientific principles. The papyrus was translated by American archaeologist James Henry Breasted (1865–1935) in 1930 and is one of the earliest known scientific documents. It may have been a manual for military surgery as it describes 48 cases of injuries, fractures, and wounds. After each case, Breasted then makes a comment in terms of early 20th century surgery. This particular excerpt describes the treatment of fracture of the humerus—upper arm.*

See also: Document 8; Document 59

CASE THIRTY-SIX

A FRACTURE of THE HUMERUS [. . .]

Examination
XII 9–10

Translation

If thou examinest a man having a break in his upper arm, (and) thou findest his upper arm hanging down, separated from its fellow, (conclusion follows in diagnosis).

Commentary

"Hang down," . . . It is not found elsewhere in the medical papyri. More literally it means simply to "be low, sink down," . . . In our passage it evidently describes the helpless hanging of the broken arm. . . . As only one arm is discussed here, it is clear that the separation mentioned is that between the two pieces of bone produced by the fracture. As in [another case] the description is incomplete; before "separated" we expect the words "one piece;" that is "(one piece) separated from its fellow."

Diagnosis
XII 10

Translation

Thou shouldst say concerning him: "One having a break in his upper arm. An ailment which I will treat."

Commentary

The terms have all been discussed above. The diagnosis, as so often in this treatise, is simply a memorandum,—nothing more indeed than the title itself, with the essential note [. . .]

Treatment
XII 10–14

Translation

Thou shouldst place him prostrate on his back, with something folded between his two shoulder-blades; thou shouldst spread out with his two shoulders, in order to stretch apart his upper arm until that break falls into its place. Thou shouldst make for him two splints of linen, (and) thou shouldst apply for him one of them both on the inside of his arm, (and) the other of them both on the under side of his arm. Thou shouldst bind it with *ymrw*, (and) treat afterward [with] honey every day until he recovers.

Commentary

This treatment is verbatim a repetition of that in the preceding case, except that the stretching apart here affects the upper arm . . . The use of, "upper arm," just noted, is of value in explaining "spread out with his two shoulders." Such a procedure would have no effect upon the upper arm unless two persons on opposite sides of the patient should each grasp an arm and pull against each other, thus stretching the fractured arm, and permitting the surgeon to fit together the fractured ends of the *humerus* [...]

"Upper arm," is commonly used as a loose designation of the arm, and its Coptic descendant . . . also seems to mean "arm," without suggesting upper arm or forearm. Nevertheless the physical situation above described makes it probable that [the symbol] is used by our surgeon to designate the upper arm. If he is speaking of a break in the forearm, we miss any indication whether it is in the ulna or the radius. Moreover, he speaks of "that break," with the demonstrative in the singular, showing that he has but one fracture in mind. Still more important is the fact that to stretch the forearm it would not be necessary to involve both shoulders; whereas the stretching of the humerus is much more naturally accomplished in the manner above described by pulling from both shoulders. The application of the bandages to the fractured humerus is prescribed in the same terms as for the fractured collar-bone in Case 85 [. . .]

CASE THIRTY-SEVEN

XII 14–21

A FRACTURE OF THE HUMERUS WITH RUPTURE OF OVERLYING SOFT TISSUE

The sole difference between this and the preceding case of fracture of the humerus lies in the injury to the overlying soft tissue. The surgeon has met two different cases of this kind. In the first the tissue is not deeply ruptured, and apparently does not bleed, at least not outwardly; in the second the wound bleeds and the rupture of the tissue penetrates clear through to the fracture itself. The surgeon regards the first case as doubtful . . . followed by treatment; but the second case is hopeless, . . . followed by no treatment. It would seem then that the laceration of the soft tissue overlying a fracture of the humerus was regarded in ancient Egyptian surgery as a fatal injury.

Translation

Instructions concerning a break in his upper arm, with a wound over it [. . .]

Translation

If thou examinest a man having a break in his upper arm, over which a wound has been inflicted, (and) thou findest that that break crepitates under thy fingers, (conclusion follows in diagnosis).

Commentary

"a wound has been inflicted," is an idiom more literally meaning "a wound has been smashed" over it (the fracture)

First Diagnosis
XII 16–17

Translation

Thou shouldst say concerning him: "One having a break in his upper arm, over which a wound has been inflicted. An ailment with which I will contend."

Commentary

The terms have all been discussed above. The diagnosis consists only of the title [. . .]

First Treatment
XII 17–19

Translation

Thou shouldst make for him two splints of linen; thou shouldst bind it with *ymrw*; (and) thou shouldst treat it afterward [with] grease, honey and lint every day until thou knowest that he has reached a decisive point.

Commentary

It is very extraordinary that we have here no instructions for setting the broken bone. In the preceding case the measures for bringing together again the two pieces of bone are carefully described, and only after this difficult operation are the two linen splints mentioned. The position of each is then carefully indicated. All this is taken for granted in Case 87, where the treatment consists chiefly of catchwords suggesting measures which are doubtless quite familiar to the surgeon. It is only on this supposition that we can understand the omission of all directions for the application of the "two bandages." The setting of the bone itself must be implied in the mere injunction to make the bandages.

Source: Breasted, James Henry. *The Edwin Smith Surgical Papyrus: Published in Facsimile and Hieroglyphic Transliteration with Translation and Commentary in Two Volumes*. Chicago, IL: University of Chicago Press, 1930, pp. 355–359.

70 Diseases in Antiquity Based on X-rays of Mummies (1931)

American geologist Roy Lee Moodie (1880–1934) found evidence of diseases in some ancient fossilized bones. He published several works that described the use of X-rays (also known as Roetgen rays) for diagnosing the diseases and condition of Peruvian and Egyptian mummies. Among opened unwrapped mummies, Moodie found evidence of tuberculosis, malaria, broken bones, trauma, arthritis, and trepanation. No syphilis was found in either Peruvian or Egyptian mummies, leading Moodie to conclude it was a modern disease. Rickets—lack of vitamin D causing bone malformation—was rare in Peruvian mummies but found among a few Egyptian child mummies. Although x-rays had been able to show conditions and diseases on unwrapped mummy limbs, x-rays through the body pack, or material that wrapped the mummy, did not. In this excerpt published in 1931, Moodie was unable to observe evidence of diseases in the mummies contained in mummy packs, likely due to the dense material of the body wrap. The excerpt is an example of the beginning of research with the use of X-rays for medical diagnosis of ancient diseases and conditions, and gives evidence of diseases and procedures found in antiquity.

Our knowledge of diseases in ancient time has been widened by the application of the Roentgen ray to the study of unopened mummy packs. A striking advance is made, especially among Peruvian material, in the possibility of studying entire skeletons. Our previous studies on pre-Columbian Peruvians have been largely restricted to consideration of isolated skeletal parts.

Roentgenologic study of unopened mummy packs has its limitations . . .

Slight surface lesions, osteoporosis, and in many cases trepannings, traumatic injuries, and even linear fractures pass unobserved in a Roentgen examination of unopened mummy packs, on account of the superimposition of materials denser than the involved areas through which the shadows are made.

We feel, however, that the advance in our knowledge of disease in ancient times more than compensates for the disadvantages incurred in such a study. Roentgenology supplements all other methods of learning of physical troubles in early times.

One great advantage in the present study is the possibility of observing the condition of many Peruvian child mummies ranging from those of premature delivery up to the age of puberty. The collections of child mummies in Field Museum are adequate to give a good cross section of the physical condition of the children of ancient Peru, in so far as the skeletal parts are concerned. We learn that there is none of the bony manifestations of rickets to be seen among the mummies of twenty-nine children less than fourteen years of age, from pre-Columbian Peru. A trace of the disease was found among the ancient Egyptians. Like syphilis, rickets apparently is a modern disease.

It is impressive to note the high percentage of disease and injury among the fifty-three mummy packs studied. Among the pre-Columbian Peruvian mummies, the incidence of disease and injury is 10.52 per cent. Among the Egyptian mummies studied the enormous figure of 40 per cent is deduced as the incidence of disease and injury, based on fifteen mummies. While among the twenty-nine pre-Columbian children from Peru the incidence is low, yet we are unable in most cases to determine the diseases of the teeth, as well as of all soft parts.

A determination of the incidence of disease and injury of the skeletal parts of the Pleistocene saber-tooth [tiger] reveals a much lower percentage, in no case over 7 per cent. This determination, however, is based on a count of about one thousand skeletons. Undoubtedly a much lower percentage would result if we could base our count on a larger series of ancient mummies. Our statistics are further vitiated by the failure of the Roentgen ray to reveal certain lesions of childhood which we know from dry skulls were prevalent among pre-Columbian children.

It is of great importance to our knowledge of disease in ancient times to develop the field by further study of additional mummy packs by the roentgenologic method.

The roentgenograms chosen illustrate representative conditions found in unopened mummy packs. To the roentgenograms of the pre-Columbian Peruvians especially have been added a number of explanatory photographs of pre-historic lesions found on material preserved in San Diego Museum. . . .

The interpretation of roentgenograms of dry bones and mummies offers further difficulties on account of the absence of shadow-casting fluids, and of all soft parts. The roentgenological appearance of mummies is quite different from that of a living body. Other difficulties are found in the intrusions of foreign bodies into the wrappings of the mummies, both intentional and unintentional. . . .

The Roentgen rays fail to reveal lesions due to trepannings, club injuries, sling shot wounds, and even linear fractures. Many of the Peruvian mummies had the skull trepanned extensively, yet I have been unable, in an examination of the many roentgenograms of mummy packs at Field Museum, to determine the presence of a single trepanning. This failure is explained in part by the conditions met with in a pre-Columbian male skull from Cinco Cerros, Peru, which had been trepanned in the frontal bone above the left orbit, possibly for the relief of a sinus headache, yet the X-rays show no evidence of the cutting, and the sinuses are clear and very large . . .

A hypertrophic spleen, indicating malaria, is suggested by the shadow on the right side of Egyptian mummy No. 30021, but the appearance may be due to the insertion into the abdomen of a parcel of intestines, wrapped in linen, smeared with pitch, with sand adherent. [. . .]

Source: Moodie, Roy Lee. *Roentgenologic Studies of Egyptian and Peruvian Mummies.* Chicago: Field Museum, 1931, pp. 13–14.

71 Eduard Pernkopf: Drawing of Head (1943)

Austrian anatomist Eduard Pernkopf's (1888–1959) Atlas of Topographical and Applied Human Anatomy *[*Topographische anatomie des menschen*] was a seven-volume work of very detailed anatomical drawings. Pernkopf, an ardent Nazi, was dean of the medical school in Vienna. He prepared the anatomy atlas along with several artists from 1937 to 1960. This detailed work from the middle of WWII likely used executed political prisoners as models. It was rumored, but not definitely confirmed, that the fresh corpses used for these drawings might have been "ordered" for specific anatomy art work and research projects. Sometimes his early SS artists wove "SS" into their signatures or wrote it in a corner of a page. Reprints later in the 20th century airbrushed these out. The drawings were used in medical journals and textbooks into the 21st century. Because of the atlas's association with German National Socialism and the more than 20 million deaths resulting from this regime, the atlas came under criticism by 2000 as to the ethics of its use.*

See also: Document 33

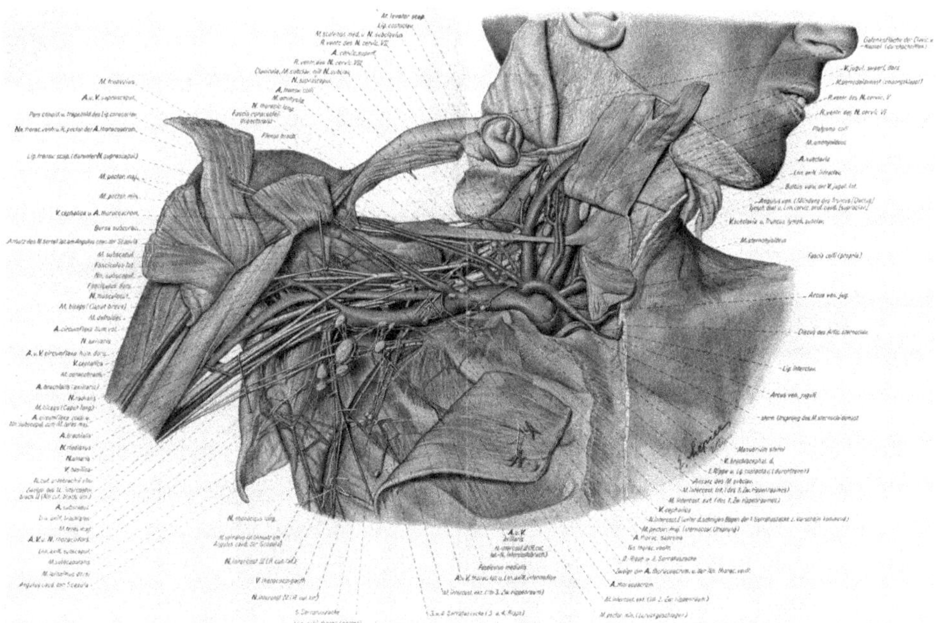

Eduard Pernkopf's drawing of a head (1943)

Source: Pernkopf, Eduard. *Topographische Anatomie des Menschen, Lehrbuch und Atlas der Regionär-Stratigraphischen Präparation.* Berlin, Urban & Schwarzenberg, 1943. Courtesy Lilly and Wells Libraries, Indiana University, Bloomington, IN.

72 Lillian Dunlap: A Nurse's Experience in the Philippines (1944)

American Brigadier General Lillian Dunlap (1922–2003) retired from the army after 33 years of service as a member of the Army Nurse Corps. She was interviewed by Cynthia A. Gurney, a colonel in the Army Nurse Corps, who compiled Dunlap's army experiences. They ranged from her first duty as an army nurse right out of nursing school in the aftermath of the bombing of Pearl Harbor to her final years in the army as Chief of the Army Nurse Corps. The interview was published in 2001 as 33 Years of Army Nursing: An Interview with Brigadier General Lillian Dunlap. *This extract of her experiences in WWII in a Philippine hospital underscores the challenges of nursing care for wounded military personnel. Dunlap discusses the understaffing of the hospital and the difficulties in evacuation of the seriously wounded. To combat infection, sulfa drugs were used and penicillin had just been introduced for use in the military. Compared to previous wars, these antibiotics reduced death rates from infections. Dunlap also had patients with malaria, scrub typhus, and other tropical conditions.*

See also: Data 4; Document 73

Treatments and Medications

I'd like to describe more of the treatments and medications that we used. In those days we gave a lot of sulpha, which was administered every four hours. The penicillin was a powdered concoction and had to be mixed up at the time we gave it. In other words, we couldn't mix it up in the morning for all the dosages we were going to give during the day. We had to mix it up just before we were going to give it. The powder and mixing solution had to be kept over in the laboratory. So the corpsman would go over to the laboratory and get the penicillin and we'd sit there and mix it up. We'd then draw up our syringes for the dosage we were going to give and fix up our tray with our penicillin. The corpsman would take a water pitcher and those envelope paper cups and the sulpha pills. The two of us would go around to the cots and we'd tap on the mosquito net. We used to laugh, because they'd stick a hand out for the sulpha and stick out their rear end where we'd poke it to give the penicillin. Then we'd go on to the next patient. So you can imagine what it was like each time the penicillins were given, some as often as every three or four hours. We were constantly mixing penicillins and getting our sulpha ready to give to the patients. They began to get some penicillin in the beeswax that was longer lasting. We'd only have to give that twice a day. But we didn't have much of that. The sulphas and penicillin were about all we had. Of course, there was atabrine for malaria and aspirin.

In addition to that we were busy doing dressings. I can remember our experience at Tacloban. We'd come on duty—this again was one long ward and one nurse covering two wards, maybe even covering 200 patients or so. We came on duty, and the dressing cart would be perhaps halfway down the ward. That's as far as they had gotten that day with changing dressings. So we'd start from that point, changing dressings and doing treatments that still needed to be done.

I saw my first gangrene in the Admiralties. Some of the Marines who had been on Cape Gloucester were sent down to us. They had received immediate medical care-morphine, bandages, and all-on the beaches, and then they were put on landing craft and sent down to us. Some of them had gangrene. They had received the antitoxin but it was outdated. Also, I saw my first scrub typhus. There is so much kunai grass up in Cape Gloucester that the sharp edges of the kunai grass cut the soldiers. The little mites had gotten into them. We saw scrub typhus and the malarias and, of course, hepatitis.

Patient Evacuation

We also had a lot of amputees, orthopedic patients, and neurosurgical patients. We did not have a means for quick evacuation of the patients. There was no scheduled evacuation. Sometimes we heard that there was a ship coming in. It took supplies on up ahead of us and it was coming back and was able to take out some patients to Australia. Well, naturally we tried to get the most critical patients we had, like the paraplegics, out. But some of the patients stayed for months before we could get them on a hospital ship to get them out to Australia. All of the transportation that they had was needed to get troops and supplies up and to bring casualties back as soon as they could. It was quite a challenge for nursing.

Source: Cynthia A. Gurney. *33 Years of Army Nursing: An Interview with Brigadier General Lillian Dunlap.* United States Army Nurse Corps, Washington, DC, 2001, pp. 28–29.

73 Karl MacMillan: Medical Diary from Burma and China in WWII (1945)

American Lt. Col. Karl MacMillan (1904–1994) was a physician and commanding officer of the 96th Field Hospital in the China-India-Burma theater of World War II during 1945. He kept a daily diary of the countryside, people, and the sanitary and health conditions as his unit slogged over the treacherous Ledo-Burma and the Burma Road in China. The diary was compiled by his niece, Ruth Clifford Engs, in 2015. The field hospital's primary battle was against deplorable sanitation, disease-carrying insects, and virulent tropical diseases. These diseases included cholera, malaria, typhoid fever, amebic dysentery, scrub typhus, bubonic plaque, and sexually transmitted diseases such as chancroid along with the more common syphilis and gonorrhea. The excerpts from the diary describe a cholera hospital and the importance of having access to clean water to prevent water-borne illnesses, being inoculated against diseases, and taking Atabrine on a daily basis to avoid contracting malaria.

See also: Data 4; Document 32; Document 72

SUNDAY APRIL 29, 1945

At 1000 we had a meeting–Capt. Sopka's office, attended by Maj. Keith, Lt. Col. Marshall (SOS surgeon), Lt. Col. Radcliffe, SOS S-4, WO. Downs S-2, etc. They also discussed the old British hospital at PANITOLA and we all drove out there and looked at it. Not too bad; the buildings were in good state of repair, mostly of Indian type, stucco sides, but 4 were thick brick structures, more or less bombproof. One operating room and 3 wards. The engineers were working on the kitchen, which will be too small for our purposes, I'm afraid. The lighting system and the water systems were in bad shape. The latrines were a disgrace, even the squat-type ones were all stopped up and all the good bowls had been taken away. Really, as far as sanitation was concerned, the place was a mess. The most incongruous sight was that every room had cow-pads in it, without exception. What entices the sacred cattle in rooms with concrete and stone floors is beyond me.

WEDNESDAY MARCH 14, 1945

We put in a tent area at the S. end of camp, near the hospital, 18th F. H. We found the latrines filthy and in bad condition. They were on one side of our area and the wash stands and showers were on the other side. A poor arrangement.

The latrines were in native-type buildings. Wood supporting structures with mud wattle walls and thatched roofs. Our mess hall and a headquarters building were of the same type. We had a shower soon after arriving, cold water, of course, but not bad.

FRIDAY, MARCH 16, 1945

All morning was spent in the open air theater, all Officers and troops, listening to orientation talks. According to their statements the VD [sexually-transmitted diseases] rate among the natives is terrific, and among the G.I.s too.

MONDAY JULY 3, 1945

Our mess put out a good meal and Brummett's generator gave the kitchen some light and ran his radio. It was a nice set up and camp. We got boiled water for our trailers and hauled water for boiling purposes.

It rained during the night, but I was quite comfortable in my bedding roll, under my mosquito net, with a couple of jungle hammocks above to keep out the rain.

SUNDAY, JULY 22, 1945

We went to the Chinese contagious hospital where they are taking care of the victims of the local cholera epidemic. A lot of the poor devils were dying here. These are the first cholera patients I have seen. They are very dehydrated and were given intravenous saline. Out in the yard, carpenters were busy making coffins, not a cheery sight for the patients, but they were too sick to care. Instead of beds, the patients were lying on wooden platforms, no mattresses or covers at all, and the floor was filling with vomitus, and partly filled, rusty bedpans were lying around the floor too.

TUESDAY, JULY 24, 1945

At 1000 we started to distribute our remaining PX supplies and most everybody received a carton of cigarettes, chewing gum, tropical candy bars, fruit juices and matches, about $3.00 worth of stuff. I bought a leather shoulder holster for my .45 automatic, why, I don't know. Had some laundry done, which was needed much more than the shoulder holster.

Arrangements were made for inoculating us with booster shots for typhus, cholera and plague at 1400 today.

WEDNESDAY AUGUST 22, 1945

We arrived at the airport at 1500, where Capt. Hogan in a jeep and Capt. Brunsen in the weapons carrier met us. On the way back, Hogan told me the news. The officers of the 3d unit had been ordered to CHUNGKING [Chongqing], but not the EM [enlisted men]. These officers were there now and [the EM] had been left behind at Kunming when we left, all but Capt. Inman, who had a bad case of infectious jaundice. Too bad, as he probably will be ill for quite a while, and may have to be evacuated to the states through India.

Lt. Holzberg, one of our unit, was down with an attack of malaria. I met him later on in the day, and he was better, but still a little weak. He said that he had stopped taking his Atabrine. We are still on ours.

Capt. Abelson, Base section III surgeon, was ill with an enlarged spleen, no diagnosis. Lt. Col. Driscoll, CO of 95th Stat. Hosp. is taking his place for the time being. Lt. O'Neil is now working up at the surgeon's office and enjoying it. Good thing, as he has not had enough to do.

It certainly felt good to get back to the unit again. It really feels like getting back home, and it was nice to take a shower and get in clean clothes. Also to get mail and be able to use my desk again, as well as all of my other things.

Source: Engs, Ruth Clifford [compiler, editor], MacMillan, Karl D.[diarist] *The Field Hospital That Never Was: Diary of Lt. Col. Karl D. Macmillan's, MD, 96th Field Hospital in China-India-Burma Theater 1945, WWII.* Bradenton, Florida: Booklocker.com, 2015. Used with permission.

74 Need for More Primary Practitioners (1994)

This United States government report in 1994 resulting from a Congressional investigation points out the need for more physicians, especially in family, general practice, and internal medicine. With a push for specialization in the post-WWII years, many medical students did not enter family or general practice medicine. Family and general practice had become a specialty in the early 1970s to help encourage young physicians to go into this field. However, there was still a shortage. A hearing was held to determine what could be done about the situation. It was found that if a medical school did not have family practice department, students and residents were less likely to go into the field. Ways to help finance training in these fields were also identified. This document pointed out the physicians' shortage in North America, and in particular the United States, at the end of the 20th century when medical education was still somewhat based upon the 1910 Flexner Report. However, the Congressional report was one of the investigations that led to major curriculum reform of medical education in most American institutions by 2005.

See also: Document 59

Since 1960, the proportion of primary care physicians—family and general practice physicians, general internists, and general pediatricians—has dropped from about 53 percent to about 35 percent of the nation's active physicians. Taking into account current health care trends emphasizing a growing need for primary care medicine, the Department of Health and Human Services (HHS) projects for the year 2000 a shortage of 35,000 generalist or primary care physicians. The decline in the proportion of active primary care physicians is related to career decisions that students make during their medical school years and later in residency training. While no single factor can explain why students pursue primary care or nonprimary care specialties, various studies indicate that the characteristics of students entering medicine and the educational process they experience may influence career decisions.

The federal government contributes to the financing of medical education and training in several ways. In 1992, the Medicare program provided a total of about $5.2 billion in support of graduate medical education. Through its funding of biomedical research, the National Institutes of Health helps support medical education at the undergraduate and graduate levels. The federal government also supports medical education and training activities through various programs authorized under the Public Health Service Act.

The federal government also contributes to the financing of graduate medical education through programs administered by the Department of Veterans Affairs, the Department of Defense, and through federal sharing in states' costs of the Medicaid program.

Concerned about the declining ratio of primary care physicians to nonprimary care physicians, you asked us to assess the role of medical education in physician specialty choice. You also asked us to assess how federal financing of medical education may influence career choices.

More specifically, we focused on the

- characteristics associated with students who are more likely to choose generalist or primary care specialties in medical school,
- curriculum requirements that expose medical students and residents to primary care training, and
- the role federal financing plays in setting the focus of medical education.

Results in Brief

Choice of career paths in medicine is associated with the characteristics of students admitted to medical schools and with the curriculum and training opportunities they receive during their medical education.

Although the strongest predictor of whether students would choose primary care careers was their stated preference for primary care before they entered medical school, we found that some features of medical schools were associated with an increased likelihood that students would go into primary care. Foremost among these was whether the medical school had a family practice department—students who attended schools with family practice departments were more likely to pursue primary care than students who attended schools without such departments. Other factors moderately favoring primary care were whether a family practice clerkship was required before career decisions were made in the fourth year and how well family practice departments were funded.

Similarly, once students graduate from medical school and enter residency programs, we found a significant association between program opportunities to expose residents to primary care faculty and the proportion of residents choosing generalist practice.

Although curriculum and training opportunities appear to influence student choice of primary care, we found that many medical schools did not require primary care experiences before students chose residency programs. Moreover, once in a residency program, residents spent only a small portion of training time on providing primary care or working in a primary care setting.

The way residency training is financed contributes to a specialist orientation for the clinical education of medical students. Only hospitals or hospital-affiliated providers are eligible to receive Medicare payments for direct training costs. Current financing mechanisms for residency training can give greater incentives to training in nonprimary care-oriented settings than in primary care-oriented settings. This can place primary care residency programs at a disadvantage because of their use of nonhospital settings for training. In our view, the Medicare payment methodology may need to be modified to provide incentives for training in nonhospital settings.

Background

Medical career decisions are usually made at three specific points during the educational continuum: (1) at the end of college when students typically apply to medical school, (2) during the fourth year of medical school when students elect the area of medicine to pursue and enter residency training, and (3) at the end of residency training when residents decide to enter practice or to train further for a subspecialty [. . .].

Matter for Congressional Consideration

. . . Congress may want to consider modifying Medicare's payment methodology for the direct costs of graduate medical education to provide incentives for training in nonhospital settings.

Source: United States General Accounting Office. *Medical Education: Curriculum and Financing. Strategies Need to Encourage Primary Care Training. Report to Congressional Requesters.* Washington, DC: GAO, October 1994, pp. 1–4, 22.

75 Measles Eradication Recommendations from a Global Meeting (1996)

Representatives from the World Health Organization (WHO), the Pan American Health Organization, and Centers for Disease Control and Prevention (CDC) met for two days at a meeting in Atlanta, Georgia in 1996 to determine if measles could be eliminated globally just as smallpox had been eradicated by the late 1970s. To accomplish this task, cooperation would be needed between all member states of the WHO, as measles obliteration would require supplementary vaccinations in higher-income nations as well as in developing countries. Many communities would also need to be educated about the seriousness of the disease, which could cause blindness, deafness, and occasionally death. Measles is highly infectious and a herd immunity of about 95 percent is needed to assure the measles virus does not spread. As part of control, new genomic tests allowed researchers to distinguish native from imported virus strains. Participants concluded based upon research that interrupting measles transmission for prolonged periods over wide geographic areas would be possible. However, geographically limited campaigns should only be conducted as part of a larger measles control or elimination strategy. The meeting and its conclusions were important as it laid out the plan for the eradication of the disease.

See also: Data 19

INTRODUCTION

During the early 1980s, in the aftermath of smallpox eradication, some scientists and public health officials urged consideration of a global effort to eradicate measles. During the mid-1980s, however, the high level of population immunity required to interrupt measles virus transmission became clear, and the prospect of measles eradication seemed to recede. As recently as 1993, a task force on disease eradication declared measles "not now eradicable". The major obstacles to eradication cited by the task force were the contagiousness of measles, the lack of a vaccine that is effective among children aged less than 9 months (most of whom have maternal antibody to measles that protects them from disease but which also inhibits the immune response to the vaccine virus), and the incorrect perception that measles is a mild illness.

Recent successes in implementing new approaches to control and eliminate measles virus transmission prompted the World Health Organization (WHO), the Pan American Health Organization (PAHO), and CDC to convene a meeting July 9–10, 1996, in Atlanta to reconsider the feasibility of global measles eradication. Among the participants were representatives of the sponsoring organizations, representatives of regions and countries that have implemented measles elimination activities, and persons affiliated with WHO Regional Offices, local and state health departments in the United States, and universities. During the meeting, presenters reviewed vaccination strategies and achievements in measles control in the Caribbean and Latin America, Canada, and the United States.

In addition, representatives of Denmark, Kuwait, Mexico, South Africa, and the United Kingdom described their recent efforts to control or eliminate measles transmission. In each of these countries, intensification of efforts to control measles has been followed by sustained declines in the number of reported cases [. . .].

Based on this information and on subsequent discussion, meeting participants were asked to address five questions:

- Is global measles eradication feasible?
- Is measles eradication feasible with current vaccines?
- What are the appropriate vaccination strategies for measles eradication?
- How should surveillance for measles be carried out?
- What role should outbreak control play in the strategy to eliminate measles?

Discussion of these questions formed the basis for the conclusions and recommendations of the meeting. The rapporteur prepared a draft of the conclusions and recommendations that was distributed and discussed in the final session of the 2-day meeting. The discussion and subsequent modification of the draft ensured that the report would reflect both points of consensus and the sense of discussions among participants.

Definitions of Measles Elimination and Eradication

To facilitate communication among participants, working definitions of two important terms were developed during the meeting. Measles elimination refers to interruption of transmission in a sizable geographic area in which vaccination would nevertheless need to continue because of the continued threat of reintroduction of the virus. Eradication, defined as the global interruption of measles transmission, represents the sum of successful elimination efforts in all countries. Once eradication is achieved, vaccination could be stopped without risk for measles outbreaks [. . .].

Status of Global Measles Control

Since the inception of the World Health Organization's Expanded Programme on Immunization (EPI) in 1974, the numbers of cases and deaths attributed worldwide to measles have declined substantially, from an estimated 100 million cases and 5.8 million deaths in 1980 to an estimated 44 million cases and 1.1 million deaths in 1995 [. . .].

Despite these achievements, measles remains one of the leading causes of child mortality in developing countries, responsible for approximately 10% of all deaths among children aged less than 5 years. These deaths typically occur among young children in countries with low vaccination coverage levels. Even countries that have achieved high levels of measles vaccination coverage and have recorded several years of low incidence frequently have experienced large measles outbreaks.

On the basis of vaccination coverage, case fatality rates, and vaccine effectiveness, WHO estimates that by 1995 measles-associated morbidity and mortality had decreased by 78% and 88%, respectively, in comparison with the pre-vaccine era (WHO, unpublished data).

Although these estimates demonstrate a marked reduction in the health burden of measles, they also indicate that the mid-decade goals of reducing measles morbidity by 90% and measles mortality by 95% have not been met [. . .]. Since 1994, a strategy of limited vaccination campaigns targeting all children aged 9 months to 5 years has been advocated to reduce measles morbidity and mortality by reaching unvaccinated children in areas in which risk for measles is high (e.g., large, densely populated urban and peri-urban centers) . . . Many children who were unvaccinated before the campaigns remained unvaccinated afterward. [. . .]

The impact of measles vaccination has varied substantially among the six WHO Regions. These interregional differences reflect disparities in routine immunization coverage levels and, more importantly, in the effectiveness of different measles control strategies. Of the six WHO Regions, the most substantial progress in measles control has been achieved in the Americas, where most countries have implemented a strategy based on a one-time-only mass vaccination campaign across a wide age group. The goals of this strategy are to achieve a rapid reduction in the number of susceptible children in the population and to interrupt the transmission of measles virus. To keep the susceptible population from exceeding the epidemic threshold requires high routine coverage and periodic "follow-up" campaigns to vaccinate children born after the previous campaigns. A strategy similar to that used in the Americas has been implemented or is being considered in at least one country in each of the other WHO regions.

Source: Center for Disease Control. "Measles Eradication: Recommendations from a Meeting Cosponsored by the World Health Organization, the Pan American Health Organization, and CDC." *MMRW* 46, no. RR11, June 13, 1997, pp. 1–20.

76 Evidence for Climate Change (2007)

In 1988, the World Meteorological Organization and the United Nations Environment Programme established the Intergovernmental Panel on Climate Change. Its purpose was to investigate the effects of greenhouse gasses that were caused by human activity and the effect on climate. Its mission was also to provide a standard reference for anyone concerned with climate change (including academia, policy makers, government, and industry) globally based upon scientific evidence. In the "Summary for Policymakers," the editors of Climate Change 2007, *condensed from the large report of Working Group II of the International Panel on Climate Changes, point out various consequences of the changing climate. This excerpt below from this report assesses the relationship between documented climate change and changes in the natural and human environment based upon data sets from 1970 to the late first decade of the 21st century. This excerpt gives evidence that indicates warming of the planet that had by the first decade of the 21st century led to issues around the world.*

See also: Data 21

Current knowledge about observed impacts of climate change on the natural and human environment

This part of the Working Group II Summary concerns the relationship between observed climate change and recent observed changes in the natural and human environment. The statements presented here are based largely on data sets that cover the period since 1970. The number of studies of observed trends in the physical and biological environment and their relationship to regional climate changes has increased greatly since the Third Assessment in 2001. There is, however, a notable lack of geographical balance in the data and literature on observed changes, with marked scarcity in developing countries.

Recent studies have allowed a broader and more confident assessment of the relationship between observed warming and impacts than was made in the Third Assessment. That Assessment concluded that "there is high confidence that recent regional changes in temperature have had discernible impacts on many physical and biological systems".

From the current Assessment we conclude the following.

Observational evidence from all continents and most oceans shows that many natural systems are being affected by regional climate changes, particularly temperature increases.

With regard to changes in snow, ice and frozen ground (including permafrost), there is high confidence that natural systems are affected. Examples are:

- enlargement and increased numbers of glacial lakes
- increasing ground instability in permafrost regions, and rock avalanches in mountain regions

- changes in some Arctic and Antarctic ecosystems, including those in sea-ice biomes, and also predators high in the food chain.

Based on growing evidence, there is high confidence that the following effects on hydrological [water] systems are occurring:

- increased runoff and earlier spring peak discharge in many glacier- and snow-fed rivers.
- warming of lakes and rivers in many regions, with effects on thermal structure and water quality.

There is very high confidence, based on more evidence from a wider range of species, that recent warming is strongly affecting terrestrial biological systems, including such changes as:

- earlier timing of spring events, such as leaf-unfolding, bird migration and egg-laying
- poleward and upward shifts in ranges in plant and animal species.

Based on satellite observations since the early 1980s, there is high confidence that there has been a trend in many regions towards earlier 'greening' of vegetation in the spring linked to longer thermal growing seasons due to recent warming.

There is high confidence, based on substantial new evidence, that observed changes in marine and freshwater biological systems are associated with rising water temperatures, as well as related changes in ice cover, salinity, oxygen levels and circulation.

These include:

- shifts in ranges and changes in algal, plankton and fish abundance in high-latitude oceans
- increases in algal and zooplankton abundance in high-latitude and high-altitude lakes

The uptake of anthropogenic carbon since 1750 has led to the ocean becoming more acidic, with an average decrease in pH of 0.1 units . . .

A global assessment of data since 1970 has shown it is likely that anthropogenic warming has had a discernible influence on many physical and biological systems.

Much more evidence has accumulated over the past five years to indicate that changes in many physical and biological systems are linked to anthropogenic warming. There are four sets of evidence which, taken together, support this conclusion:

1. The Working Group I Fourth Assessment concluded that most of the observed increase in the globally averaged temperature since the mid-20th century is very likely due to the observed increase in anthropogenic [human] greenhouse gas concentrations.

2. Of the more than 29,000 observational data series, from 75 studies, that show significant change in many physical and biological systems, more than 89% are consistent with the direction of change expected as a response to warming.

3. A global synthesis of studies in this Assessment strongly demonstrates that the spatial agreement between regions of significant warming across the globe and the locations of significant observed changes in many systems consistent with warming is very unlikely to be due solely to natural variability of temperatures or natural variability of the systems.

4. Finally, there have been several modelling studies that have linked responses in some physical and biological systems to anthropogenic warming by comparing observed responses in these systems with modelled responses in which the natural forcings (solar activity and volcanoes) and anthropogenic forcings (greenhouse gases and aerosols) are explicitly separated. . . . The consistency between observed and modelled changes in several studies and the spatial agreement between significant regional warming and consistent impacts at the global scale is sufficient to conclude with high confidence that anthropogenic warming over the last three decades has had a discernible influence on many physical and biological systems .

Other effects of regional climate changes on natural and human environments are emerging, although many are difficult to discern due to adaptation and non-climatic drivers

Effects of temperature increases have been documented in the following (medium confidence):

- effects on agricultural and forestry management at Northern Hemisphere higher latitudes, such as earlier spring planting of crops, and alterations in disturbance regimes of forests due to fires and pests
- some aspects of human health, such as heat-related mortality in Europe, infectious disease vectors in some areas, and allergenic pollen in Northern Hemisphere high and midlatitudes.
- some human activities in the Arctic (e.g., hunting and travel over snow and ice) and in lower-elevation alpine areas (such as mountain sports).

Recent climate changes and climate variations are beginning to have effects on many other natural and human systems. However, based on the published literature, the impacts have not yet become established trends. Examples include:

- Settlements in mountain regions are at enhanced risk of glacier lake outburst floods caused by melting glaciers. Governmental institutions in some places have begun to respond by building dams and drainage works.
- In the Sahelian region of Africa, warmer and drier conditions have led to a reduced length of growing season with detrimental effects on crops. In southern Africa, longer dry seasons and more uncertain rainfall are prompting adaptation measures.

- Sea-level rise and human development are together contributing to losses of coastal wetlands and mangroves and increasing damage from coastal flooding in many areas.

Source: Parry, M. L., et. al., Eds. "Summary for Policymakers." In *Climate Change 2007: Impacts, Adaptation and Vulnerability, Contribution of Working Group II to the Fourth Assessment Report of the Intergovernmental Panel on Climate Change.* Cambridge, United Kingdom: Cambridge University Press, 2007, pp. 8–9. Used with permission of the IPCC.

77 Tuning in to Secure Food (2011)

Gary Humphreys, a journalist for the World Health Organization (WHO), wrote an article in 2011 concerning food security in Africa. He addressed solutions for achieving adequate food and nutrition—a World Health Organization Millennium Development Goal 1 for 2015. A solution he described was the introduction of technology that was adapted for use on small farms in Africa. This was the use of the mobile phone along with a weekly agricultural radio program that discussed issues common to the local area. With two-way communication, farmers could talk to each other and discuss problems and possible solutions for farming activities. Climate change, crop diseases, increasing population, increasing food prices, internal conflict, lack of rain and desertification led to farming becoming more difficult by the second decade of the 21st century. Few crops meant a lack of money for the family and also a lack of food to eat. Many of the farmers were women. This excerpt is important as it shows the plight of small African farmers and some solutions to their farming issues.

See also: Data 5

When Winnie Asege's crop was hit by cassava brown streak disease a few years ago she was faced with two problems. "She had very little to eat and nothing to sell," says Emily Arayo, Uganda national coordinator of the African Radio Research Initiative, a project run by Canadian nongovernmental organization Farm Radio International. This is food security, or rather food insecurity, at its most basic: a woman standing in a field looking at rotten tubers and wondering how she and her children are going to survive.

The impact is global too. In recent years rising food prices have sparked civil unrest, fuelled [*sic*] inflation and led to economic measures by some countries. Global food prices hit new record highs in December 2010, according to the Food and Agriculture Organization (FAO). While the reasons for volatile food prices are as diverse as climate change, commodity speculation, changing dietary habits, increased population and global trade issues, at bottom food security is simple: it means everyone gets to eat.

This is the idea enshrined in the United Nations Millennium Development Goal 1, part of which seeks to cut by half the prevalence of underweight children aged less than five years and to halve the proportion of the global population struggling to survive below the minimum level of dietary energy consumption of about 1825 calories a day (FAO definition) between 1990 and 2015.

So, with four years to go, how close are we to achieving this goal? According to the United Nation's Millennium Development Goals report, released in September 2010, not very: "Overall progress in reducing the prevalence of hunger has not been sufficient to reduce the number of undernourished people," the report says. In other words there has been no change since the MDGs were announced in 2000.

A similarly discouraging picture is painted by the FAO, which also released a report in September 2010 stating that, while the number of hungry people worldwide had decreased from more than one billion in 2009 to 925 million people in 2010, this small decline was largely attributable to resumed economic growth and a fall in food prices since 2008. The preceding period saw a similar lack of progress. From 1990–2000, the proportion of undernourished people declined globally from 16% to 14%.

"The reality is that the proportion of hungry people in the world has only decreased by half a percent from 14% in 2000 to 13.5% today," says Oxfam's food and agriculture spokesperson Chris Leather, adding that any improvement that may have happened—and he has doubts about the numbers—has more to do with two years of good harvests rather than good policy. "Some countries may be doing better in terms of food security compared to 10 years ago," Leather says, citing Brazil, Ghana, Malawi and Viet Nam as examples, "but overall the picture remains fairly bleak". This is particularly true of the developing world, where, according to FAO economist David Dawe, 16% of the total population lives in hunger. "Finding ways to enable those people to feed themselves is one of the biggest challenges we face," Dawe says.

This situation is unlikely to change unless international development partners and national governments live up to pledges made in the past few years, and notably in July 2009 in the Italian city of L'Aquila, where world leaders pledged US$ 20 billion in aid over three years to a food security initiative. But money alone will not bring about change either. "There needs to be new thinking," says Dawe. "We are going to need 70% more production by 2050 just to keep up with population growth and changing eating habits. This increase cannot be achieved simply by increasing the land under cultivation. The best land is already being farmed while both water and fertilizer are becoming more scarce, and expensive." Dawe believes that one of the ways production can be increased is by the judicious introduction of technology, but technology adapted for use on small farms . . .

It was just this kind of technology that helped Asege. All that was involved was a radio, or more precisely, a radio programme and some mobile phones. The programme in question was a weekly farm show that features interactive, entertaining, multi-format items on agriculture themes selected by area farmers . . . While broadcast in the local language and rooted in the local agricultural context, the shows are generated by radio station staff with the support of Farm Radio International, which works with about 350 radio broadcasters in 39 African countries. "We are coming up to 1000 scripts," says Farm Radio International Chief Executive Officer Kevin Perkins, who says that their programmes reach around 39 million farmers every week . . .

"One of the things that radio can do really well is to bring people together, but that is not all it does," Perkins says, arguing that what makes radio particularly exciting right now in the developing world is the emergence of technologies that make it not only cheap but interactive. "The lowering of the cost of recording equipment, the availability of open-source editing software, and the introduction of cell phones has made it possible to connect people who are otherwise isolated in remote rural areas," Perkins says, stressing the fact that people don't just listen, they call in to share their views in talk radio segments.

Farmers talk to farmers about problems as diverse as animal enclosure, composting techniques, low-cost crop storage methods and the introduction of new crop varieties. Perkins says: "Radio becomes a platform for conversations and dialogue involving farmers, extension workers, policy-makers and researchers. It no longer has to be a one-way medium that lectures farmers—instead, they can participate in finding the solutions and share their knowledge with each other."

Source: Humphreys, Gary. "Tuning in to Secure Food." *Bulletin of the World Health Organization* 89, no. 2, February 2011, pp. 86–87. Used by permission of the World Health Organization.

78 WHO: Report on the Global Tobacco Epidemic (2015)

This excerpt from the executive report on the effects of raising taxes on tobacco was published by the World Health Organization in 2015. It describes the issues, failures, and successes in reducing tobacco use through taxes in a number of nations. Smoking and tobacco are one of the major factors in morbidity (illness) and mortality (death) of noncommunicable diseases such as heart disease, cancers, and strokes. This summary provides data and facts from the larger report. In 2008, WHO launched MPOWER, a policy group, globally to reduce the tobacco epidemic. MPOWER stands for: 1) Monitor tobacco use and prevention policies, 2) Protect people from tobacco smoke, 3) Offer help to quit tobacco, 4) Warn about the dangers of tobacco, 5) Enforce bans on tobacco advertising, promotion, and sponsorship, and 6) Raise taxes on tobacco. MPOWER is a resource for the key methods and strategies to reduce tobacco use and offers information and actions to help nations in this public health effort. Many of these suggestions have been adapted globally although increasing taxes has not been as successful and differences between regions exist.

See also: Data 29

Overview

There has been steady progress in global tobacco control. Today, more than half of the world's countries, with 40% of the world's population (2.8 billion people) have implemented at least one MPOWER measure at the highest level of achievement (not including the Monitoring and Mass media measures, which are assessed separately). This progress more than doubles the number of countries and nearly triples the number of people covered since 2007.

Despite the fact that raising tobacco taxes to more than 75% of the retail price is among the most effective and cost-effective tobacco control interventions (it costs little to implement and increases government revenues), only a few countries have increased tobacco taxes to best practice level. Raising taxes is the least implemented MPOWER measure—with only 10% of the world's people living in countries with sufficiently high taxes—and is the measure that has seen the least improvement since WHO started assessing these data. Even so, by 2014, 11 countries had raised taxes to represent more than 75% of the retail price of a pack of cigarettes, joining the 22 countries that already had similarly high taxes in place in 2008. However, there are still many countries with extremely low tobacco tax rates, and some countries that do not levy any tobacco taxes at all.

Many countries have implemented multiple MPOWER measures at the highest level of achievement. A total of 49 countries with nearly 20% of the world's population are covered by two or more MPOWER measures at the highest level, tripling the number of people protected by at least two fully implemented tobacco control measures to 1.4 billion people since 2007. Seven countries, five of which are low- and middle-income, have implemented four or more MPOWER measures at the highest level. Six of these countries (four of which are low- and middle-income countries with more than 4% of the world's population—more than 300 million people), are only one step away from having all MPOWER measures in place at the highest level.

Key findings

Over the past 2 years, there has been notable progress in global tobacco control. Since the previous WHO report on the global tobacco epidemic, 2013, which reported data from 2012, the global population covered by at least one MPOWER measure at the highest level has increased from 2.3 billion to 2.8 billion, an increase of half a billion people (7% of the world's population). The number of countries implementing at least one MPOWER measure at the highest level has increased by 11 since 2012, from 92 to 103.

Each MPOWER measure saw new countries implementing best tobacco control practice since 2012.

- Five countries with a combined population of 187 million people, (Chile, Jamaica, Madagascar, Russian Federation and Suriname) implemented a comprehensive smoke-free law covering all indoor public places and workplaces.
- Six countries (Argentina, Belgium, Brunei Darussalam, Malta, Mexico and the Netherlands) implemented appropriate cessation services. Because one country reduced services after 2012, the net gain for offering assistance to quit was five countries and 173 million people.
- Twelve countries with a combined population of 370 million people (Bangladesh, Costa Rica, Fiji, Jamaica, Namibia, Philippines, Samoa, Solomon Islands, Trinidad and Tobago, Turkmenistan, Vanuatu and Vietnam) implemented large graphic pack warnings.
- Seven countries (Kiribati, Nepal, Russian Federation, Suriname, United Arab Emirates, Uruguay and Yemen) introduced a complete ban on all tobacco advertising, promotion and sponsorship (TAPS) activities, thus protecting an additional 209 million people from exposure to TAPS.
- Seven countries (Bangladesh, Bosnia and Herzegovina, Croatia, Kiribati, New Zealand, Romania and Seychelles) raised taxes on cigarettes to more than 75% of the retail price (because four countries did not maintain sufficiently high taxes after 2012, and one country did not provide data, the net gain for raising taxes was only two countries and 154 million people

Conclusion

Progress spurred by the WHO Framework Convention on Tobacco Control and the consistent MPOWER measures over the past decade has helped protect 40% of the world's people through at least one MPOWER measure at the highest level of achievement. As countries continue the process of adopting and implementing effective tobacco control strategies, they can look for inspiration and guidance to other countries that have successfully moved to advance their policies to the best practice level.

The focus of this report, Raising Tobacco Taxes, is the MPOWER measure that has experienced least progress. Only one in 10 of the world's people live in the 33 countries that levy taxes of more than 75% of the cigarette retail price, making it the least-implemented MPOWER measure and the one with least improvement since 2007. More than 80% of countries have no tobacco taxation in place at the highest level of achievement despite clear evidence that increasing taxes to a sufficiently high level is an extremely effective—including cost-effective—intervention; it reduces tobacco use, costs governments relatively little to implement, and increases government revenues, sometimes substantially.

It can be difficult to generate sufficient political will to overcome opposition—including from the tobacco industry—to raising tobacco taxes. The tobacco industry has long opposed any strengthening of tobacco control measures, and is particularly active in attempting to prevent any type of tax increase leading to actual higher prices. The industry makes spurious claims of economic harm caused by higher taxes, which are not borne out by the evidence. One particular claim is that higher taxes lead to increased smuggling and illicit trade, but again the evidence does not support this. But because tobacco taxes are generally better accepted than other types of taxes, it is possible to achieve widespread public support, even among tobacco users, especially if at least some of the new tax revenues are used for tobacco control, health promotion and other public health programmes.

All countries have an obligation to protect the health of their people, and all Parties to the WHO CTC have made specific commitments to implement strong tobacco control policies as an important means of providing that protection. There has been substantial progress in the past decade, but we must now recommit ourselves to continuing our global tobacco control efforts so that all the people of the world are fully protected from the tobacco epidemic and its harm.

Source: World Health Organization. *Report on the Global Tobacco Epidemic, 2015–Executive Summary. Raising Taxes on Tobacco.* 2015, pp. 1–2, 4. http://www.who.int/tobacco/global_report/2015/en/. Used with permission of the World Health Organization.

79 WHO: Recommendations for the Prevention of Childhood Obesity (2017)

In 2017, the Commission on Ending Childhood Obesity of the World Health Organization (WHO) published a fact sheet outlining the dangers of childhood obesity globally and gave recommendations for its prevention. From 1990 to 2013, the number of overweight or obese infants and children under the age of 5 years increased almost 76 percent. In the WHO African Region alone, this situation more than doubled. The rate of increase in developing nations has been more than 30 percent higher compared to developed nations. A curious paradox exists in that poorer people and nations are more likely to be overweight or obese compared to the financially better off segments of the population. This is due to the poor or uneducated eating inexpensive and readily available highly processed foods high in fat and sugar. If the overweight and obesity trend continues, these children are likely to become overweight and obese adolescents and adults. Obesity in childhood is associated with a wide range of serious health complications. This WHO excerpt on childhood obesity points out that nations need to develop health-promotion interventions and measures to help slow this epidemic. These include more physical activity and improving nutrition among children.

Consequences of obesity in childhood

Obese children are more likely to develop a variety of health problems as adults. These include:

- cardiovascular disease
- insulin resistance (often an early sign of impending diabetes)
- musculoskeletal disorders (especially osteoarthritis—a highly disabling degenerative disease of the joints)
- some cancers (endometrial, breast and colon)
- disability.

Contributors to obesity in infants and children

Every aspect of the environment in which children are conceived, born and raised can contribute to their risk of becoming overweight or obese. During pregnancy, gestational diabetes (a form of diabetes occurring during pregnancy) may result in increased birth weight and risk of obesity later in life.

Choosing healthy foods for infants and young children is critical because food preferences are established in early life. Feeding infants energy-dense, high-fat, high-sugar and high-salt foods is a key contributor to childhood obesity.

Lack of information about sound approaches to nutrition and poor availability and affordability of healthy foods contribute to the problem. The aggressive marketing of energy-dense foods and beverages to children and families further exacerbate it. In some societies, longstanding cultural norms (such as the widespread belief that a fat baby is a healthy baby) may encourage families to over-feed their children.

The increasingly urbanized and digitalized world offers fewer opportunities for physical activity through healthy play. Being overweight or obese further reduces children's opportunities to participate in group physical activities. They then become even less physically active, which makes them likely to become more overweight over time.

Prevention of childhood obesity

Overweight and obesity are largely preventable. Supportive policies, environments, schools and communities are fundamental in shaping parents' and children's choices, making the healthier choice of foods and regular physical activity the easiest choice (accessible, available and affordable), and therefore preventing obesity.

For infants and young children, WHO recommends:

- early initiation of breastfeeding within one hour of birth;
- exclusive breastfeeding for the first 6 months of life; and
- the introduction of nutritionally-adequate and safe complementary (solid) foods at 6 months together with continued breastfeeding up to two years of age or beyond.

Complementary foods should be rich in nutrients and given in adequate amounts. At six months, caregivers should introduce foods in small amounts and gradually increase the quantity as the child gets older. Young children should receive a variety of foods including meat, poultry, fish or eggs as often as possible. Foods for the baby can be specially prepared or modified from family meals. Complementary foods high in fats, sugar and salt should be avoided.

School-aged children and adolescents should:

- limit energy intake from total fats and sugars;
- increase consumption of fruit and vegetables, as well as legumes, whole grains and nuts;
- engage in regular physical activity (60 minutes a day).

The food industry can play a significant role in reducing childhood obesity by:

- reducing the fat, sugar and salt content of complementary foods and other processed foods;
- ensuring that healthy and nutritious choices are available and affordable to all consumers;
- practicing responsible marketing especially those aimed at children and teenagers.

WHO response

Adopted by the World Health Assembly in 2004, the WHO Global Strategy on Diet, Physical Activity and Health calls for action at global, regional and local levels to improve diets and increase physical activity.

The Political Declaration of the High Level Meeting of the United Nations General Assembly on the Prevention and Control of Noncommunicable Diseases of September 2011 recognizes the critical importance of reducing the level of exposure of individuals and populations to unhealthy diet and physical inactivity. The Political Declaration commits to advance the implementation of the WHO Global Strategy on Diet, Physical Activity and Health, including, where appropriate, the introduction of policies and actions aimed at promoting healthy diets and increasing physical activity.

At the 2012 World Health Assembly, countries agreed to work towards halting any further increases in the proportion of overweight children. This is one of the six global nutrition targets aimed at improving maternal, infant and young child nutrition by 2025.

The World Health Assembly in 2014 adopted the "Global Action Plan for the prevention and control of noncommunicable diseases 2013–2020" which aims to achieve the commitments of the UN Political Declaration on NCDs. The action plan will contribute to progress on 9 global NCD targets to be attained in 2025, including halting of the global obesity rates in school-aged children, adolescents and adults.

Source: World Health Organization. Commission on Ending Childhood Obesity. *Facts and Figures on Childhood Obesity.* October 13, 2017. http://www.who.int/end-childhood-obesity/facts/en/ Used with permission of the World Health Organization.

About the Editor and Contributors

Editor

Ruth Clifford Engs, PhD, is Professor Emerita, School of Public Health, Indiana University, Bloomington, Indiana. Her research has focused upon student drinking patterns in addition to social reform movements of the early 20th century. Her many works include *The Field Hospital That Never Was* (2015), *Unseen Upton Sinclair* (2009), *The Eugenics Movement* (2005), *The Progressive Era's Health Reform Movement* (2003), and *Clean Living Movements: American Cycles of Health Reform* (2000). Other major works include two oral histories, *Conversations in the Abbey: Senior Monks of Saint Meinrad Archabbey Reflect on their Lives* (2008) and *Conversations in the Abbey, Volume 2* (2016).

Contributors

Deborah Brunton was awarded a doctorate from the University of Pennsylvania in 1990 and was, until recently, senior lecturer in the history of medicine at the Open University in Milton Keynes in Britain. She has researched extensively on public health, particularly smallpox prevention. She is author of *The Politics of Vaccination: Practice and Policy in England, Wales, Ireland and Scotland, 1800–1874* and of *Medicine in Modern Britain: 1780–1950.*

Joseph P. Byrne, PhD, is a historian and professor of humanities in the honors program at Belmont University in Nashville, Tennessee. He has written *The Black Death* (Greenwood, 2004), *Daily Life during the Black Death* (Greenwood, 2006), the *Encyclopedia of the Black Death* (ABC-CLIO, 2012), and *The World of Renaissance Italy: A Daily Life Encyclopedia* (Greenwood, 2017). He has also edited the *Encyclopedia of Pestilence, Pandemics, and Plagues* (Greenwood, 2008).

William H. York, PhD, earned his doctorate in the history of science, medicine, and technology from the Johns Hopkins University with a focus on medieval and early modern European history. He is a member of the faculty in the Honors College at Portland State University, where he teaches courses on the history of science and medicine, environmental history, and the history of animals. He is currently serving as the president of Medica: The Society for the Study of Healing in the Middle Ages.

Index

Boldface numbers refer to volume numbers.